Earth Science & Astronomy for the Logic Stage

Teacher Guide

Earth Science & Astronomy for the Logic Stage Teacher Guide

Second Edition (Third Printing, 2020)

ISBN# 978-1-935614-60-9

Printed in the USA for worldwide distribution

For more copies write to:
Elemental Science
PO Box 79
Niceville, FL 32588
support@elementalscience.com

Copyright Policy

Earth Science & Astronomy for the Logic Stage
Teacher Guide Table of Contents

Earth Science & Astronomy for the Logic Stage Introduction

In *Success in Science: A Manual for Excellence in Science Education*, we state that the middle school student is "a bucket full of unorganized information that needs to be filed away and stored in a cabinet."[1] The goals of science instruction at the logic level are to begin to train the students' brain to think analytically about the facts of science, to familiarize the students with the basics of the scientific method through inquiry-based techniques, and to continue to feed the students with information about the world around them. *Earth Science & Astronomy for the Logic Stage* integrates the above goals using the Classic Method of middle school science instruction as suggested in our book. This method is loosely based on the ideas for classical science education that are laid out in *The Well-Trained Mind: A Guide to Classical Education at Home* by Jessie Wise and Susan Wise Bauer.

This guide includes the four basic components of middle school science instruction as explained in *Success in Science*.

1. **Hands-on Inquiry** — Middle school students need to see real-life science, to build their problem solving skills and to practice using the basics of the scientific method. This can be done through experiments or nature studies. In this guide, the weekly experiments fulfill this section of middle school science instruction.
2. **Information** — Middle school students need to continue to build their knowledge base along with learning how to organize and store the information they are studying. The information component is an integral part of this process. In this guide, the reading assignments, vocabulary and sketches contain all of the necessary pieces of this aspect of middle school science instruction.
3. **Writing** — The purpose of the writing component is to teach the students how to process and organize information. You want them to be able to read a passage, pull out the main ideas and communicate them to you in their own words. The assigned outlines or reports in this guide give you the tools you need to teach this basic component to the students.
4. **The Science Project** — Once a year, all middle school student should complete a science project. Their project should work through the scientific method from start to finish on a basic level, meaning that their question should be relatively easy to answer. The science fair project, scheduled as a part of unit three fulfills the requirements of this component.

Earth Science & Astronomy for the Logic Stage also includes the two optional components of middle school science instruction as explained in *Success in Science.*

1. **Around the Web** — Middle school students should gain some experience with researching on the Internet. So for this optional component, the students should, under your supervision, search the Internet for websites, YouTube videos, virtual tours and activities that relate to what they are studying. In this guide, the Want More lessons recommend specific sites and activities for you to use.
2. **Quizzes or Tests** — During the middle school years it is not absolutely necessary that

[1]Bradley R. Hudson & Paige Hudson, Success in Science: A Manual for Excellence in Science Education, (Elemental Science, 2012) 52

you give quizzes or tests to the students. However, if you want to familiarize them with test-taking skills, we suggest that you give quizzes or tests that will set the students up for success. With that in mind, we have included optional tests for you to use with each unit.

My goal in writing this curriculum is to provide you with the tools to explore the field of earth science and astronomy while teaching the basics of the scientific method. During the years, the students will work on their observation skills, learn to think critically about the information they are studying, and practice working independently. *Earth Science & Astronomy for the Logic Stage* is intended to be used with sixth through seventh grade students.

What this guide contains in a nutshell

This guide includes the weekly student assignment sheets, all the sketches pre-labeled for you and discussion questions to help you guide the discussion time. This guide also contains information for each experiment, including the expected results and an explanation of those results. There is a list of additional activities that you can choose to assign for each week. Finally, this guide includes possible schedules for you to use as you guide the students through *Earth Science & Astronomy for the Logic Stage.*

Student Guide

The Student Guide, which is sold separately, is designed to encourage independence in the students as they complete *Earth Science & Astronomy for the Logic Stage.* The Student Guide contains all the student assignment sheets, pre-drawn sketches ready for labeling, experiment pages, and blank report pages. The guide also includes blank date sheets as well as all the sheets they will need for the Science Fair Project. In short, the Student Guide contains all the pages the students will need and it is essential for successfully completing this program.

Student Assignment Sheets

This Teacher Guide contains a copy of each of the student assignment sheets that are in the Student Guide. This way you can stay on top of what the students are studying. Each of the student assignment sheets contains the following:

✓ **Experiment**

Each week will revolve around a weekly topic that it to be studied. The students will be assigned an experiment that poses a question related to the topic. Each of these experiments will walk the students through the scientific method. (*See the Appendix pg. 239 for a brief explanation of the scientific method.*) In a nutshell, the scientific method trains the brain to examine and observe before making a statement of fact. It will teach the students to look at all the facts and results before drawing a conclusion. If this sounds intimidating, it's not. You are simply teaching the students to take the time to discover the answer to a given problem by using the knowledge they have and the things they observe during an experiment.

Each week, the student assignment sheet will contain a list of the materials needed and the instructions to complete the experiment. The student guide contains an experiment sheet for the students to fill out. Each experiment sheet contains an introduction that is followed by a list of materials, a hypothesis, a procedure, an observation and a conclusion section. The introduction will give the students specific background information for the experiment. In the hypothesis section, they will predict the answer to the question posed in the lab. In the materials listed section, the students will fill out what they will use to complete the experiment. In the procedure section, they will recount step by step what was done during their experiment, so that someone else could read their report and replicate their experiment. In the observation section, the students will write what they saw. Finally, in the conclusion section they will write whether or not their hypothesis was correct and share any additional information they have learned from the experiment. If the students' hypotheses were not correct, discuss why and have them include that on their experiment sheet.

Vocabulary & Memory Work

Throughout the year, the students will be assigned vocabulary for each week. They will need to write out the definitions for each word on the Unit Vocabulary Sheet found in the Student Guide on the week that they are assigned. You may want to have the students also make flash cards to help them work on memorizing the words. This year, the students will also memorize several lists of facts that correspond to each unit. There is a complete listing of the vocabulary words and memory work for each unit on the unit overview sheet in this guide along with a glossary and a list of the memory work in the Student Guide.

Sketch

Each week the students will be assigned a sketch to complete and label. The Student Guide contains an unlabeled sketch for them to use. They will color the sketch, label it and give it a title according to the directions on the Student Assignment Sheet. The information they need will be in their reading, but the sketch is not always identical to the pictures found in the encyclopedia. So, these sketch assignments will make the student think. This guide contains a completed sketch for you to use when checking their work.

Writing Assignments

Each week the students will be assigned pages to read in the spine text, the *Kingfisher Science Encyclopedia* or the *Usborne Science Encyclopedia.* The students will read the assigned pages, and then discuss what they have read with you. After you have finished reading and discussing the reading assignment, you have three options for the students' writing assignment.

- ***Option 1: Have your student write an outline from the spine text.***
  A typical sixth grader completing this program should be expected to write a two level outline for the two page spread assigned for the week. This outline should include the main point from each paragraph on the page along with one to three supporting points.
- ***Option 2: Have your student write a narrative summary from the spine text.***
  A typical sixth grader completing this program should be expected to write a two to four paragraph summary (or six to ten sentences) about what they have read in the spine text.
- ***Option 3: Have the students write both an outline and a written report***
  First, have the students read the assigned pages in the spine text. Then, have them write a two level outline or list of seven to nine facts for the two page spread. Next have the students do some additional reading on the topic from one or more of the

additional research assignments. Each topic will have pages assigned from these reference books for their research. The following encyclopedias are scheduled to be used as additional reference books:

- 🕮 *The DK Encyclopedia of Science, 2016 Edition* (DKEOS) – This resource is a slightly more advanced reference work than the *Kingfisher Science Encyclopedia.*
- 🕮 *DK Eyewitness Books: Astronomy, 2013 Edition* (DK Astro) – This resource is only for the astronomy study and is also approaching the high school level.
- 🕮 *Exploring the Night Sky, 1987 Edition* (ENS) – This is more of a stargazing guide, but several pages are scheduled throughout the astronomy unit.

Once the students complete the additional research reading, have them write a report of two to four paragraphs in length, detailing what they have learned from their research reading.

Your writing goal for middle school students is to have them write something (narrative summary, outline, or list of facts) every day you do school, either in science or in another subject. So, the writing option you choose for this curriculum will depend on the writing the students are already doing in their other subjects.

When evaluating the students' report, make sure that the information they have shared is accurate and that it has been presented in a grammatically correct form (i.e. look for spelling mistakes, run-on sentences, and paragraph form). In the Student Guide, there are two blank lined sheets for the students to use when writing their outlines and/or summaries. If you are having the students type their report, have them glue a copy of it into their Student Guide.

🕒 **Dates**

Each week the dates of important discoveries within the topic and the dates from the readings are given on the student assignment sheet. The students will enter these dates onto one of their date sheets. The date sheets are divided into the four time periods as laid out in *The Well-Trained Mind* by Susan Wise Bauer and Jessie Wise (Ancients, Medieval-Early Renaissance, Late Renaissance-Early Modern, and Modern). Completed date sheets are available for you to use in the Appendix of this guide on pp. 234-237.

Schedules

Earth Science & Astronomy for the Logic Stage is designed to take up to three to four hours per week. You and the students can choose whether to complete the work over five days or over two days. Each week I have included two scheduling options for you to use as you lead them through this program. They are meant to be guides, so feel free to change the order to better fit the needs of the students. I also recommend that you begin to let them be in charge of choosing how many days they would like to do science as this will help to begin to foster independence in their school work. I have included two blank scheduling templates for you to use in the Appendix of this guide on pp. 245-246.

Additional Information Section

The Additional Information Section includes tools that you will find helpful as you guide the students through this study. It is only found in the Teacher Guide, and it contains the following:

☞ **Experiment Information**

Each week, the Additional Information Section includes the expected experiment results and an explanation of those results for you to use with the students. When possible, you will also find suggestions on how to expand the experiment in the Take if Further section.

Discussion Questions

Each week the Additional Information Section includes possible discussion questions from the main reading assignment, along with the answers. These are designed to aid you in leading the discussion time with the students. I recommend that you encourage them to answer in complete sentences, as this will help them organize their thoughts for writing their outline or report. I have also included a list of the discussion questions without the answers at the end of each unit's material in this guide. This is so you can give them to the students ahead of time, if you desire, or you can use them to review for the unit test. If they are already writing outlines or lists of facts, you do not need to have them write out the answers to the discussion questions before hand as there is plenty of writing required in this program already.

Want More

Each week, the Additional Information Section includes a list of activities under the Want More section. ***These activities are totally optional.*** The Want More activities are designed to explore the science on a deeper level by researching specific topics or through additional projects to do. The students do not have this information in their guide, so it is up to you whether or not to assign these.

☑ **Sketch**

Each week, the Additional Information Section includes copies of the sketches that have been labeled. These are included in this guide for you to use as you correct the students' work.

Tests

The students will be completing a lot of work each week that will help you to assess what they are learning, so testing is not absolutely necessary. However, I have included end of unit tests that you can use with the students if you feel the need to do so. The tests and the answers to them are included after the material for each unit in this guide. You can choose to give the tests orally or copy them for the students to fill out.

What a typical two day schedule looks like

A typical two day schedule will take one and a half to two hours per day. Here's a breakdown of how a normal two day week would work using week one:

- **Day 1: *Define the vocabulary, do the experiment as well as complete the experiment sheet and record the dates.***
  Begin day 1 by having the students do the "Can I calculate the speed of light using a microwave?" experiment. Have them read the introduction and then perform the experiment using the directions provided. Next have them complete the necessary calculations, discuss their results with you and then write a conclusion for their experiment. Finish the day by having them look up and define "universe" using the

glossary in their guide and adding the dates to their date sheets.

- **Day 2:** ***Read the assigned pages and discuss together, prepare an outline or narrative summary and complete the sketch.***

Begin by having the students read pg. 386-387 in the *Kingfisher Science Encyclopedia.* Then using the questions provided, discuss what they have read. Have them complete the sketch using the directions on the Student Assignment Sheet. Finally have them write an outline or narrative summary. Here is what that could look like:

Sample two level outline of the spine text for Week 1

I. The universe consists of everything in space.
   A. The universe contains atoms, people, our Earth, our solar system and countless galaxies.
   B. We cannot see everything that is included in the universe.
II. Measuring distances in the universe is different than measuring distances on Earth.
   A. We use Astronomical Units to measure distances within our solar system.
   B. We use light years to measure distances in the universe outside of our solar system.
III. Everything in the universe is moving.
   A. Planets spin on their axis and orbit the Sun.
   B. Galaxies in the universe move with the expansion of the universe.

Sample Narrative Summary from the spine text only for Week 1

The universe is a dynamic entity that consists of everything in existence. It contains the smallest particles, like atoms as well as countless stars and galaxies. Our planet and solar system are all a part of the universe. It is so large that we cannot see everything that is included in the universe.

Astronomers cannot use the same unit to measure distances in the universe that they use on Earth. On Earth we use either the metric or the US Customary system to measure distances. However distances in the universe are too great to use meters or feet to measure. Instead astronomers use Astronomical Units to measure distances within our solar system and light years to measure distances in the rest of the universe.

The universe is always changing because it is constantly moving. The planets in our solar system are moving by spinning on their axis. The stars and other objects in our galaxy are moving by orbiting around a central point in the Milky Way. Then there are other galaxies that are moving with the expansion of the universe. Finally, the universe itself is continually expanding.

What a typical five day schedule looks like

A typical five day schedule will take thirty to forty-five minutes per day. Here's a breakdown of how a normal five day week would work using week one:

- **Day 1:** ***Do the experiment and complete the experiment sheet***
Begin day 1 by having the students do the "Can I calculate the speed of light using a microwave?" experiment. Have them read the introduction and then perform the experiment using the directions provided. Next have them complete the necessary calculations, discuss their results with you and then write a conclusion for their experiment.
- **Day 2:** ***Read the assigned pages, discuss together and write an outline or list of facts.***
Begin by having the students read pg. 386-387 in the *Kingfisher Science Encyclopedia.* Then using the questions provided, discuss what they have read. Then have the students write a two level outline or a list of facts. Here's a sample list of facts:

Sample list of facts from the spine text for Week 1

1. The universe contains atoms, people, our Earth, our solar system and countless galaxies.
2. We cannot see everything that is included in the universe.
3. We use Astronomical Units to measure distances within our solar system.
4. We use light years to measure distances in the universe outside of our solar system.
5. Everything in the universe is moving.
6. Planets spin on their axis and orbit the Sun.
7. Galaxies in the universe move with the expansion of the universe.

- **Day 3:** ***Record the dates, define the vocabulary and complete the sketch.***
Have the students look up and define "universe" using the glossary in their guide and adding the dates to their date sheets. Then have them complete the sketch using the directions on the Student Assignment Sheet.
- **Day 4:** ***Read from the additional reading assignments and prepare a written report***
Begin by having the students read pg. 154-155 in the *The Usborne Science Encyclopedia.* Then have the students use their outline or list facts along with what they have just read to write a three to five paragraph summary of what they have learned. Here's a sample of what that summary could look like:

Sample Written Report for Week 1

The universe is the term used to describe all the atoms, people, planets, galaxies, and space that exists. It is large that we can't see most of the universe. Scientists use light years to measure distances in the portions of the universe that we can see. A light year is distance that light can travel within one year.

The universe is always changing because it is constantly moving. The planets in our solar system are moving by spinning on their axis. The stars and other objects in our galaxy are moving by orbiting around a central point in the Milky Way. Then there are other galaxies that are moving with the expansion of the universe. Finally, the universe itself is continually expanding.

The constant expansion of the universe and a week signal from deep space have led scientist to create the Big Bang theory as an explanation of how the universe began. The Big Bang Theory states that a big bang created a huge fireball, which cooled and formed into tiny particles, called matter. This matter then spread out forming thick clouds of hydrogen and helium. Over time, these clouds separated and formed the galaxies and planets we know today.

- **Day 5:** ***Complete one of the Want More activities***
  Have the students spend some time observing the universe or use this day to discuss the Big Bang Theory.

The Science Fair Project

I have scheduled time for the students complete a science fair project during unit three. *Janice VanCleave's A+ Science Fair Projects* is excellent resources for choosing a project topics within the field of earth science or astronomy. You can call your local school system to see if it allows homeschooled students to participate in the local school science fair or get information on national science fairs from them. Another option would be to have the students present their project in front of a group of friends and family.

How to Include Younger Students

I recognize that many homeschool families have a range of different student ages. If you wish to have all the students studying the topic of earth science and astronomy you have two options for the elementary students when using this program with the middle school students:

- ***Option 1: Have the younger students use Earth Science & Astronomy for the Grammar Stage***
  I recommend this option if the younger students are in first through third grade and/or the older student is ready for some independence. You will need to rearrange the units in *Earth Science & Astronomy for the Logic Stage* so that all the students will remain on similar topics. I suggest that you do the units in the following order: Unit 4, Unit 6, Unit 5, Unit 2, Unit 3, and Unit 1.
- ***Option 2: Have the younger students use Earth Science & Astronomy for the Logic Stage along with the older students***
  I recommend this option if the younger students are in third through fourth grade and/or the older students are not ready to work independently. You will need to adjust the work load for the younger student. Here are some suggestions on how to do that:
  - ✓ Have them watch and observe the experiments. Do not expect them to predict the outcome of the experiment (hypothesis);
  - ✓ Add in some picture books from the library for each of the topics;
  - ✓ Read the reading assignments to them and have them narrate it back to you;
  - ✓ Let them color the sketches and then tell them how to label them.

  As for the reading assignments, you may find that the spines scheduled are too much for the younger students. If so, you can read to them out of the *Usborne Science Encyclopedia*, which is scheduled as an additional research reading resource or you can use the following books instead:

  - 🕮 *DK First Space Encyclopedia, 2016 Edition*

🕮 *DK First Earth Encyclopedia, 2010 Edition*

I have included a chart coordinating these resources in the Appendix of this guide on pp. 240-242.

Helpful Articles

Our goal is to provide you with the information you need to be successful in your quest to educate your students in the sciences at home. This is the main reason we share tips and tools for homeschool science education on our blogs. As you prepare to guide your students through this program, you may find the following articles from there helpful:

- *Classical Science Curriculum for the Logic Stage Student* – This article explains the goals of logic stage science and demonstrates how the classical educator can utilize the tools they have at their disposal to reach these goals.
  - http://elementalblogging.com/classical-science-curriculum-logic/
- *Scientific Demonstrations vs. Experiments* – This article shares information about these two types of scientific tests and points out how to employ scientific demonstrations or experiments in your homeschool.
  - https://elementalscience.com/blogs/news/89905795-scientific-demonstrations-or-experiments
- *A Simple Explanation of the Scientific Method* – This article details the steps of the scientific method, along with why it is so important to teach.
  - https://elementalscience.com/blogs/news/simple-explanation-of-the-scientific-method/

Additional Resources

The following page contains quick links to the activities suggested in this guide along with several helpful downloads:

https://elementalscience.com/blogs/resources/esals

Final Thoughts

If you find that this program contains too much work, please tailor it to the needs of your student. As the author and publisher of this curriculum I encourage you to contact me with any questions or problems that you might have concerning *Earth Science & Astronomy for the Logic Stage* at support@elementalscience.com. I will be more than happy to answer them as soon as I am able. I hope that you and your student enjoy *Earth Science & Astronomy for the Logic Stage*!

Book List

The following books were used when planning this study. (**Note**—*The editions noted here are the most current editions. However, the past two editions of each of these resouces will also work.*)

Encyclopedias for Reading Assignments

The following books are the main spines of this program. You will need to purchase both of these to complete the reading assignments scheduled in this program.

- 🕮 *The Kingfisher Science Encyclopedia, 2017 Edition* (KSE)
- 🕮 *The Usborne Science Encyclopedia, 2015 Edition* (USE)

References for Reports

The following encyclopedias are scheduled for additional reference reading. They are optional, but I suggest that you purchase one or two to use throughout the year. The first encyclopedia was scheduled in previous logic stage programs.

- 🕮 *The DK Encyclopedia of Science, 2016 Edition* (DKEOS) – This resource is a slightly more advanced reference work than the *Kingfisher Science Encyclopedia.*
- 🕮 *DK Eyewitness Books: Astronomy 2013 Edition* (DK Astro) – This resource is only for the astronomy study and is also approaching the high school level.
- 🕮 *Exploring the Night Sky, 1987 Edition* (ENS) – This is more of a stargazing guide, but several pages are scheduled throughout the astronomy unit.

Sequence of Study

Astronomy Units (15 weeks)

Unit 1: Space (5 weeks)
- ✓ Universe
- ✓ Galaxies
- ✓ Stars
- ✓ Constellations
- ✓ Constellations: Research Project

Unit 2: Our Solar System (6 Weeks)
- ✓ Sun
- ✓ Inner Planets
- ✓ Earth/Moon
- ✓ Outer Planets
- ✓ Dwarf Planets
- ✓ Comets, Meteorites

Unit 3: Astronomers & Their Tools (4 Weeks)
- ✓ Astronomers
- ✓ Looking into Space
- ✓ Exploring Space
- ✓ Satellites

Earth Science Units (20 weeks)

Unit 4: Our Planet (7 weeks)
- ✓ Inside the Earth
- ✓ Maps and Mapping
- ✓ Rivers
- ✓ Oceans
- ✓ Glaciers
- ✓ Natural Cycles
- ✓ Biomes and Habitats

Unit 5: Geology (7 weeks)
- ✓ Continents
- ✓ Volcanoes
- ✓ Earthquakes
- ✓ Mountains

- ✓ Rocks
- ✓ Ores and Gems
- ✓ Erosion and Weathering

Unit 6: Weather (6 Weeks)

- ✓ Atmosphere
- ✓ Climates
- ✓ Weather
- ✓ Clouds
- ✓ Extreme Weather
- ✓ Forecasting

End-of-the-year Test (1 week)

Materials Listed by Week

Astronomy Units

Unit 1: Space

Week	Materials
1	Large chocolate bar, large plate, microwave
2	4 Types of Galaxies article (in appendix of SG), galaxy cards
3	Aluminum foil, large piece of cardboard (large enough to fit under the glass bowl), glass bowl, flashlight, scissors
4	Shoebox, black construction paper, pin, flashlight
5	*No supplies needed.*

Unit 2: Our Solar System

Week	Materials
6	2 glass jars or 2 clear glasses, Plastic wrap, 2 black tea bags, Water, Instant read thermometer
7	3 heavy duty plastic bottles, 3 balloons, 3 tsp of yeast (1 ½ packages), 3 TBSP of sugar, Water , White vinegar
8	Apple, Fork, Flashlight, Partner
9	Wooden Dowel, Foil, Paper clip, Toaster
10	Construction paper, Paints or crayons
11	Marble, Rubber bouncy ball, Foam ball, Tennis ball, Cake pan, Cornstarch, Ruler

Unit 3: Astronomers & Their Tools

Week	Materials
12-14	Materials will vary depending on the Science Fair Project that your student has chosen to do

Earth Science Units

Unit 4: Our Planet

Week	Materials
16	Modeling clay (you will need yellow, orange, red, blue, and green), Ruler
17	Blue balloon (with the continents drawn or printed on it), Flat map, Pin
18	Pitcher for water, Water, Cookie sheet, Paper cup, Straw, Dirt or sand, Small rocks, Clay or play dough, Books, Tape

Unit 4: Our Planet (continued)

Week	Materials
19	Aluminum bread pan or Plastic bin, Air dry clay, Water, Sand (1 cup), 2 Straws
20	Glacier Melt Model (make using cup, water, pebbles, sand), Large cutting board with a handle, Large rubber band
21	Cup, Baggie, Water, Rubber band
22	Paper towels, Wax paper, Rubber band, Water

Unit 5: Geology

Week	Materials
23	Marshmallow creme (or whipping cream), Graham crackers, 3 Plates, Bowl with water
24	Mentos™, Cardboard cereal box, 1-Liter bottle of cola (or orange soda), 1 Can of Great Stuff™ Foam, Paints, Aluminum oil
25	Partner, Slinky, Rope
26	Several different colors of crayons, Grater, Butter knife, Pencil sharpener, Foil, Bowl, Warm water, Foil muffin cups
27	7 to 10 Rocks collected from outside, Rock & Mineral field guide, Plastic baggie, Sharpie Marker, White-out
28	5 to 8 More rocks collected from outside, Rock & Mineral field guide, Foam board, Sharpie Marker, White-out
29	Dirt or sand, Grass seed, Water, Pitcher, 2 Aluminum Pans ***NOTE:*** *You will need to plant your grass seed mountain at least 7 days before doing this experiment so that it will grow in time to do the experiment.*

Unit 6: Weather

Week	Materials
30	3 Cups, 2 Colors of food coloring, Hot and cold water
31	3 Foil muffin cups, Soil from outside, Sand, Water , Desk lamp
32	Balloon, Two permanent markers of different colors, A partner
33	2 Liter bottle, Water, Matches
34	Large clear round container, Warm water , Red food coloring, Blue ice cubes
35	Battery powered toothbrush, Sound recording device

Astronomy Unit 1

Space

Astronomy Unit 1: Space
Overview of Study

Sequence of Study

Week 1: Universe (Optional: Big Bang Theory)
Week 2: Galaxies
Week 3: Stars
Week 4: The Big and Little Dipper
Week 5: Constellations

Materials by Week

Week	Materials
1	Large chocolate bar, large plate, microwave
2	4 Types of Galaxies article (in appendix of SG), galaxy cards
3	Aluminum foil, large piece of cardboard (large enough to fit under the glass bowl), glass bowl, flashlight, scissors
4	Shoebox, black construction paper, pin, flashlight
5	Shoebox planetarium from previous week, black construction paper, pin & a flashlight

Vocabulary for the Unit

1. **Universe** – The collection of all the matter, space, and energy that exists, also known as the cosmos.
2. **Galaxy** – A body held together by gravity that is made of millions of stars, gas, and dust.
3. **Cluster** – A group of galaxies that are found close together.
4. **Supercluster** – The largest structure in the universe, composed of many galaxy clusters.
5. **Star** – A massive, hot, shining ball of gas.
6. **Nebulae** – Clouds of dust and gas found in space.
7. **Black hole** – Formed by a collapsed star, has a very strong gravitational pull.
8. **Constellation** – The pattern that a group of stars seems to make in the sky.
9. **Planetarium** – A device used to project images of the stars or depict the solar system.
10. **Zodiac** – The twelve constellations through which the sun, moon, and planets appear to move.

Memory Work for the Unit

Types of Stars

1. Blue giant – A large, hot star off the main sequence.
2. Red giant – An older star with a cooler outer layer.
3. Neutron star – The tightly-packed collapsed core of a larger star.
4. Main-sequence star – A star plotted in the left-to-right band across the HR diagram.

5. Black hole – A gravitationally dense region of space-time where nothing can escape, not even light.
6. White dwarf – A stellar core remnant of a low to medium mass star.
7. Red dwarf – A cool, small star on the main sequence.

Constellations of the Zodiac

1. Aquarius
2. Aries
3. Cancer
4. Capricorn
5. Gemini
6. Leo
7. Libra
8. Pisces
9. Sagittarius
10. Scorpio
11. Taurus
12. Virgo

Notes

Student Assignment Sheet Astronomy Week 1
Universe

Experiment: Can I calculate the speed of light using a microwave?

Materials

- ✓ Large chocolate bar
- ✓ Large plate
- ✓ Microwave
- ✓ Ruler

> **CAUTION**
> ***Melted chocolate is very hot and can burn, DO NOT touch!***

Procedure

1. Read the introduction to this experiment and answer the question.
2. Unwrap the chocolate bar and place it on the plate. Remove the turntable from your microwave and set the plate inside.
3. Begin by heating the chocolate bar for 1 minute; check to see if it has begun to melt. (*You are looking to see if there are two spots that have begun to melt. You DO NOT want the entire chocolate bar to melt.*) If the bar has not begun to melt, continue to heat it for 30-second intervals, checking each time to see if melting has begun.
4. Once melting has begun, carefully remove the plate from the microwave and measure the distance between the centers of the two melted points.
5. Record the distance on your experiment sheet and complete the calculations.
6. Draw conclusions and complete your experiment sheet.

Vocabulary & Memory Work

- ☐ Vocabulary: universe
- ☐ Memory Work – Work on memorizing the Types of Stars.

Sketch Assignment: Contents of the Universe

- Label the following: Earth, Our Solar System, Milky Way Galaxy, Cluster of Galaxies, The Universe

Writing Assignment

- Reading Assignment: *Kingfisher Science Encyclopedia* pg. 386-387 The Universe
- Additional Research Readings
  - Big Bang Theory: *KSE* pg. 388-389
  - The Universe: *USE* pg. 154-155

Dates to Enter

- 1929 – Edwin Hubble proves that the universe is expanding.
- 1965 – Scientists find heat waves in the universe that they believe are leftover from a vast explosion.
- 1992 – The satellite *Cosmic Background Explorer* traces background radiation and ripples in the universe that are thought to be leftover from the Big Bang.

Schedules for Week 1

Two Days a Week

<table>
<tr><th>Day 1</th><th>Day 2</th></tr>
<tr><td>☐ Define universe on SG pg. 14
☐ Do the "Can I calculate the speed of light?" experiment, then fill out the experiment sheet on SG pp. 18-19
☐ Enter the dates onto the date sheets on SG pp. 8-12</td><td>☐ Read pp. 386-387 from the Kingfisher Science Encyclopedia, then discuss what was read
☐ Color and label the "Contents of the Universe" sketch on SG pg. 17
☐ Prepare an outline or narrative summary, write it on SG pp. 20-21</td></tr>
<tr><td colspan="2">Supplies I Need for the Week
✓ Large chocolate bar
✓ Large plate
✓ Microwave
✓ Ruler</td></tr>
<tr><td colspan="2">Things I Need to Prepare</td></tr>
</table>

Five Days a Week

<table>
<tr><th>Day 1</th><th>Day 2</th><th>Day 3</th><th>Day 4</th><th>Day 5</th></tr>
<tr><td>☐ Do the "Can I calculate the speed of light?" experiment, then fill out the experiment sheet on SG pp. 18-19</td><td>☐ Read pp. 386-387 from the Kingfisher Science Encyclopedia, then discuss what was read
☐ Write an outline or list of facts on SG pg. 20</td><td>☐ Define universe on SG pg. 14
☐ Enter the dates onto the date sheets on SG pp. 8-12
☐ Color and label the "Contents of the Universe" sketch on SG pg. 17</td><td>☐ Read one or all of the additional reading assignments
☐ Prepare your report, write the report on SG pg. 21</td><td>☐ Complete one of the Want More Activities listed
OR
☐ Study a scientist from the field of Astronomy</td></tr>
<tr><td colspan="5">Supplies I Need for the Week
✓ Large chocolate bar
✓ Large plate
✓ Microwave
✓ Ruler</td></tr>
<tr><td colspan="5">Things I Need to Prepare</td></tr>
</table>

Additional Information Astronomy Week 1

Experiment Information

- **Introduction** – (*from the Student Guide*) The universe is the vast expanse of space in which all things are found. It contains us, our planet, our solar system, our galaxy and at least 100 billion other galaxies. Astronomers have studied what they call the observable universe since Galileo invented the first telescope in 1609. As astronomers began to record their observations, they found the need to calculate distances, so that they could give approximate locations for the objects in the universe. Since the distances in the universe are so large, astronomers began to use light years to calculate them. A light year is the distance a wavelength of light will travel in one year, or about 5.88 trillion miles. In this experiment, you are going to try to calculate the speed of light, which scientists then multiply by the time in one year to calculate a light year.
- **Results** – Depending on the strength of your microwave, the students will measure the distance between the two spots to be between five to ten centimeters. Here is a sample calculation for a student that measured a 6 centimeters (0.06 meters) distance in a 2450 Mega Hertz (MHz) microwave.

  Calculation #1: 0.06 m x 2 = 0.12 m (wavelength)

  Calculation #2: 2450 MHz x 1,000,000 = 2,450,000,000 Hz (cycles per second)

  Calculation #3: 0.12 m x 2,450,000,000 Hz =294,000,000 m/s (close to the speed of light)

  When the students complete the calculations, they should see that their speed is close to the actual speed of light (299, 792, 452 m/s).
- **Explanation** – Microwave ovens have an electromagnetic wave that has the same frequency and wavelength as light. In a microwave, the energy, or heat, is concentrated at the peaks of the waves. So the chocolate will melt first at the points where the wavelength entered and exited the chocolate bar (*see diagram*). If you measure the distance between the centers of the two melted spots, you are measuring the distance between two nodes of a standing wave, which is half of the wavelength. You then multiple that times 2, to get the full wavelength. Then multiple the wavelength by the frequency or number of hertz, or cycles per second (which you can find on the back of your microwave). This will give you the speed in meters per second, which should be close to the speed of light.

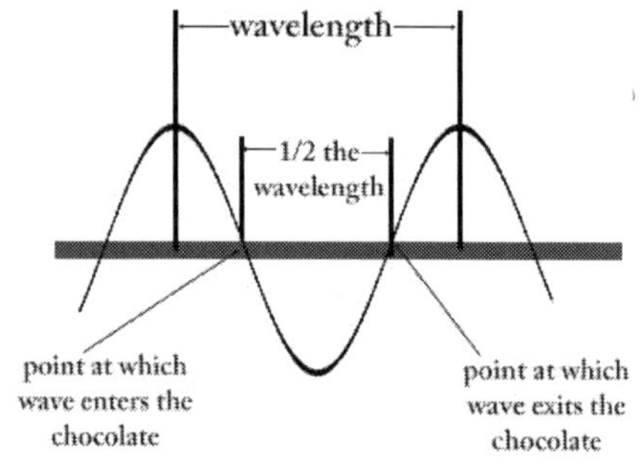

- **Troubleshooting** – This is a challenging experiment for middle schoolers. In case you don't get the right results, here are a few troubleshooting tips.
  - *You only saw one melted hole in the center of your chocolate bar.*

    Solution – Be sure your chocolate bar is at least 12 cm long and make sure that your plate is not spinning. You may need to remove both the plate and the spinner from your microwave before doing this experiment.
  - *Your answer is way off from the speed of light.*

    Solution – Units! In this experiment we used several units of measurement that are common in science, but may not be familiar to the students. I have included a chart explaining each of the units for your reference.

Unit Abbreviation	What it stands for	What it's used for
cm	Centimeters	Measurement of length 100 cm = 1 m
m	Meters	
MHz	Mega Hertz	Frequency or cycles per second, 1MHz = 1,000,000 Hz
Hz	Hertz	
m/s	Meters per Second	Measurement of speed

- *If you are still having problems, the following video will give you a good visual reference of this experiment.*
  - https://www.youtube.com/watch?v=kpB1wezpJeE

Discussion Questions

1. How can we see other galaxies? (*We can see other galaxies by using a telescope.*) How many do we know about? (*Astronomers know about approximately 100 billion galaxies that can be seen from Earth.*)
2. How do astronomers measure distances in the universe? (*Within our solar system, astronomers use the Astronomical Unit (AU) to measure objects. The AU is equal to the distance between the Earth and the Sun, which is about 93 million miles. Outside of our solar system, astronomers use light years to measure objects in the universe. A light year is the distance that light travels in one year, which is about 5.88 trillion miles.*)
3. What does everything in the universe do? (*Everything in the universe moves.*)

Additional Notes

If you want to introduce your students to the Big Bang theory, this is the week to do so. The pages for this are scheduled as an additional resource reading assignment, which gives you the option to assign them or not. I want to encourage you to do so, even if you don't hold to the Big Bang theory as the truth of how the universe began. In today's world, most astronomers do believe in the Big Bang theory. It is often referred to as the most plausible explanation for the origins of the universe, so it is important that students are familiar with what it says. It is also equally as important that as teachers/parents, we share with our students what we hold to be true about the origins of the universe. I believe that logic stage is a good time to begin having those discussions. If you do decide to include these pages, here are some discussion questions for you to use.

1. Explain the Big Bang theory.(*Many astronomers believe that there was a huge explosion that created a large amount of energy. This energy was then transformed into subatomic particles, which after 300,000 years, turned into a soup of elements. After a billion years, gravity pulled the elements into clouds, which then formed the first galaxies and stars.*)
2. What evidence do astronomers use to support the Big Bang theory? (*Astronomers use the fact that galaxies are moving farther apart to support the Big Bang theory. They use this fact because it suggests that the galaxies were once concentrated in a single place.*)

3. What evidence for the Big Bang still eludes scientists? (*Scientists still haven't found the majority of the universe's matter or the stuff that the universe is composed of.*)
4. What do many cosmologists believe will happen to our universe? (*Many cosmologists believe that our universe will expand to a certain point and then it will begin to contract. Eventually it will collapse inward and implode in an event they call the Big Crunch. This will destroy everything, but it will be followed by another Big Bang.*)

I have also included a couple of questions to help you and your students as you examine the Big Bang Theory in your homeschool.

1. **Theory vs. Fact**
   - In science, what is a theory? (*The word theory comes from the ancient Greek word theoria, which means "a looking at, viewing or beholding". In science, a theory is an analytical tool used for understanding, explaining or making predictions about a certain subject matter. Theories are meant to be tested by experimentation and observation to determine if they are fact.*)
   - In science, what is fact? (*The word fact is comes from the Latin word factum, which means "a thing done or performed". In science, a fact is an objective and verifiable observation. Facts can be verifiable through repeatable experimentation.*)
2. **Origins**
   - Where did the energy for the Big Bang come from? (*We know from the first law of thermodynamics that energy is conserved. The first law of thermodynamics states: Energy can be neither created nor destroyed. It can only change forms. Therefore the energy for the Big Bang had to come from somewhere. If the Big Bang is true, where did the original energy for it come from? There's no real answer to this question, it's something that scientists are still trying to figure out and one of the main reasons that the Big Bang theory remains a theory instead of fact.*)

Want More

- **Observe the Universe** – There are many things about our universe that can be observed from Earth by the naked eye or by using a telescope. Take some time this week to record what you can observe. Go outside at night, take pictures of what you see and use a field guide to identify what you have observed (*Exploring the Night Sky* or *Usborne Discovery Astronomy* are two good options.) Have the students create a mini-book or journal detailing what they have seen. You can add to this project as you continue to work your way through the astronomy units.

Sketch Assignment Week 1

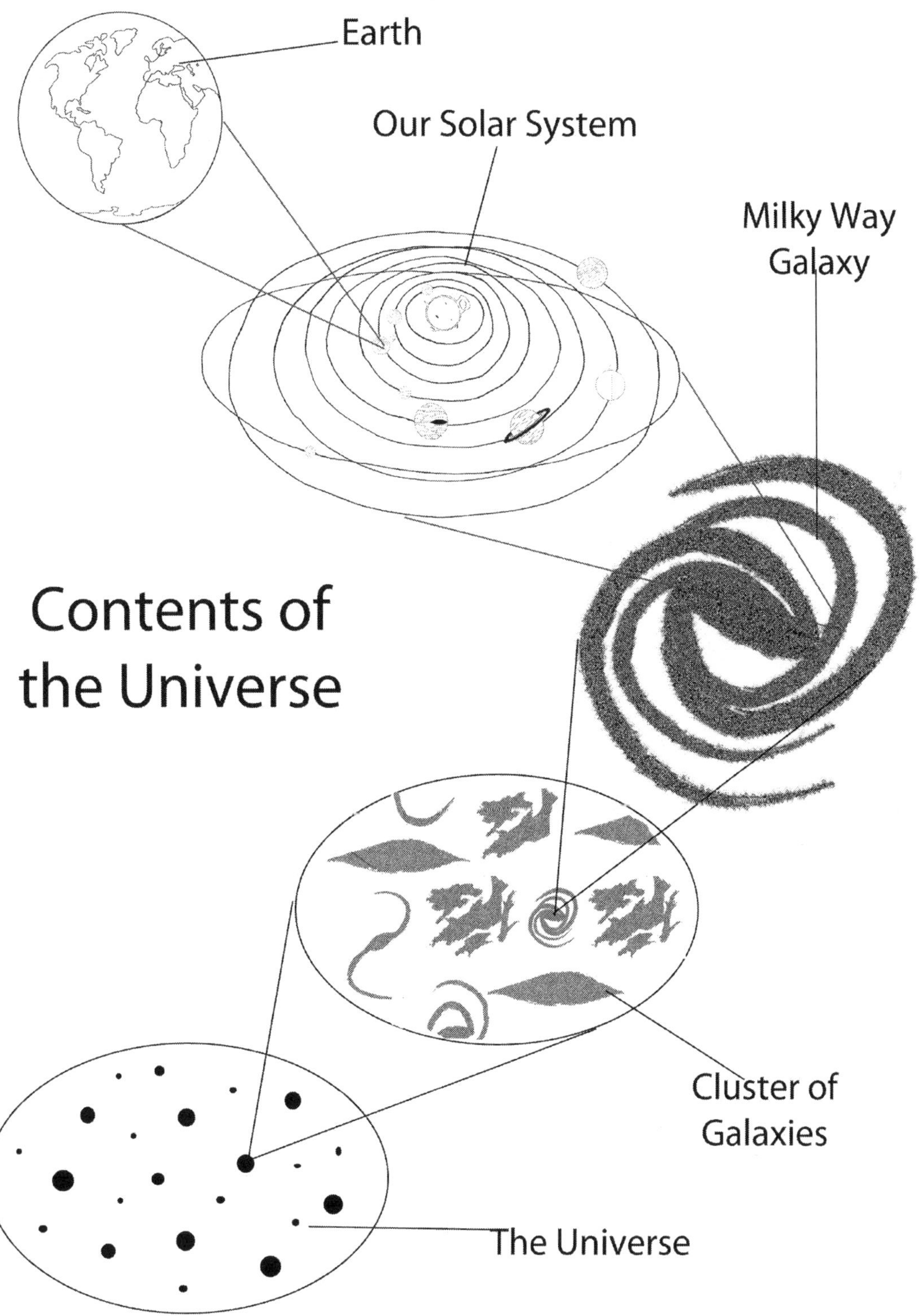

Student Assignment Sheet Astronomy Week 2
Galaxies

Experiment: Identifying Galaxies

Materials

- ✓ Galaxy cards (See Appendix pg. 247)

Procedure

1. Read the introduction to this experiment and answer the question.
2. Read "Four Types of Galaxies" found on pg. 246 of the SG Appendix. Then, fill in the Galaxy Information Chart on your experiment sheet with the information.
3. Next, look at each of the galaxy cards, determine which type of galaxy they are by using the information included, and then check your answers with your teacher.
4. Write what you have learned in the conclusion section of your experiment sheet.

Vocabulary & Memory Work

- Vocabulary: galaxy, cluster, supercluster
- Memory Work – Continue to work on memorizing the Types of Stars.

Sketch Assignment: 4 Types of Galaxies

- Label the following: irregular galaxy, elliptical galaxy, spiral galaxy and barred spiral galaxy

Writing Assignment

- Reading Assignment: *Kingfisher Science Encyclopedia* pg. 390-391 Galaxies
- Additional Research Readings
  - Galaxies: *USE* pg. 156-157
  - Our Galaxy and Beyond: *DK Astro* pg. 62-63

Dates to Enter

- 1784 – Charles Messier finds several blurry objects that he records as nebulae. These are later discovered to be galaxies.
- 1845 – Lord Rosse draws the galaxy M51, without knowing what it is.
- 1924 – Edwin Hubble presents the first evidence of other galaxies.

Schedules for Week 2

Two Days a Week

Day 1	Day 2
☐ Define galaxy, cluster, supercluster on SG pg. 14 ☐ Do the "Identifying Galaxies" experiment, then fill out the experiment sheet on SG pp. 24-25 ☐ Enter the dates onto the date sheets on SG pp. 8-12	☐ Read pp. 390-391 from the *Kingfisher Science Encyclopedia*, then discuss what was read ☐ Prepare an outline or narrative summary, write it on SG pp. 26-27 ☐ Color and label the "4 types of galaxies" sketch on SG pg. 23
Supplies I Need for the Week ✓ Galaxy Information Sheet ✓ Galaxy Trading Cards	
Things I Need to Prepare	

Five Days a Week

Day 1	Day 2	Day 3	Day 4	Day 5
☐ Do the "Identifying Galaxies" experiment, then fill out the experiment sheet on SG pp. 24-25	☐ Read pp. 390-391 from the *Kingfisher Science Encyclopedia*, then discuss what was read ☐ Write an outline or list of facts on SG pg. 26	☐ Define galaxy, cluster, supercluster on SG pg. 14 ☐ Enter the dates onto the date sheets on SG pp. 8-12 ☐ Color and label the "4 types of galaxies" sketch on SG pg. 23	☐ Read one or all of the additional reading assignments ☐ Prepare your report, write the report on SG pg. 27	☐ Complete one of the Want More Activities listed **OR** ☐ Study a scientist from the field of Astronomy
Supplies I Need for the Week ✓ Galaxy Information Sheet ✓ Galaxy Trading Cards				
Things I Need to Prepare				

Additional Information Astronomy Week 2

Experiment Information

- **Introduction** – (*from the Student Guide*) All galaxies are massive celestial bodies made up of stars, gas and dust. They are held together by gravity and classified by their shape. There are four main types of galaxy shapes, spiral, elliptical, barred spiral, and irregular. In this experiment, you are going to read more about each type of galaxy shape and then identify several galaxies using what you have learned.
- **Galaxy Cards** – The galaxy cards can be found in the Appendix of this guide on pg. 247-250. Simply print them out, fold them in half and glue them together.
- **Results** – The students' charts should look like this:

Type of Galaxy	Spiral	Elliptical	Barred Spiral	Irregular
Shape	pinwheel shaped	round or oval shape	pinwheel shaped with a bar of stars, dust & gas running across the center	no regular shape
Bulge & Disks	bulge and thin disk present	bulge, but no disk	bulge and thin disk present	may show signs of a disk and a halo
Gas & Dust	rich in gas & dust	little cool gas & dust	rich in gas & dust	usually rich in gas & dust
Types of Stars	young & old stars are present	mainly old stars are present	young & old stars are present	young & old stars are present
Examples (from Galaxy Cards)	NGC 7217 Messier 100 Andromeda	NGC 4881 NGC 3377	NGC 4156 Milky Way	NGC 5253

Discussion Questions

1. What is the name of the galaxy our solar system is in? (*Our solar system is found in the Milky Way Galaxy.*)
2. How are galaxies classified? (*Galaxies are classified according to their shape.*)
3. What are two things that astronomers believe help to determine the shape of a galaxy? (*Astronomers believe that the amount of material, the speed of spin and the rate at which stars form all help to determine the shape of a galaxy.*)
4. Describe the typical active galaxy. (*The typical active galaxy has a luminous core that emits huge jets of material. The center also has a glowing ring of gas and dust that surrounds a black hole.*)
5. Which cluster of galaxies does the Milky Way belong to? (*The Milky Way belongs to the Local Group cluster of galaxies.*)

Want More

- **Galaxy Cards** – Print out an extra set of galaxy cards and use them to play games like Go

Fish or Memory. You could also have the students match the information to the galaxy for more of a challenge.

- **Deep Space Art** – Have the students make a chalk drawing of the planets and the galaxy. Directions can be found at the following website:
  - http://www.deepspacesparkle.com/2009/03/planets-and-galaxy-project-for-fifth/

Sketch Assignment Week 2

4 Main Types of Galaxies

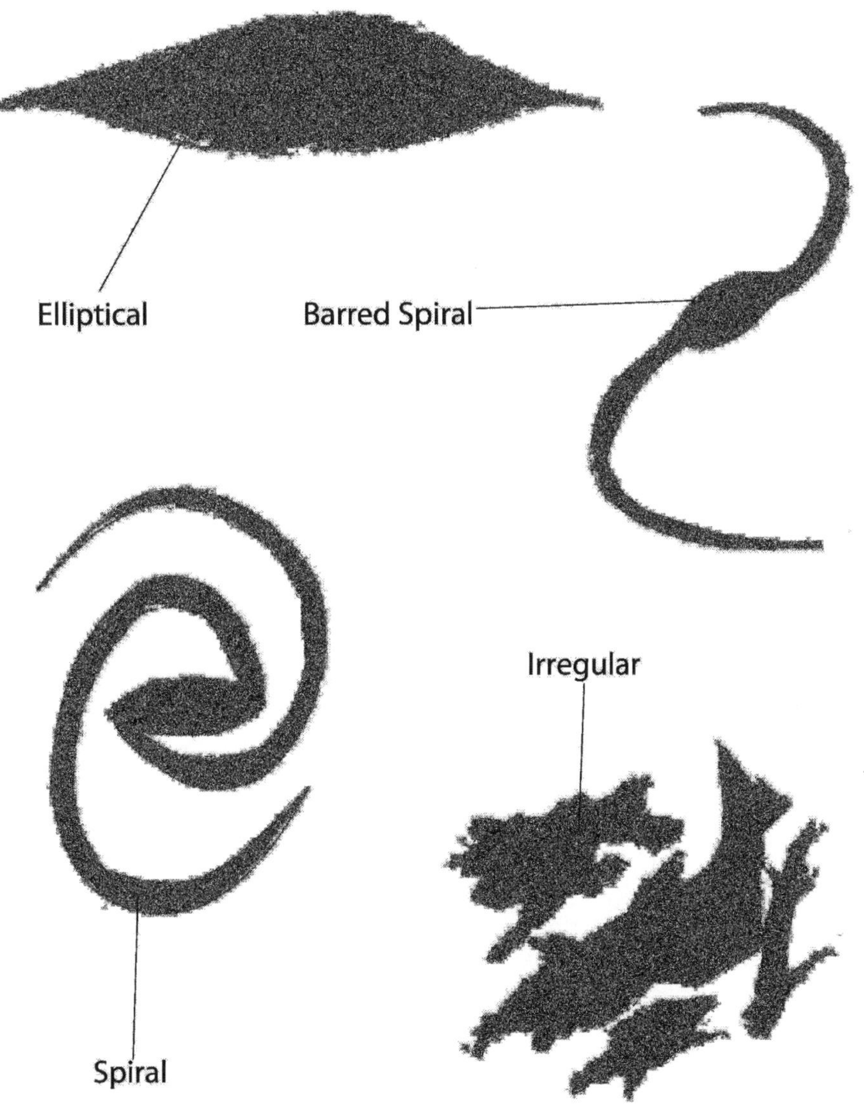

Student Assignment Sheet Astronomy Week 3
Stars

Experiment: Why do stars twinkle?

Materials
- ✓ Aluminum foil
- ✓ Large piece of cardboard (large enough to fit under the glass bowl)
- ✓ Glass bowl
- ✓ Flashlight
- ✓ Scissors

Procedure
1. Read the introduction to this experiment and answer the question.
2. Cut out small pieces of aluminum foil, shape them into stars and glue them onto the cardboard.
3. Fill up two thirds of the bowl with water and place it on top of the cardboard.
4. Turn off the lights in the room you are in and shine your flashlight on the top of the bowl.
5. Tap the side of the bowl and record what happens.
6. Discuss with your teacher, draw conclusions, and finish your experiment sheet.

Vocabulary & Memory Work
- ☐ Vocabulary: star, nebulae, black hole
- ☐ Memory Work – Continue to work on memorizing the Types of Stars.

Sketch Assignment: Life Cycle of a Star
- Label the following: stellar nebulae, average star, red giant, planetary nebula, neutron star, the material condenses and begins to burn by converting hydrogen to helium, helium starts to convert to carbon and the star gets larger, the fuel in the core is used up and the outer layers are pushed out into space, the core shrinks to the size of a small planet

Writing Assignment
- Reading Assignment: *Kingfisher Science Encyclopedia* pg. 392-393 Stars
- Additional Research Readings:
  - Stars: *USE* pg. 158-159
  - The birth and death of stars: *DK Astro* pg. 60-61

Dates to Enter
- 1824-1910 – British astronomer William Huggins lives. He is the first to use spectroscopy in astronomy.
- 1906 – Ejnar Hertzsprung, a Danish astronomer, discovers that a star's temperature and luminosity are linked. He then arranges them into families, from hot and bright to cool and dim.

Schedules for Week 3

Two Days a Week

<table>
<tr><th>Day 1</th><th>Day 2</th></tr>
<tr><td>☐ Define star, nebulae, black hole on SG pg. 14
☐ Do the "Why do stars twinkle?" experiment, then fill out the experiment sheet on SG pp. 30-31
☐ Enter the dates onto the date sheets on SG pp. 8-12</td><td>☐ Read pp. 392-393 from the Kingfisher Science Encyclopedia, then discuss what was read
☐ Prepare an outline or narrative summary, write it on SG pp. 32-33
☐ Color and label the "Life Cycle of a Star" sketch on SG pg. 29</td></tr>
<tr><td colspan="2">Supplies I Need for the Week
✓ Aluminum foil
✓ Large piece of cardboard (large enough to fit under the glass bowl)
✓ Glass bowl
✓ Flashlight
✓ Scissors</td></tr>
<tr><td colspan="2">Things I Need to Prepare</td></tr>
</table>

Five Days a Week

<table>
<tr><th>Day 1</th><th>Day 2</th><th>Day 3</th><th>Day 4</th><th>Day 5</th></tr>
<tr><td>☐ Do the "Why do stars twinkle?" experiment, then fill out the experiment sheet on SG pp. 30-31</td><td>☐ Read pp. 392-393 from the Kingfisher Science Encyclopedia, then discuss what was read
☐ Write an outline or list of facts on SG pg. 32</td><td>☐ Define stars, nebulae, black hole on SG pg. 14
☐ Enter the dates onto the date sheets on SG pp. 8-12
☐ Color and label the "Life Cycle of a Star" sketch on SG pg. 29</td><td>☐ Read one or all of the additional reading assignments
☐ Prepare your report, write the report on SG pg. 33</td><td>☐ Complete one of the Additional Activities listed
OR
☐ Study a scientist from the field of Astronomy</td></tr>
<tr><td colspan="5">Supplies I Need for the Week
✓ Aluminum foil
✓ Large piece of cardboard (large enough to fit under the glass bowl)
✓ Glass bowl
✓ Flashlight
✓ Scissors</td></tr>
<tr><td colspan="5">Things I Need to Prepare</td></tr>
</table>

Additional Information Astronomy Week 3

Experiment Information

☞ **Introduction** – (*from the Student Guide*) Stars are the most numerous heavenly bodies in our universe. Our galaxy alone has about 200 billion of them. Stars are balls of hot, glowing gas that produce light that we can see from Earth. Stars vary in size, but all appear very small from the Earth because they are so far away. At times stars appear to sparkle in the night sky. In this experiment, you are going to figure out why they appear to twinkle.

☞ **Results** – The students should see that the foil reflects the light coming from the flashlight. They should see that when they tap the side of the bowl, the reflected light appears to twinkle.

☞ **Explanation** – The light reflecting from your aluminum stars appears to twinkle when the water moves. This is because the light is being refracted or bent by the molecules in the moving water, so it appears to be moving. The same is true for light coming from stars in the Universe. When the light rays hit our atmosphere, some of them are refracted or bent slightly. This refraction of light gives the stars the appearance of twinkling in the night sky.

Discussion Questions

1. What does light coming from a star tell an astronomer about a star? (*Light coming from a star tells an astronomer what the star consists of, how big it is and how hot it is.*)
2. Name three types of energy that are produced by a star. (*Stars produce heat energy, light energy, UV radiation and x-rays.*)
3. How does a star's mass affect it? (*The larger a star's mass the greater its luminosity or brightness and the quicker it will use up its fuel.*)
4. Name two characteristics that are common to all stars. (*All stars start with a hydrogen core that is converted into helium. All stars are born from nebulae or small clouds of gas and dust.*)
5. What are the two types of star clusters? Explain both. (*The two types of star clusters are open clusters, which is a group of young stars that are loosely collected and will eventually disperse, and globular clusters, which is a group of older stars that have spend their lives together and will die together.*)
6. What happens to the core of a star when it dies? (*The core of larger stars will continue to collapse and eventually form a black hole. The core of smaller stars will form a neutron star.*)

Want More

✐ **Life Cycle of a Star Mobile** – Cut a paper plate into a spiral. Punch a hole in the center of the spiral and tie a string through it, so that you can hang up your mobile. Use a pulled out white cotton ball to make a stellar nebula with its cloud of dust and gas. Then use a small yellow pompom for the average star and a large red pompom for the red giant. Next paint a cotton ball purple, orange and a bit of blue. Pull it out of shape and use it for the planetary nebula. Finally use a small white bead or sequin for the white dwarf.

Sketch Assignment Week 3

The students may find this week's sketch to be a bit difficult as the pictures in the spine book do not clearly explain the entire life cycle of a star. The information is all in their reading, but you may need to guide them as they complete this sketch assignment.

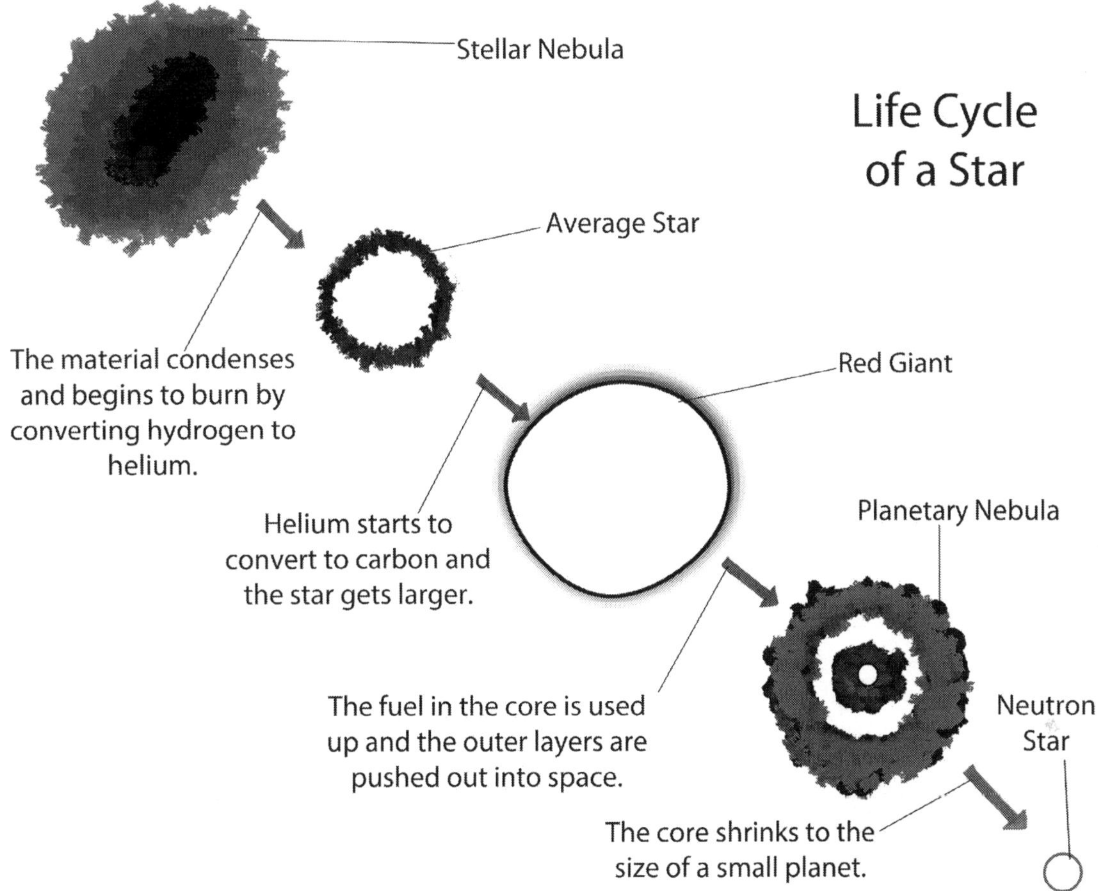

Student Assignment Sheet Astronomy Week 4
The Big and Little Dipper

Experiment: Shoebox Planetarium

Materials

- ✓ Shoebox
- ✓ Black construction paper
- ✓ Pin
- ✓ Flashlight

Procedure

1. Read the introduction on your experiment sheet.
2. At one end of the shoebox, cut out a hole that is a little less than 3 inches wide and 5 inches long.
3. Cut out two rectangles from the black construction paper measuring 3 inches by 5 inches. Then using the templates from your experiment sheet and a pin, punch out the necessary holes to make the Big Dipper and the Little Dipper constellations.
4. Tape one of the cards in front of the hole that was cut in the shoebox earlier. Place the flashlight in the box and cover with the lid. Turn off the lights in the room, angle the shoebox towards a wall, and observe what you see.
5. Repeat with the second card.

Vocabulary & Memory Work

- ☐ Vocabulary: constellation, planetarium
- ☐ Memory Work – Begin to work on memorizing the Constellations of the Zodiac: Aquarius, Aries, Cancer, Capricorn, Gemini, Leo, Libra, Pisces, Sagittarius, Scorpio, Taurus, Virgo

Sketch Assignment: Big Dipper & Little Dipper

- Label the following: Ursa Major, Ursa Minor, Polaris, Dubhe, Merak, Mizar, Benetnasch

Writing Assignment

- Reading Assignment: "Ursa Major and Ursa Minor," "Callisto and Arcas," and "The Two Bears" from *The Stars and their Stories* (found in the Appendix of the SG pp. 115-117)
- Additional Research Readings
  - None this week

Dates to Enter

- 2nd century – Ptolemy names forty-eight different constellations in his book *Almagest.*
- 17th-18th centuries – Forty more constellations are named, for a total of eighty-eight named constellations.

Schedules for Week 4

Two Days a Week

Day 1	Day 2
☐ Define constellation, planetarium on SG pp. 14 & 15 ☐ Do the "Shoebox Planetarium" experiment, then fill out the experiment sheet on SG pg. 36 ☐ Enter the dates onto the date sheets on SG pp. 8-12	☐ Read *The Stars and their Stories: The Two Bears* on SG pp. 247-250 and then discuss what was read ☐ Prepare an outline or narrative summary, write it on SG pp. 38-39 ☐ Color and label the "Big Dipper & Little Dipper" sketch on SG pg. 35
Supplies I Need for the Week ✓ Shoebox ✓ Black construction paper ✓ Pin ✓ Flashlight	
Things I Need to Prepare	

Five Days a Week

Day 1	Day 2	Day 3	Day 4	Day 5
☐ Do the "Shoebox Planetarium" experiment, then fill out the experiment sheet on SG pg. 36	☐ Read *The Stars and their Stories: The Two Bears* on SG pp. 247-250 and then discuss what was read ☐ Write an outline or list of facts on SG pg. 38	☐ Define constellation, planetarium on SG pp. 14 & 15 ☐ Enter the dates onto the date sheets on SG pp. 8-12 ☐ Color and label the "Big Dipper & Little Dipper" sketch on SG pg. 35	☐ Read one or all of the additional reading assignments ☐ Prepare your report, write the report on SG pg. 39	☐ Complete one of the Want More Activities listed **OR** ☐ Study a scientist from the field of Astronomy
Supplies I Need for the Week ✓ Shoebox ✓ Black construction paper ✓ Pin ✓ Flashlight				
Things I Need to Prepare				

Additional Information Astronomy Week 4

Experiment Information

- **Introduction** – (*from the Student Guide*) A constellation is the pattern or shape that a group of stars makes in the sky. There are 88 named constellations in our sky. Your position on the Earth and the time of year determine which constellations you can see. The most recognized constellations in the Northern Hemisphere are the Big Dipper and the Little Dipper. In this experiment, you are going to make your own planetarium, or device used to project images of the stars, so that you can view these constellations at anytime.
- **Results** – The students should see the two constellations projected on the wall in front of them.

Discussion Questions

1. Why are the constellations Ursa Major and Ursa Minor called the Big Dipper and Little Dipper? (*Ursa Major and Ursa Minor are called the Big Dipper and Little Dipper because they resemble dippers.*)
2. Tell the story of the two bears in your own words. (*Student's answer should highlight the following: Jupiter fell in love with Callisto, Jupiter's wife Juno was jealous, Callisto had a son, but she went out hunting one day. Callisto ran into Juno who turned her into a bear, years later Callisto ran into her son and he shot her through the heart. Jupiter had not forgotten Callisto, he turned her son into a bear also. He reunited Callisto with her son by placing both of them up into the sky where they would always be together.*)
3. What are some other names for the constellation Ursa Major? (*Ursa Major is also known as the Big Dipper, David's Chariot, Seven Oxen of the Plowshare.*)

Want More

- **Make More Constellation Cards** – There are 88 named constellations, have the students choose several of them and make cards for their planetarium.

Sketch Assignment Week 4

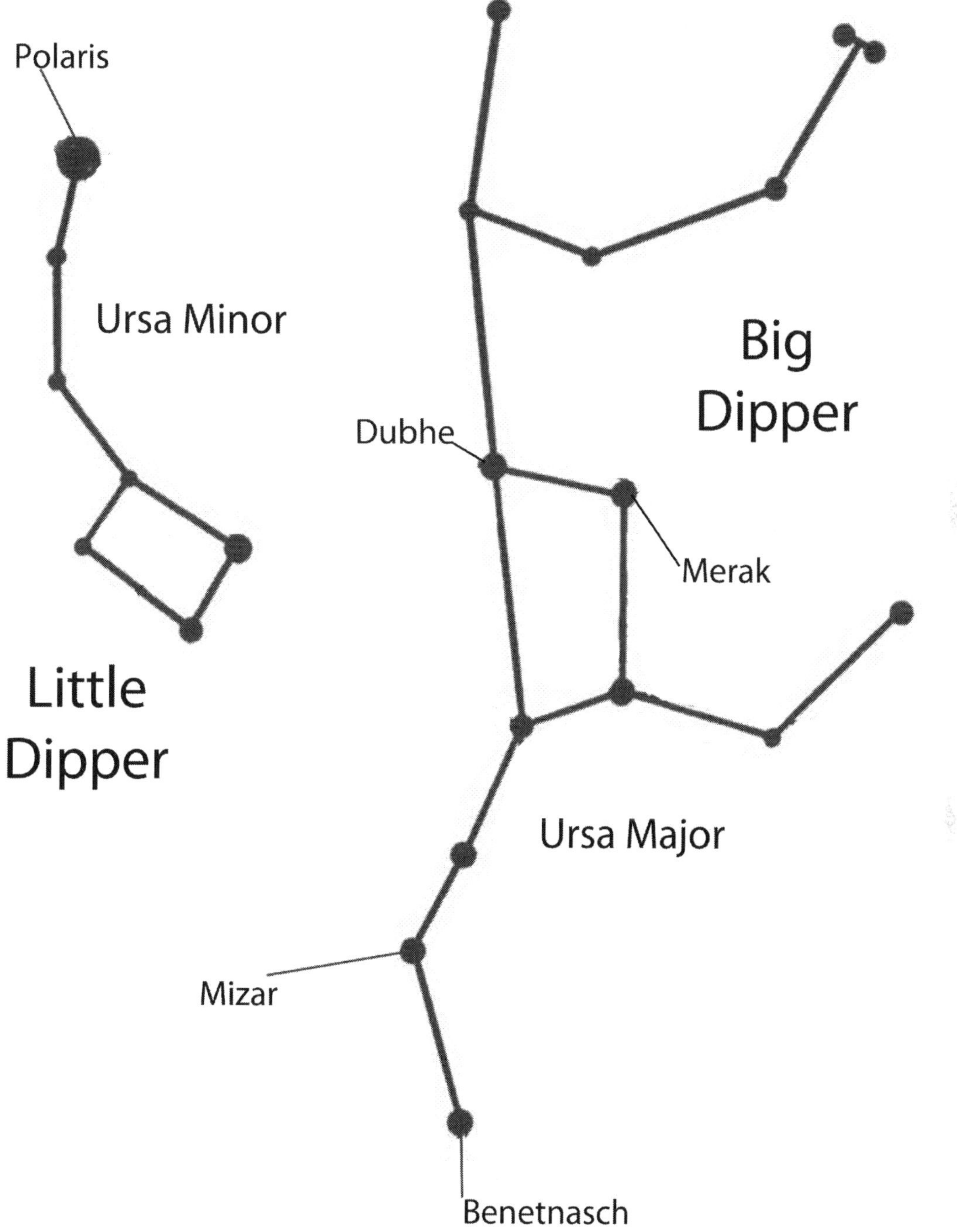

Student Assignment Sheet Astronomy Week 5
Constellations

Experiment: Constellations Research Project

This week you will spend part of the week on researching a constellation of the Zodiac and creating a profile page for that constellation.

Steps to Follow

1. Choose a Constellation – Choose one of the constellations of the Zodiac for an in-depth profile.
2. Do some research about the constellation – Use the internet and the resources you have in your home or at your library to find out more about your chosen constellation. Answer the following questions from your research:
   - ✓ What is the English translation of the Latin name of the constellation?
   - ✓ Where is the constellation found?
   - ✓ What are the major stars found in the constellation?
   - ✓ What is the best season to view the constellation?
   - ✓ What is the story behind the constellation's name?
   - ✓ Write down any interesting facts you have learned on individual index cards.
3. Complete the profile page for your constellation – Write the Latin name for your constellation on the blank at the top of the page. Then, fill out the remaining information. Your summary of the story behind the constellation should be four to five sentences long. Finally, draw your constellation in the box.

Writing Assignment

- Reading Assignment: *Kingfisher Science Encyclopedia* pg. 396-397 Constellations
- Additional Research Readings:
  - Constellations: *USE* pg. 160
  - Astrology: *DK Astro* pg. 16-17

Vocabulary & Memory Work

- ☐ Vocabulary: zodiac
- ☐ Memory Work – Continue to work on memorizing the Constellations of the Zodiac

Sketch Assignment: Constellations

- Label the following constellations and tell whether the are found in the Northern or Southern Hemisphere: The Southern Cross, Libra, Scorpio, Leo, Pegasus

Dates to Enter

- 7th century BC – Babylonian astronomers use a coordinate system resembling the Zodiac.
- ca. 50 BC – A relief called the Dendera zodiac is the first known depiction of the classical zodiac of twelve signs.

Schedules for Week 5

Two Days a Week

Day 1	Day 2
☐ Do the Constellation Research Project, then fill out the Constellation Profile Page on SG pp. 42-43 ☐ Define zodiac on SG pg. 15 ☐ Enter the dates onto the date sheets on SG pp. 8-12	☐ Read pp. 396-397 from the *Kingfisher Science Encyclopedia*, then discuss what was read ☐ Color and label the "Constellations" sketch on SG pg. 41
Supplies I Need for the Week ✓ No supplies needed	
Things I Need to Prepare	

Five Days a Week

Day 1	Day 2	Day 3	Day 4	Day 5
☐ Begin the Constellation Research Project ☐ Complete your research	☐ Fill out the Constellation Profile Page on SG pp. 42-43	☐ Read pp. 396-397 from the *Kingfisher Science Encyclopedia*, then discuss what was read ☐ Define zodiac on SG pg. 15	☐ Color and label the "Constellations" sketch on SG pg. 41 ☐ Enter the dates onto the date sheets on SG pp. 8-12	☐ Complete one of the Want More Activities listed **OR** ☐ Study a scientist from the field of Astronomy ☐ Take the Unit 1 Test
Supplies I Need for the Week ✓ No supplies needed				
Things I Need to Prepare				

Additional Information Astronomy Week 5

Constellation Research Project

☞ This week the students will be doing a mini-research project. They will be choosing a constellation from the Zodiac to profile. All the instructions they need are on the Student Assignment Page, but they may need you to walk them through the process depending on how much experience they have with doing research prior to this assignment.

Constellation Profile Sample Page

Constellation Profile Page

Aquila

English Translation: The Eagle

Location: a few degrees north of the celestial equator

Major Stars: Altair

Best Season to View the Constellation: the Summer

Story Behind the Name:

In ancient Greece there was a great eagle named Aquila, who was Zeus's pet. Prometheus, one of the Titan gods, angered Zeus by stealing a ray of sunshine. Zeus tied Prometheus to a mountain and had Aquila attack him repeatedly. Hercules, as a favor to Prometheus, killed Aquila with an arrow. Zeus took his beloved pet eagle and set him in the sky so that he could soar forever.

Discussion Questions

There is no additional writing assignment for this week because of the constellation research project. However, I suggest that you still discuss what your students read with the following questions.

1. What is a constellation? (*A constellation is a dot-to-dot picture in the night sky. Some are animals, imaginary creatures, and figures from mythology.*)

2. How many constellations have astronomers given names to? (*Astronomers have named 88 constellations that they use to help find their way around in the night sky.*)
3. What is the zodiac? (*The zodiac is a group of 12 constellations that the sun, moon, and planets appear to move through.*)

Want More

- **Make More Constellation Cards** – Have the students make constellation cards for the constellations in the Zodiac for their planetarium.
- **Make Another Constellation Profile Page** – Choose another one of the constellations of the Zodiac to profile.

Sketch Assignment Week 5

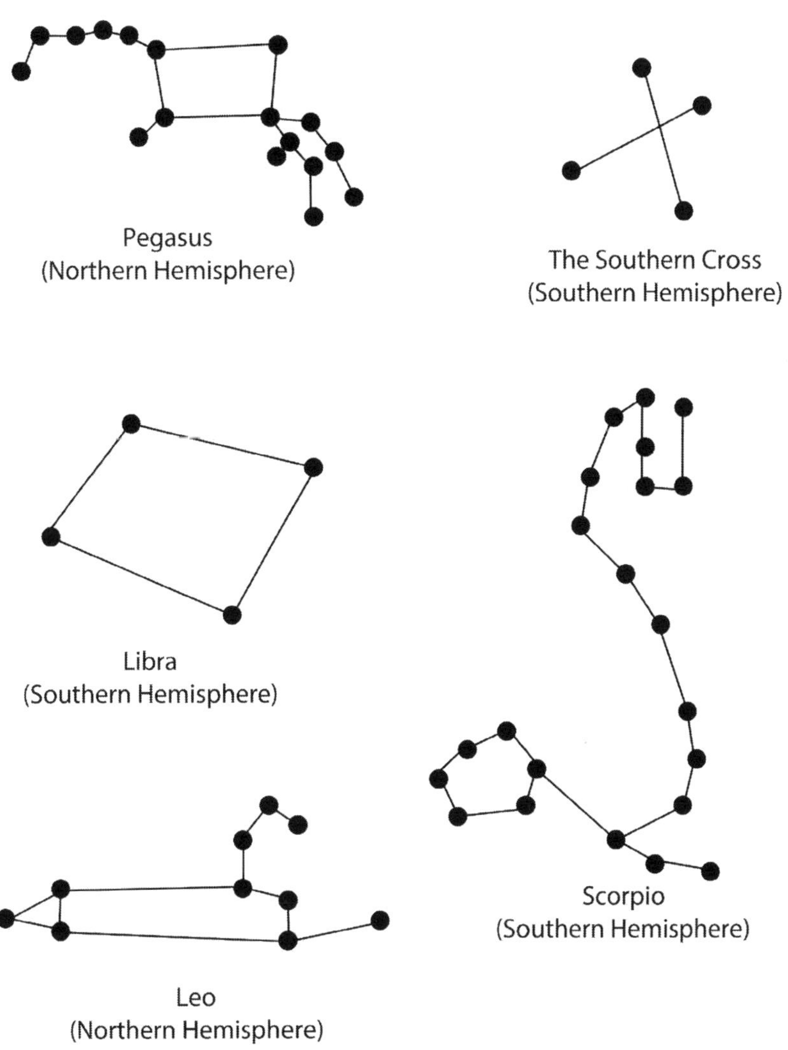

Astronomy Unit 1: Space
Discussion Questions

Week 1

1. How can we see other galaxies? How many do we know about?
2. How do astronomers measure distances in the universe?
3. What does everything in the universe do?

Week 2

1. What is the name of the galaxy our solar system is in?
2. How are galaxies classified?
3. What are two things that astronomers believe help to determine the shape of a galaxy?
4. Describe the typical active galaxy.
5. Which cluster of galaxies does the Milky Way belong to?

Week 3

1. What does light coming from a star tell an astronomer about a star?
2. Name three types of energy that are produced by a star.
3. How does a star's mass affect it?
4. Name two characteristics that are common to all stars.
5. What are the two types of star clusters? Explain both.
6. What happens to the core of a star when it dies?

Week 4

1. Why are the constellations Ursa Major and Ursa Minor called the Big Dipper and Little Dipper?
2. Tell the story of the two bears in your own words.
3. What are some other names for the constellation Ursa Major?

Week 5

1. What is a constellation?
2. How many constellations have astronomers given names to?
3. What is the zodiac?

Astronomy Unit 1: Space
Unit Test Answers

Vocabulary

1. B
2. E
3. A
4. H
5. D
6. I
7. G
8. F
9. C

True or False

1. False (*Astronomers know about approximately100 billiong galaxies.*)
2. True
3. True
4. False (*Galaxies are classified according to their shape.*)
5. True
6. True
7. False (*Ursa Minor is also known as the Little Dipper.*)
8. True
9. True
10. False (*The zodiac is a group of 12 constellations that the sun, moon, and planets appear to move through.*)

Short Answer

1. Answers should include 4 of the following: Blue Giant-hot, large star; Red Giant-cooler outer layer, large star; Main-sequence star-the typical star, such as the sun; Red Dwarf-cool, small star; White Dwarf-very cool, small star; Neutron star-tightly packed remnants of a star; Black hole-a star that has collapsed on its self
2. Within our solar system, astronomers us the Astronomical Unit (AU) to measure objects. The AU is equal to the distance between the Earth and the Sun, which is about 93 million miles. Outside of our solar system, astronomers use light years to measure objects in the universe. A light year is the distance that light travels in one year, which is about 5.88 trillion miles.
3. Astronomers believe that the amount of material, the speed of spin and the rate at which stars form all help to determine the shape of a galaxy.
4. All stars start with a hydrogen core that is converted into helium. All stars are born from nebulae or small clouds of gas and dust.
5. Answers should include 7 of the following: Aquarius, Aries, Cancer, Capricorn, Gemini, Leo, Libra, Pisces, Sagittarius, Scorpio, Taurus, Virgo

Astronomy Unit 1: Space
Unit Test

Vocabulary Matching

1. Universe
2. Galaxy
3. Cluster
4. Supercluster
5. Star
6. Nebulae
7. Black hole
8. Constellation
9. Zodiac

A. A group of galaxies that are found close together.

B. The collection of all the matter, space, and energy that exists, also known as the cosmos.

C. The twelve constellations through which the sun, moon, and planets appear to move.

D. A massive, hot, shining ball of gas.

E. A body held together by gravity that is made of millions of stars, gas, and dust.

F. The pattern that a group of stars seems to make in the sky.

G. Formed by a collapsed star, has a very strong gravitational pull.

H. The largest structure in the universe, composed of many galaxy clusters.

I. Clouds of dust and gas found in space.

True or False

1. ______________________ Astronomers know of less than 2 million galaxies in our universe.

2. ______________________ Everything in our universe moves.

3. ______________________ The galaxy that our solar system is found on is called the Milky Way galaxy.

4. ______________________ Galaxies are classified according to their size.

5. ______________________ A star produces heat and light energy, as well as UV radiation and X-rays.

6. ____________________ After the death of a star, its core can collapse and form a black hole or a neutron star.

7. ____________________ Ursa Minor is also know as the Little Star.

8. ____________________ Ursa Major is also known as the Big Dipper, David's Chariot and the Seven Oxen of the Plowshare.

9. ____________________ A constellation is a dot-to-dot picture in the night sky.

10. ____________________ The zodiac is a group of 100 constellations that the sun, moon, and planets appear to move through

Short Answer

1. Name and describe four types of stars that can be found in our universe.

2. Explain how astronomer's measure distances in our universe. (*HINT – There are 2 ways.*)

3. Name two things that astronomers believe help to shape a galaxy.

4. Name two characteristics that are common to all stars.

5. Name at least 7 of the constellations of the Zodiac.

Astronomy Unit 2

Our Solar System

Astronomy Unit 2: Our Solar System
Overview of Study

Sequence of Study

Week 6: Sun
Week 7: Inner Planets (Mercury, Venus, Mars)
Week 8: Earth/Moon
Week 9: Outer Planets (Jupiter & Saturn)
Week 10: Outer Planets (Uranus & Neptune) & Minor Members
Week 11: Comets, Meteorites

Materials by Week

Week	Materials
6	2 glass jars or 2 clear glasses, Plastic wrap, 2 Black tea bags, Water, Instant read thermometer
7	3 Heavy duty plastic bottles, 3 Balloons, 3 tsp of yeast (1 ½ packages), 3 TBSP of sugar, Water, White vinegar
8	Apple, Fork, Flashlight, Partner
9	Wooden Dowel, Foil, Paper clip, Toaster
10	Construction paper, Paints or crayons
11	Marble, Rubber bouncy ball, Foam ball, Tennis ball, Cake pan, Cornstarch, Ruler

Vocabulary for the Unit

1. **Photosphere** – The surface of the Sun.
2. **Prominence** – Large eruptions or loops of flaming gas from the Sun's surface.
3. **Solar wind** – A constant stream of particles that flow into space from the Sun.
4. **Sunspot** – Dark, cooler areas of the Sun's photosphere.
5. **Crater** – The hole formed in a planet's surface by the impact of a meteorite.
6. **Planet** – A large globe composed of rock, liquid, or gas that revolves around a star.
7. **Axis** – An imaginary line through the center of a planet, around which it rotates.
8. **Orbit** – The path of one celestial body around another.
9. **Moon** – A celestial body in orbit around a planet.
10. **Eclipse** – When one celestial body casts a shadow on another celestial body.
11. **Galilean moons** – Jupiter's 4 largest moons, Io, Ganymede, Callisto and Europa, they are named after Galileo, who discovered them.
12. **Gas giant** – A large planet that is mostly composed of gas.
13. **Dwarf planet** – A minor planet in the solar system.
14. **Asteroid** – Large chunks of rock and metal that orbit the sun in the region between Mars and Jupiter.

15. Comet – A chunk of frozen gas and dirt that has an orbit.
16. Meteor – A meteoroid that starts to burn as it enters the atmosphere.
17. Meteoroid – A small piece of space debris.

Memory Work for the Unit

Planet Order *(along with the planet's gravity relative to Earth)*

1. Sun
2. Mercury (Gravity: 0.38)
3. Venus (Gravity: 0.90)
4. Earth (Gravity: 1 or 9.8 m/s^2) [Moon (Gravity: 0.17)]
5. Mars (Gravity: 0.38)
6. Jupiter (Gravity: 2.34)
7. Saturn (Gravity: 0.93)
8. Uranus (Gravity: 0.90)
9. Neptune (Gravity: 1.13)

Notes

Student Assignment Sheet Astronomy Week 6
Sun

Experiment: Do the sun's rays contain heat?

Materials
- ✓ 2 glass jars or 2 clear glasses
- ✓ Plastic wrap
- ✓ 2 black tea bags
- ✓ Water
- ✓ Instant read thermometer

Procedure

****NOTE** – You will need to do this experiment on a sunny day.**

1. Read the introduction to this experiment and answer the question.
2. Fill each jar with the same amount of water. Take the temperature of the water in each jar. Then, place a tea bag in each jar and cover with the plastic wrap.
3. Set one of the jars outside in a sunny spot and leave the other jar inside your house.
4. After two hours, bring the jar you left outside into the house. Then, measure the temperature of the water and observe any changes to the appearance of the water. Write your results on your experiment sheet.
5. Draw conclusions and complete your experiment sheet.

Vocabulary & Memory Work

- ☐ Vocabulary: photosphere, prominence, solar wind, sunspot
- ☐ Memory Work – Begin to work on memorizing the Planet Order.
  1. Sun
  2. Mercury (Gravity: 0.38)
  3. Venus (Gravity: 0.90)
  4. Earth (Gravity: 1 or 9.8 m/s^2) [Moon (Gravity: 0.17)]
  5. Mars (Gravity: 0.38)
  6. Jupiter (Gravity: 2.34)
  7. Saturn (Gravity: 0.93)
  8. Uranus (Gravity: 0.90)
  9. Neptune (Gravity: 1.13)

Sketch Assignment: Parts of the Sun

- Label the Following: chromosphere, flare, facula, prominence, sunspot, hydrogen core, photosphere

Writing Assignment

- Reading Assignment: *Kingfisher Science Encyclopedia* pp. 394-395 The Sun
- Additional Research Readings
  - The Sun: *USE* pp. 192-193
  - The Sun: *DK Astro* pp. 38-39

Dates to Enter:

- 1930 – French astronomer, Bernard Lyot, invents the coronagraph, allowing scientists to view the Sun without waiting for a total solar eclipse.
- 1868-1938 – George Hale lived. He was an American astronomer who studied sunspots and discovered the magnetic fields within them.

Schedules for Week 6

Two Days a Week

Day 1	Day 2
☐ Define photosphere, prominence, sunspot, solar wind on SG pg. 46 ☐ Do the "Do the Sun's rays contain heat?" experiment, then fill out the experiment sheet on SG pp. 50-51 ☐ Enter the dates onto the date sheets on SG pp. 8-12	☐ Read pp. 394-395 from the *Kingfisher Science Encyclopedia*, then discuss what was read ☐ Prepare an outline or narrative summary, write it on SG pp. 52-53 ☐ Color and label the "Parts of the Sun" sketch on SG pg. 49

Supplies I Need for the Week

- ✓ 2 glass jars or 2 clear glasses
- ✓ Plastic wrap
- ✓ 2 black tea bags
- ✓ Water
- ✓ Instant read thermometer

Things I Need to Prepare

Five Days a Week

Day 1	Day 2	Day 3	Day 4	Day 5
☐ Do the "Do the Sun's rays contain heat?" experiment, then fill out the experiment sheet on SG pp. 50-51	☐ Read pp. 394-395 from the *Kingfisher Science Encyclopedia*, then discuss what was read ☐ Write an outline or list of facts on SG pg. 52	☐ Define photosphere, prominence, sunspot, solar wind on SG pg. 46 ☐ Enter the dates onto the date sheets on SG pp. 8-12 ☐ Color and label the "Parts of the Sun" sketch on SG pg. 49	☐ Read one or all of the additional reading assignments ☐ Prepare your report, write the report on SG pg. 53	☐ Complete one of the Want More Activities listed **OR** ☐ Study a scientist from the field of Astronomy

Supplies I Need for the Week

- ✓ 2 glass jars or 2 clear glasses
- ✓ Plastic wrap
- ✓ 2 black tea bags
- ✓ Water
- ✓ Instant read thermometer

Things I Need to Prepare

Additional Information Astronomy Week 6

Experiment Information

- **Introduction** – (*from the Student Guide*) The sun is the closest star to the earth. It is a giant ball of a constantly exploding gas called hydrogen. The surface of the sun is around 9,932°F, but the core is much hotter. It is the largest object in our Solar System. The sun's gravitational pull is so strong that all the planets in our Solar System revolve around it. The sun is important to the earth in many ways. In this experiment, you are going to look specifically at the sun's rays affect the objects on our planet.
- **Results** – The students should see that the jar that was outside in the sun has a greater temperature increase than the jar that was inside. They should also observe that the water in the jar that was outside in the sun is much darker than the jar that was inside. They may also observe that the water in the jar that was inside did not noticeably change color.
- **Explanation** – The jar that was left inside acts as a control because it did not receive any of the sun's rays. The jar that was outside in the sun received direct rays from the sun, which caused several changes to the water. The sun's rays carry energy in the form of heat which causes the temperature of the water to increase. This temperature increase also causes tea molecules to be released into the water, changing the color & taste of the water.

Discussion Questions

1. What is the sun? (*The sun is a star or a giant ball of hot gas.*)
2. What causes sunspots? (*Sunspots are caused by magnetic fields in the sun. They are so strong that they slow down the flow of heat within the sun.*)
3. What is the chromosphere of the sun composed of? (*The chromosphere of the sun is composed of hydrogen and helium gas.*)
4. Briefly explain the expected life of the sun. (*The sun was born from a nebula. It has been combusting ever since and scientists believe that its life is halfway over. They think that when half of its hydrogen core has been converted into helium, the core will collapse. Then the outer layer will cool and swell out. The sun will have become a red giant. Once the helium turns to carbon, the sun will have cooled further and turned yellow. The outer layer will shrink and the inner layers will collapse, turning the sun into a white dwarf. Then the sun will slowly fade out and die.*)

Want More

- **Make a solar system fact book** – This week make the page for the sun and the cover for the book. Have the students cut out pictures of the solar system and the sun. A template has been included for you to use in the appendix of this guide on pg. 251. Fold one piece of construction paper in half and cut. Label one half with "Solar System Fact Book" and glue the solar system picture to it. Glue the sun picture on the other half sheet of construction paper and label it with "The Sun". Then turn the sheet over and glue a piece of blank paper on the back. Have the students write 5-6 keys facts that they learned about the sun on the piece of paper. They will continue this project throughout the unit.

Sketch Assignment Week 6

Parts of the Sun

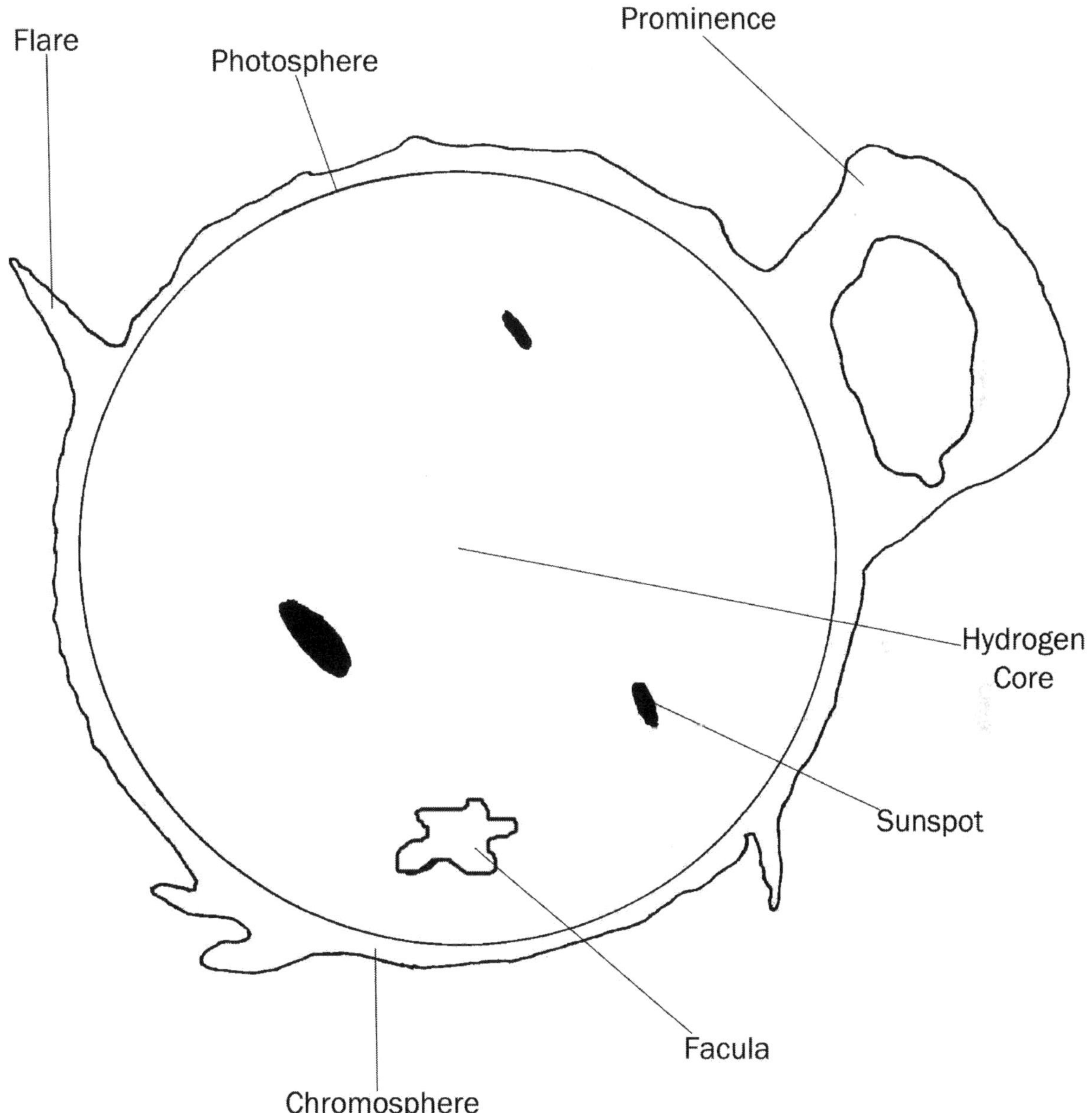

Student Assignment Sheet Astronomy Week 7
Inner Planets-Mercury, Venus, and Mars

Experiment: Can yeast survive on Mercury or Venus?

Materials
- ✓ 3 heavy duty plastic bottles
- ✓ 3 balloons
- ✓ 3 tsp of yeast (1 ½ packages)
- ✓ 3 TBSP of sugar
- ✓ Water
- ✓ White vinegar

> **CAUTION**
>
> ***Hot water is very dangerous and can cause injury. Be sure to have an adult handle the hot water at all times. ALWAYS use proper protection when handling hot water!***

Procedure
1. Read the introduction to this experiment and answer the question.
2. Label the bottles, "Mercury," "Venus," and "Earth." Use a funnel to carefully add 1 ½ cups of warm (between 125°F and 130°F) water to the Earth bottle. Use a funnel to carefully add 1½ cups of ice cold (below 40°F) water to the Mercury bottle. Have an adult use a funnel to carefully add 1 cup of hot (above 140°F) water and ½ cup of vinegar to the Venus bottle.
3. Add 1 tsp of yeast and one TBSP of sugar to each of the bottles, and then quickly cover the top of the bottle with a balloon.
4. Wait 30 minutes. Then, make observations and measure the circumference of each balloon.
5. Draw conclusions and complete your experiment sheet.

Vocabulary & Memory Work
- Vocabulary: crater, planet
- Memory Work – Continue to work on memorizing on Planet Order

Sketch Assignment: Inner Planets
- Label the Following: Mercury, Caloris Basin, crater-covered surface; Venus, multiple layers of dense clouds; Mars, Polar regions covered with water, ice and carbon dioxide ice

Writing Assignment
- Reading Assignment: *Kingfisher Science Encyclopedia* pg. 403 Mercury & pg. 404 Venus, pg. 405 Mars
- Additional Research Readings
  - The Inner Planets: *USE* pg. 164-165
  - Mercury: *DK Astro* pg. 44-45, Venus: *DK Astro* pg. 46-47, Mars: *DK Astro* pg. 48-49
  - Venus & Mercury: *ENS* pg. 28-29, *ENS* pg. 30-31

Dates to Enter
- 1974-1975 – *Mariner 10* flies past Mercury three times to take overlapping photos of the surface of the planet.
- 1990-1994 – *Magellan* maps 98% of the surface of Venus.
- 1976 – Two American space probes land on Mars to test for signs of life, but find none.
- 1997 – *Pathfinder* lands on Mars and delivers the robotic rover *Sojourner* to explore the surface of Mars.
- 2004 – Mobile robots, called *Spirit* and *Opportunity,* explore the surface of Mars.

Schedules for Week 7

Two Days a Week

Day 1	Day 2
☐ Define crater, planet on SG pg. 46 ☐ Do the "Can yeast survive on Mercury or Venus?" experiment, then fill out the experiment sheet on SG pp. 56-57 ☐ Enter the dates onto the date sheets on SG pp. 8-12	☐ Read pp. 403-405 from the *Kingfisher Science Encyclopedia*, then discuss what was read ☐ Prepare an outline or narrative summary, write it on SG pp. 58-59 ☐ Color and label the "Inner Planets" sketch on SG pg. 55

Supplies I Need for the Week
- ✓ 3 heavy duty plastic bottles
- ✓ 3 balloons
- ✓ 3 tsp of yeast (1 ½ packages)
- ✓ 3 TBSP of sugar
- ✓ Water, White vinegar

Things I Need to Prepare

Five Days a Week

Day 1	Day 2	Day 3	Day 4	Day 5
☐ Do the "Can yeast survive on Mercury or Venus?" experiment, then fill out the experiment sheet on SG pp. 56-57	☐ Read pp. 403-405 from the *Kingfisher Science Encyclopedia*, then discuss what was read ☐ Write an outline or list of facts on SG pg. 58	☐ Define crater, planet on SG pg. 46 ☐ Enter the dates onto the date sheets on SG pp. 8-12 ☐ Color and label the "Inner Planets" sketch on SG pg. 55	☐ Read one or all of the additional reading assignments ☐ Prepare your report, write the report on SG pg. 59	☐ Complete one of the Want More Activities listed **OR** ☐ Study a scientist from the field of Astronomy

Supplies I Need for the Week
- ✓ 3 heavy duty plastic bottles
- ✓ 3 balloons
- ✓ 3 tsp of yeast (1 ½ packages)
- ✓ 3 TBSP of sugar
- ✓ Water, White vinegar

Things I Need to Prepare

Additional Information Astronomy Week 7

Experiment Information

- **Introduction** – (*from the Student Guide*) Each planet has its own unique atmosphere or layer of gas surrounding the planet. The atmosphere and the planet's proximity to the Sun affect the surface conditions and temperature of the sphere. The atmosphere around Earth is perfectly suited to support live on the planet. In this experiment, you are going to test and see if Mercury and Venus could also support life.
- **Results** – The students should see that their Earth bottle inflates quite a bit. The circumferences will vary based on the size of your balloon and the freshness of your yeast. The Mercury and Venus bottles balloons may inflate a bit, but probably not at all.
- **Explanation** – The Earth bottle contains warm water which is the perfect temperature for the yeast to thrive in. The Mercury bottle contains ice cold water to simulate how cold the planet gets when it is not facing the sun because of its thin atmosphere. The Venus bottle contains hot water and vinegar to simulate the thick and acidic atmosphere found on the planet. Yeasts will only grow and reproduce at within the right temperature and acidity range, just like life on a planet will only thrive under the proper conditions.
- **Troubleshooting** – It can take an hour or more to see results, depending upon the age and health of the yeast you use. If you don't see results after 30 minutes, give it another hour before you toss the bottles to see if the results changes.

Discussion Questions

Mercury pg. 403

1. What is the surface of Mercury like? (*The surface of Mercury is covered in craters and crossed by ridges and craters that can be up to a mile high. It is extremely hot during the day (842°F) and bitterly cold at night (-274°F).*)
2. What two factors contribute to the fact that a day on Mercury is longer than a year? (*Mercury's day is longer than its year due to its fast orbit and slow spin.*) ***NOTE****: A year is defined as the time it takes for a planet to make one revolution around the Sun, while a day is defined as the time it takes for the planet to revolve once on its axis.*

Venus pg. 404

1. Why does Venus appear as a bright star in our sky? (*Venus appears as a bright star in our sky because sunlight is reflected from its cloud tops.*)
2. What are two reasons why humans could not survive on Venus? (*Humans could not survive on Venus because the air pressure is 90 times greater than what it is on Earth, the atmosphere contains toxic sulfuric acid and the average surface temperature is 867°F.*)
3. What is the surface of Venus like? (*The surface of Venus is very hot. It is a relatively smooth planet with volcanic craters and lava flows.*)

Mars pg. 405

1. Why is Mars known as the Red Planet? (*Mars is known as the Red Planet due to its red surface and sky. The surface is red because of the rock that is rich in iron oxide. The sky is red because of the dust from the surface.*)
2. Has life been found on Mars? (*No*) What have explorers found? (*Explorers have found*

evidence of the past existence of water on the planet of Mars.)

3. What is the surface of Mars like? (*Mar's surface is a rock-filled desert. It has craters from meteors and dusty red dunes. Mars also has large mountains and deep canyons.*)

Want More

- **Make a solar system fact book** – This week make the pages for Mercury, Venus, and Mars. Have the students cut out pictures of the three planets. A template has been included for you to use in the appendix of this guide on pp. 252-253. Fold three pieces of construction paper in half and cut. Glue the picture of Mercury on one half sheet of construction paper and label it with "Mercury". Then turn the sheet over and glue a piece of blank paper on the back. Have the students write 5-6 keys facts that they learned about Mercury on the piece of paper. Repeat this for Venus and Mars. Add to the pages they made the previous week.

Sketch Assignment Week 7

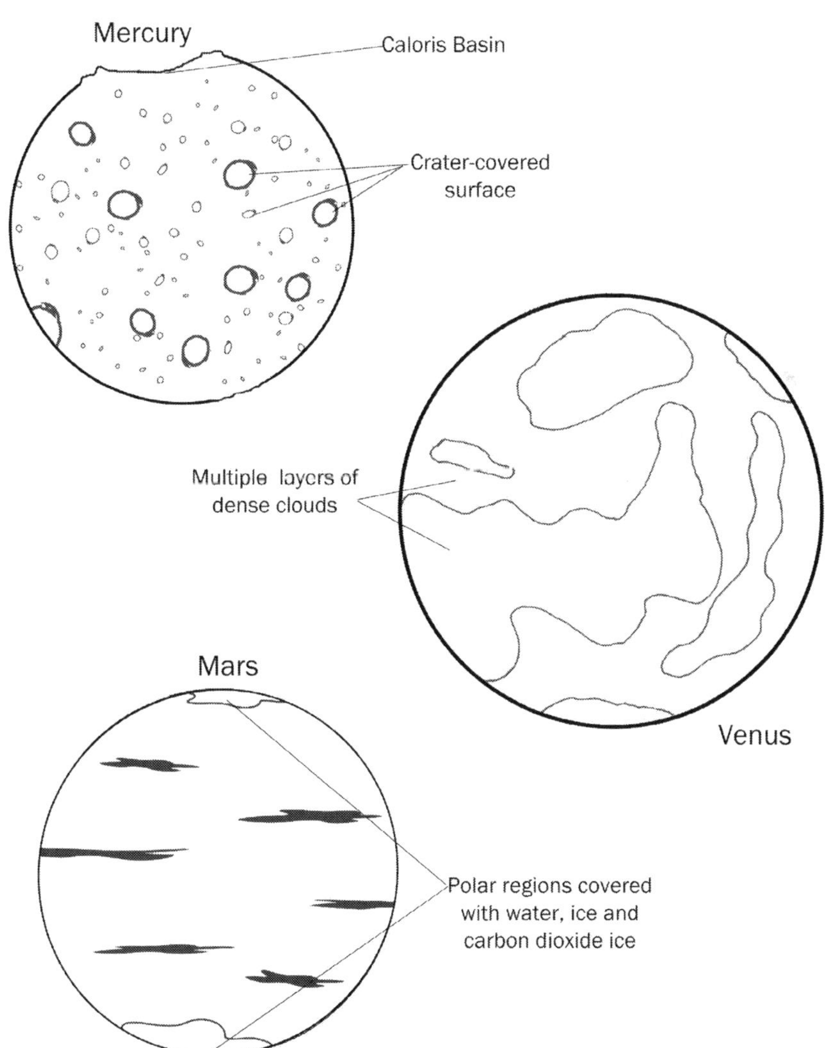

Student Assignment Sheet Astronomy Week 8
Earth and the Moon

Experiment: Does the moon change size?

Materials
- ✓ Apple
- ✓ Fork
- ✓ Flashlight
- ✓ Partner

Procedure
1. Read the introduction to this experiment and answer the question.
2. Secure the apple on the end of the fork.
3. Have your partner stand 5 feet away from you and shine the flashlight in your direction.
4. Hold the fork with the apple at arm's length in front of the flashlight and a little above the beam. ***(Note** – The apple should appear darkened.)*
5. Keep the apple in the same place and turn slowly counterclockwise around an imaginary circle with the apple as the center. Continue until you have completed your circle and are back to your starting point. ***(Note** – You may need to duck down a bit as you turn so that you don't block the flashlight beam with your body.)*
6. Write down your observations about what happened to your apple as you were turning.
7. Draw conclusions and complete your experiment sheet.

Vocabulary & Memory Work
- ☐ Vocabulary: axis, orbit, moon, eclipse
- ☐ Memory Work – Continue to work on memorizing the Planet Order

Sketch Assignment: Phases of the Moon
- Label the following and color in the portion of the moon that the labels represent: New Moon, Waxing Crescent, First Quarter, Gibbous Waxing, Full Moon, Gibbous Waning, Last Quarter, and Waning Crescent

Writing Assignment
- Reading Assignment: *Kingfisher Science Encyclopedia* pg. 400-401 Earth and the Moon, pg. 402 Eclipses
- Additional Research Readings
  - The Earth and the Moon: *USE* pg. 166-167
  - Earth: *DK Astro* pg. 42-43
  - Moon: *DK Astro* pg. 40-41

Dates to Enter
- 1647 – Johannes Hevelius publishes the first lunar atlas.
- October 1959 – Russian spacecraft *Luna 3* transmits the first images of the far side of the moon back to the Earth.
- July 20, 1969 – US astronauts Neil Armstrong and Edwin Aldrin became the first humans to walk on the moon.

Schedules for Week 8

Two Days a Week

Day 1	Day 2
☐ Define axis, orbit, moon, eclipse on SG pg. 46 & 47 ☐ Do the "Does the moon change size?" experiment, then fill out the experiment sheet on SG pp. 62-63 ☐ Enter the dates onto the date sheets on SG pp. 8-12	☐ Read pp. 400-402 from the *Kingfisher Science Encyclopedia*, then discuss what was read ☐ Prepare an outline or narrative summary, write it on SG pg. 64-65 ☐ Color and label the "Phases of the Moon" sketch on SG pg. 61
Supplies I Need for the Week ✓ Apple ✓ Fork ✓ Flashlight ✓ Partner	
Things I Need to Prepare	

Five Days a Week

Day 1	Day 2	Day 3	Day 4	Day 5
☐ Do the "Does the moon change size?" experiment, then fill out the experiment sheet on SG pp. 62-63	☐ Read pp. 400-402 from the *Kingfisher Science Encyclopedia*, then discuss what was read ☐ Write an outline or list of facts on SG pg. 64	☐ Define axis, orbit, moon, eclipse on SG pg. 46 & 47 ☐ Enter the dates onto the date sheets on SG pp. 8-12 ☐ Color and label the "Phases of the Moon" sketch on SG pg. 61	☐ Read one or all of the additional reading assignments ☐ Prepare your report, write the report on SG pg. 65	☐ Complete one of the Want More Activities listed **OR** ☐ Study a scientist from the field of Astronomy
Supplies I Need for the Week ✓ Apple ✓ Fork ✓ Flashlight ✓ Partner				
Things I Need to Prepare				

Additional Information Astronomy Week 8

Experiment Information

☞ **Introduction** – (*from the Student Guide*) The moon is a ball of rock that orbits around the Earth. It takes 27.3 days to complete its orbit around our planet. As the moon travels around the Earth it appears to be smaller or larger to us. In this experiment, you are going to determine if the moon actually changes size as it orbits around us by using an apple for the moon, a flashlight for the sun and your head for the Earth.

☞ **Results** – The students should see that the apple begins to be illuminated as their rotate away from the flashlight. Once their back is to the flashlight, they should be able to see the entire apple. As they continue around the imaginary circle, the apple will begin to darken again.

☞ **Explanation** – The portion of the moon that is illuminated by the sun depends upon the angle that the moon is relative to the sun. In other words, when the moon is positioned 90° from the sun, we see that half of the moon's surface is illuminated. In the experiment the angle the apple was from the flashlight beam determined how much of the apple was illuminated. So that when the apple was 90° from the flashlight beam, half of the apple was illuminated.

Discussion Questions

Earth and the Moon pg. 400-401

1. What makes the Earth unique to our solar system? (*The Earth is unique because it is the largest rock planet in the solar system. It is also very wet compared to other planets and full of life.*)
2. How long does it take for the Earth to orbit the sun one time? (*It takes the Earth 365.25 days to orbit the sun one time.*) How long does it take the Earth to complete one spin on its axis? (*It takes the Earth 23.9 hours to complete one spin on its axis.*)
3. Why do we only see one side of the moon from the Earth? (*We are only able to see one side of the moon from the Earth because one orbit of the moon around the Earth takes the same time as one complete spin on the moon's axis.*)
4. What is a moon phase? (*A moon phase is the size of the sun-lit part of the moon that we can see from Earth.*) How long does it take the moon to complete one cycle of its phases? (*It takes the moon 29.5 days to complete one cycle of its phases.*)

Eclipses pg. 402

1. What is the difference between a solar eclipse and a lunar eclipse? (*In a solar eclipse the moon blocks the sun and prevents its light from reaching Earth. In contrast, a lunar eclipse happens when the moon is in the Earth's shadow, preventing the moon from reflecting the Sun's light.*)

Want More

✐ **Make a solar system fact book** – This week make a page for the Earth and its moon. Have the students cut out pictures of the Earth and the moon. A template has been included for you to use in the appendix of this guide on pg. 253. Fold one piece of construction paper in half and cut. Glue the picture of the Earth and the moon on one half sheet of construction paper and label it with "Earth and its moon". Then turn the sheet over and glue a piece of blank paper on the back. Have the students write 5-6 keys facts that they learned about the Earth and the moon on the piece of paper. Add to the page they made the previous week.

- **Keep a Moon Diary** – Have the students make their own moon diary. You can do this by going out to observe the moon every night just after the sky darkens. Then have the students take a picture or draw what they see. Make sure they label each picture with the day and time that they observed the moon (i.e. Day 12, 8:45 PM). Have them keep the diary for at least 30 days so they can see a complete moon phase cycle.

Sketch Assignment Week 8

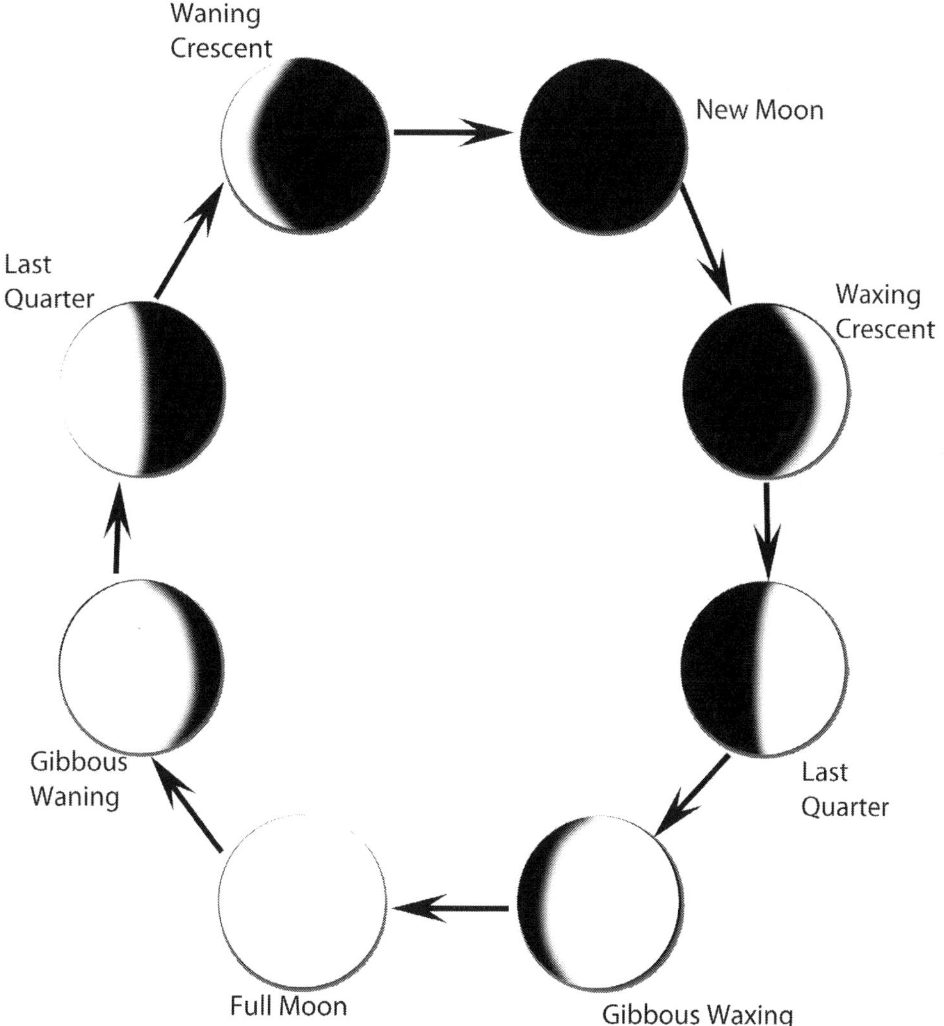

Student Assignment Sheet Astronomy Week 9
Outer Planets-Jupiter and Saturn

Experiment: Does the heat in Jupiter's core affect the storms on its surface?

Materials

- ✓ Wooden dowel rod
- ✓ Paper clip
- ✓ 4 inch square of aluminum foil (not heavy duty)
- ✓ Toaster

> **CAUTION:**
> ***Be careful not to touch your toaster or your foil kite until they have time to cool. They will be very hot and can burn you.***

Procedure

1. Read the introduction to this experiment and answer the question.
2. Begin by making a kite. First, unbend your paper clip halfway. Place the remaining loop of the paper clip over your wooden dowel (it should be a tight fit.) Then, puncture the corner of your aluminum foil with the straight end of the paper clip. Finally, bend the straight end of the paper clip over so that the foil is secure.
3. Turn your toaster on and wait 1 minute. Move your foil kite so that it is about a foot above the toaster's opening. Observe what happens to your kite and write it down on your experiment sheet.
4. Remove your kite from over the heat and turn off the toaster. Observe what happens to your kite and write it down on your experiment sheet.
5. Draw conclusions and complete your experiment sheet.

Vocabulary & Memory Work

- ☐ Vocabulary: Galilean moons, gas giants
- ☐ Memory Work – Continue to work on memorizing the Planet Order

Sketch Assignment: Jupiter & Saturn

- Label the following: Jupiter, the Red Spot, bands of storms, Saturn, rings, bands of ammonia, water and methane clouds

Writing Assignment

- Reading Assignment: *Kingfisher Science Encyclopedia* pg. 406 Jupiter, pg. 407 Saturn
- Additional Research Readings
  - The Outer Planets: *USE* pg. 168-169
  - Jupiter: *DK Astro* pg. 50-51, *ENS* pg. 32-33
  - Saturn: *DK Astro* pg. 52-53, *ENS* pg. 34-35

Dates to Enter

- 1610 – Galileo makes the first systematic study of Jupiter's 4 largest moons.
- 1660 – Robert Hooke reports a giant spot on Jupiter's surface.
- 1655 – Dutch scientist, Christiaan Huygens, correctly identifies Saturn's rings.
- 1979 – *Pioneer II* explores Saturn's rings.
- 1995 – The *Galileo* probe reaches Jupiter. It studies Jupiter's atmosphere and its moons.
- 2004 – *Cassini* arrives at Saturn to study the planet's moons and rings.

Schedules for Week 9

Two Days a Week

Day 1	Day 2
❑ Define Galilean moons & gas giants on SG pg. 47 ❑ Do the "Does the heat in Jupiter's core affect the storms on its surface?" experiment, then fill out the experiment sheet on SG pp. 68-69 ❑ Enter the dates onto the date sheets on SG pp. 8-12	❑ Read pp. 406-407 from the *Kingfisher Science Encyclopedia*, then discuss what was read ❑ Prepare an outline or narrative summary, write it on SG pp. 70-71 ❑ Color and label the "Jupiter & Saturn" sketch on SG pg. 67
Supplies I Need for the Week ✓ Wooden dowel rod ✓ Paper clip ✓ 4 inch square of aluminum foil (not heavy duty) ✓ Toaster	
Things I Need to Prepare	

Five Days a Week

Day 1	Day 2	Day 3	Day 4	Day 5
❑ Do the "Does the heat in Jupiter's core affect the storms on its surface?" experiment, then fill out the experiment sheet on SG pp. 68-69	❑ Read pp. 406-407 from the *Kingfisher Science Encyclopedia*, then discuss what was read ❑ Write an outline or list of facts on SG pg. 70	❑ Define Galilean moon & gas giants on SG pg. 47 ❑ Enter the dates onto the date sheets on SG pp. 8-12 ❑ Color and label the "Jupiter & Saturn" sketch on SG pg. 67	❑ Read one or all of the additional reading assignments ❑ Prepare your report, write the report on SG pg. 71	❑ Complete one of the Want More Activities listed **OR** ❑ Study a scientist from the field of Astronomy
Supplies I Need for the Week ✓ Wooden dowel rod ✓ Paper clip ✓ 4 inch square of aluminum foil (not heavy duty) ✓ Toaster				
Things I Need to Prepare				

Additional Information Astronomy Week 9

Experiment Information

- ☞ **Introduction** – (*from the Student Guide*) Jupiter is a very turbulent planet. Its many bands and prominent red spot are evidence of a stormy atmosphere that surrounds the planet. Jupiter's Red Spot is known as the solar system's oldest hurricane. The high pressure that is found on the planet contributes to the perpetuation of these storms, but there are other factors involved as well. In this experiment, you will examine whether the heat from Jupiter's core is able to create winds that help to perpetuate the storms that cover the planet.
- ☞ **Results** – The students should see that the kite flutters when it is held over the toaster and it is still when not over the heat of the toaster.
- ☞ **Explanation** – The kite flutters because when hot air rises and meets with the cool air. Wind is created due to convection, or the tendency of a hotter material to rise. Jupiter is under a tremendous amount of pressure, which crushes the planet's material towards the interior and releases heat. The heat then causes the atmospheric gases to boil up from the warmer more interior layers. Those gases then meet with the cooler exterior layers of the atmosphere, which creates powerful winds. These winds help to fuel the storms that cover the planet's exterior.

Discussion Questions

Jupiter pg. 406

1. Describe what Jupiter is like. (*Jupiter is the largest planet in our solar system. Its surface is gaseous with liquid below. Jupiter does have a solid core.*)
2. What are two factors that contribute to Jupiter's stormy atmosphere? (*Two factors that contribute to Jupiter's stormy atmosphere are its rapid spin and the heat rising from the interior of the planet. The students may also include pressure as a factor in their answer.*)

Saturn pg. 407

1. What is the outer surface of Saturn like? (*The outer surface of Saturn is not solid. It is made of bands of ammonia, water and methane clouds. These clouds are colored by phosphorus and other elements.*)
2. What are Saturn's rings made from? (*Saturn's rings are made from billions of pieces of ice-covered rock that orbit around the planet.*) Where are the largest pieces of Saturn's rings found? (*The largest pieces of Saturn's rings are found closest to the planet.*)

Want More

- **Make a solar system fact book** – This week make a page for the Jupiter and Saturn. Have the students cut out pictures of Jupiter. A template has been included for you to use in the appendix of this guide on pg. 254. Fold one piece of construction paper in half and cut. Glue the picture of Jupiter on one half sheet of construction paper and label it with "Jupiter". Then turn the sheet over and glue a piece of blank paper on the back. Have the students write 5-6 keys facts that they learned about Jupiter on the piece of paper. Repeat this for Saturn. Add to the pages they made the previous week.

Sketch Assignment Week 9

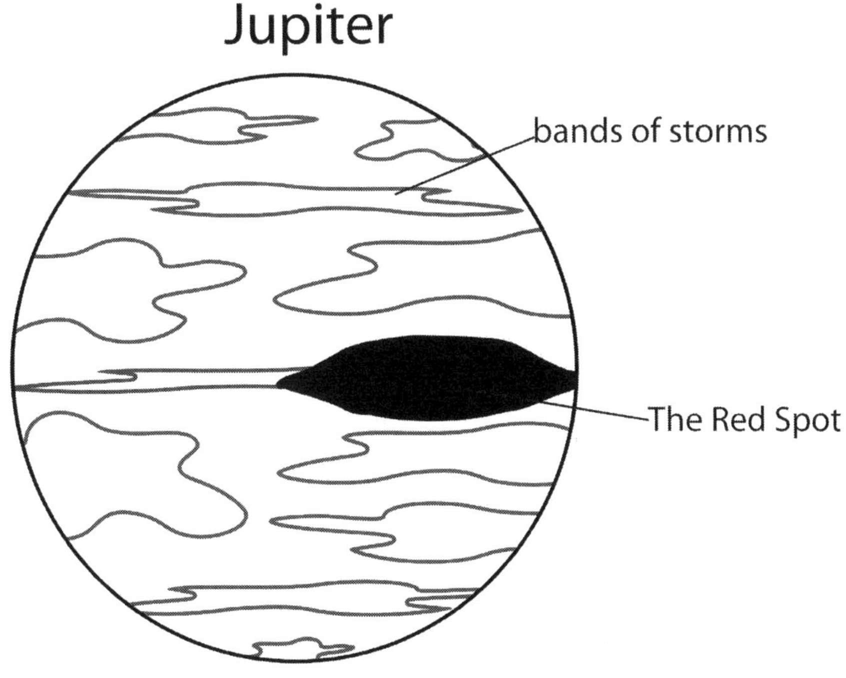

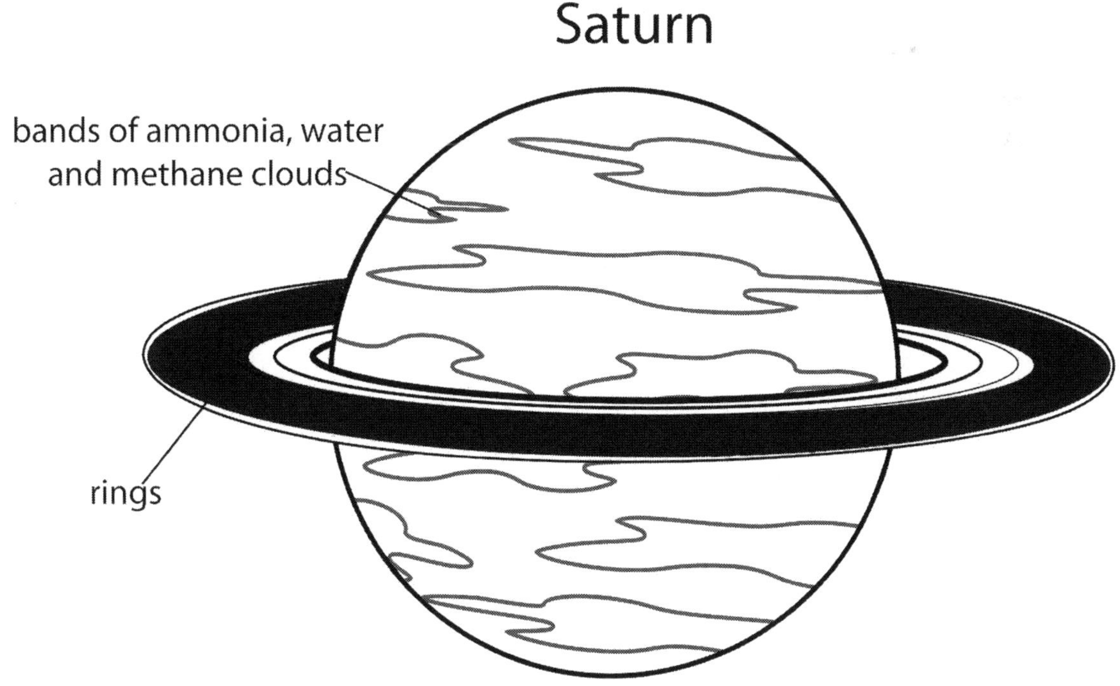

Student Assignment Sheet Astronomy Week 10
Outer Planets-Uranus, Neptune, and Minor Members

Experiment: Scaled Model of the Solar System

Materials
- ✓ Construction paper
- ✓ Paints or crayons

Procedure
1. This week you will be making a scaled version of the solar system, using the chart on your experiment sheet for your placements. Try to make your planets look as realistic as possible by painting or drawing the major features onto your models. For the Sun, tape four pieces of construction paper together lengthwise and then trim them up to look like a portion of a circle. Add solar flares, a prominence, sunspots, and facula.

	Distance from the Sun	Scale diameter of planet
Mercury	2 inches	3/4 inch
Venus	3 inches	1 3/4 inches
Earth	4 inches	2 inches
Mars	6 inches	1 1/8 inches
Jupiter	1 foot, 9 inches	22 inches
Saturn	3 feet, 2 inches	20 inches
Uranus	6 feet, 5 inches	8 inches
Neptune	10 feet, 1 inch	7 1/2 inches
Pluto (Optional)	13 feet, 3 inches	1/2 inches

2. Take a picture of your model and write what you have learned about the solar system from making the model on your experiment sheet.

Vocabulary & Memory Work
- ☐ Vocabulary: dwarf planet, asteroid
- ☐ Memory Work – Continue to work on memorizing the Planet Order

Writing Assignment
- Reading Assignment: *Kingfisher Science Encyclopedia* pg. 408 Uranus, pg. 409 Neptune and pg. 410-411 The Solar System's Minor Members
- Additional Research Readings:
  - The Outer Planets: *USE* pg. 170-171
  - Uranus: *DK Astro* pg. 54-55
  - Neptune & Pluto: *DK Astro* pg. 56-57

Dates to Enter
- March 13, 1781 – William Herschel discovers Uranus using a homemade telescope.
- 1846 – Johann Galle finds the planet Neptune.
- 1930 – Clyde Tombaugh, a US astronomer, discovers Pluto.
- 2006 – Pluto is reclassified as a dwarf planet.

Schedules for Week 10

Two Days a Week

Day 1	Day 2
☐ Define dwarf planet & asteroid on SG pg. 47 ☐ Make the Scaled Model of the Solar System, then fill out the experiment sheet on SG pp. 73	☐ Read pp. 408-411 from the *Kingfisher Science Encyclopedia*, then discuss what was read ☐ Prepare an outline or narrative summary, write it on SG pp. 74-75 ☐ Enter the dates onto the date sheets on SG pp. 8-12
Supplies I Need for the Week ✓ Construction paper ✓ Paint or crayons	
Things I Need to Prepare	

Five Days a Week

Day 1	Day 2	Day 3	Day 4	Day 5
☐ Begin working on the Scaled Model of the Solar System ☐ Define dwarf planet & asteroid on SG pg. 47	☐ Finish the Scaled Model of the Solar System, then fill out the experiment sheet on SG pp. 73 ☐ Enter the dates onto the date sheets on SG pp. 8-12	☐ Read pp. 408-411 from the *Kingfisher Science Encyclopedia*, then discuss what was read ☐ Write an outline or list of facts on SG pg. 74	☐ Read one or all of the additional reading assignments ☐ Prepare your report, write the report on SG pg. 75	☐ Complete one of the Want More Activities listed **OR** ☐ Study a scientist from the field of Astronomy
Supplies I Need for the Week ✓ Construction paper ✓ Paint or crayons				
Things I Need to Prepare				

Additional Information Astronomy Week 10

Experiment Information

The students' assignment this week is to make a scaled model of the solar system using wall space to display it.

If you don't have the wall space or do not wish to have this project on the wall, here are directions on how to scale the solar system to paper:

- ☞ **Directions** – Begin by getting two 11"x 17" sheets of black construction paper or three 8 ½" x 11" sheets together to make an 11" x 34" or 8 ½"x 33" sheet of paper. Place the Sun on the far left, then measure the distances of the planet. Use a pencil and a string so that you can draw a semi-circle since some of the planets will be very close and you may need to stagger them. Use the chart below for the distances.

Planet	Distances, in centimeters, from the Sun on your model
Mercury	1 cm
Venus	1.5 cm
Earth	2 cm
Mars	3 cm
Jupiter	10.6 cm
Saturn	19 cm
Uranus	38.6 cm
Neptune	60.6 cm
Pluto	0.8 cm

- ☞ **NOTE** – I have not included scaled diameters of the planets as some of them would be too small to cut out. Just have the students make their planets relative in size. For example, Pluto is the smallest planet, Earth is 4 times the size of Pluto, Saturn is 10 times the size of Earth and so on.

Discussion Questions

Uranus pg. 408

1. What are some key features of Uranus? (*Uranus receives little heat and light, so it's cold and dark. The planet travels around the sun on its side, so its rings and moons orbit around its middle. Uranus's surface consists mostly of hydrogen and helium, plus a little methane which gives the planet its blue-green appearance.*)

Neptune pg. 409

1. What are some key features of Neptune? (*Neptune is a bright blue gas giant. The planet is bluer than Uranus due to increased methane in its upper clouds. Neptune's surface is also dotted with dark spots and white clouds.*)
2. How was Neptune discovered? (*Astronomers studying Uranus noticed that the planet's path was being affected by an unknown body. That unknown body was later identified as*

Neptune.)

The Solar System's Minor Members pg. 410-411

1. What are the four main groups of minor members in our solar system? (*The first main group of minor members in our solar system is asteroids that can be found in the Asteroid Belt, which is between Mars and Jupiter. The second main group of minor members in our solar system is asteroids that can be found in the Kuiper Belt which can be found after Neptune. The third main group of minor members in our solar system is comets which can be found in the Ort Cloud. The fourth main group of minor members in our solar system is dwarf planets. The three main dwarf planets in our solar system are Pluto, Ceres and Eris.*)
2. Why does Pluto's distance from the Sun vary? (*Pluto's distance from the sun varies because its orbit is not circular, plus the planet's orbit is tilted slightly.*)
3. Why are the asteroids in the asteroid belt called the minor planets? (*The asteroids in the asteroid belt are called minor planets because they are each rocky bodies that orbit the sun.*)

Want More

- **Make a solar system fact book** – This week make a page for the Uranus, Neptune, and Dwarf Planets. Have the students cut out pictures of the three planets. A template has been included for you to use in the appendix of this guide on pp. 255-256. Fold one piece of construction paper in half and cut. Glue the picture of Uranus on one half sheet of construction paper and label it with "Uranus". Then turn the sheet over and glue a piece of blank paper on the back. Have the students write 5-6 keys facts that they learned about Uranus on the piece of paper. Repeat for Neptune and Dwarf Planets and then add to the pages they made the previous week.
- **Research Report** – Pluto wasn't always considered a dwarf planet. Up until 2006, it was still considered the ninth planet in our solar system. Have the students research and write a report on why Pluto is now known as a dwarf planet.

Student Assignment Sheet Astronomy Week 11
Comets and Meteors

Experiment: Does the size of a meteor change the impact it will have on a planet's surface?

Materials
- ✓ Marble
- ✓ Rubber bouncy ball
- ✓ Tennis ball
- ✓ Cake pan
- ✓ Cornstarch
- ✓ Ruler
- ✓ Foam ball (a little larger than the tennis ball)

Procedure
1. Read the introduction to this experiment and answer the question.
2. Pour a layer of cornstarch on the bottom of the cake pan about ½ inch deep. Shake lightly so that the surface is smooth.
3. Drop the marble from a height of 2 feet, aiming for the center of the pan. Observe what happens. Remove the marble, being careful not disturb the cornstarch, and measure the width and depth of the crater created. Record the measurement on your experiment sheet and shake the pan lightly so that the surface is smooth.
4. Repeat step #3 for the rubber bouncy ball, foam ball, and tennis ball.
5. Draw conclusions and complete your experiment sheet.

Vocabulary & Memory Work
- ☐ Vocabulary: comet, meteor, meteoroid
- ☐ Memory Work – Continue to work on memorizing the Planet Order

Sketch Assignment: Anatomy of a Comet
- Label the following: nucleus, dust tail, gas tail

Writing Assignment
- Reading Assignment: *Kingfisher Science Encyclopedia* pg. 412 Comets, pg. 413 Meteors and Meteorites
- Additional Research Readings
  - Space Debris: *USE* pg. 172-173
  - Travelers in Space: *DK Astro* pg. 58-59

Dates to Enter
- 1997 – The comet *Hale-Bopp* is in the Earth's night sky. It won't return for another 2,400 years.
- 1656-1742 – English astronomer, Edmond Halley lives. He correctly predicts that a comet will return to Earth's night sky in 1758, 1835, and 1910.
- 1976 – The second largest iron & nickel meteorite in the United States is found.
- 1986 – The space probe *Giotto*, is sent inside Halley's comet, giving people the first look at a comet's nucleus.

Schedules for Week 11

Two Days a Week

Day 1	Day 2
☐ Define comet, meteor, meteorite on SG pg. 47 ☐ Do the "Does the size of a meteor change the impact it will have on a planet's surface?" experiment, then fill out the experiment sheet on SG pp. 78-79 ☐ Enter the dates onto the date sheets on SG pp. 8-12	☐ Read pp. 412-413 from the *Kingfisher Science Encyclopedia*, then discuss what was read ☐ Prepare an outline or narrative summary, write it on SG pp. 80-81 ☐ Color and label the "Anatomy of a Comet" sketch on SG pg. 77
Supplies I Need for the Week ✓ Marble, Rubber bouncy ball, Foam ball, Tennis ball ✓ Cake pan ✓ Cornstarch ✓ Ruler	
Things I Need to Prepare	

Five Days a Week

Day 1	Day 2	Day 3	Day 4	Day 5
☐ Do the "Does the size of a meteor change the impact it will have on a planet's surface?" experiment, then fill out the experiment sheet on SG pp. 78-79	☐ Read pp. 412-413 from the *Kingfisher Science Encyclopedia*, then discuss what was read ☐ Write an outline or list of facts on SG pg. 80	☐ Define comet, meteor, meteorite on SG pg. 47 ☐ Enter the dates onto the date sheets on SG pp. 8-12 ☐ Color and label the "Anatomy of a Comet" sketch on SG pg. 77	☐ Read one or all of the additional reading assignments ☐ Prepare your report, write the report on SG pg. 81	☐ Complete one of the Want More Activities listed **OR** ☐ Study a scientist from the field of Astronomy ☐ Take the Unit 2 Test
Supplies I Need for the Week ✓ Marble, Rubber bouncy ball, Foam ball, Tennis ball ✓ Cake pan ✓ Cornstarch ✓ Ruler				
Things I Need to Prepare				

Additional Information Astronomy Week 11

Experiment Information

- **Introduction** – (*from the Student Guide*) Bits of space dust and iron-rich rock, called meteoroids, can be found throughout the solar system. They are constantly bombarding the planets. On Earth, most of these meteors burn up before they hit the surface due to our atmosphere, but this is not always the case on other planets. The surfaces of those planets are dotted with impact craters from the meteors. In this experiment, you are going to test whether the size of the meteor affects the size of the crater it will make.
- **Results** – The students should see that the tennis ball created the largest crater, while the foam ball barely made a dent. The marble and the rubber bouncy ball should fall somewhere in between.
- **Explanation** – The size and weight of a meteor affects the impact crater. The reason the foam ball created the smallest crater was because it weighed the least. It created less of an impact force when it hits the ground because there was less weight behind it. It is actually the weight, not the size, that determines how much of an impact a meteoroid will have on the surface.

Discussion Questions

Comet pg. 412

1. What is common to all comets? (*All comets orbit around the sun. Also, they all are potato-shaped balls composed of snow and rock dust.*)
2. Why do comets grow a tail when they are closer to the sun? (*As a comet's orbit gets close to the sun, the heat from the sun turns the surface of the comet's snowball nucleus to gas and this causes some of the dust to be released. The gas and dust are blown away to form the tail of the comet.*)

Meteors & Meteorites pg. 413

1. What is a shooting star? (*A shooting star is a meteor that is burning up as it enters Earth's atmosphere.*)
2. What are meteorites? (*Meteorites are large rocks falling from space that do not completely burn up in our atmosphere. They once were comets or asteroids.*)

Want More

- **Make a solar system fact book** – This week make a page for comets and asteroids. Have the students cut out pictures of a comet and asteroids. A template has been included for you to use in the appendix of this guide on pp. 256-257. Fold one piece of construction paper in half and cut. Glue the picture of a comet on one half sheet of construction paper and label it with "Comets". Then turn the sheet over and glue a piece of blank paper on the back. Have the students write 5-6 keys facts that they learned about comets on the piece of paper. Repeat for asteroids/meteors. Add to the pages they made the previous week and bind the book together.
- **Make a Comet** – Follow the directions found on this website:
  http://www.proteacher.org/a/35553_Make_a_Comet.html

Sketch Assignment Week 11

Anatomy of a Comet

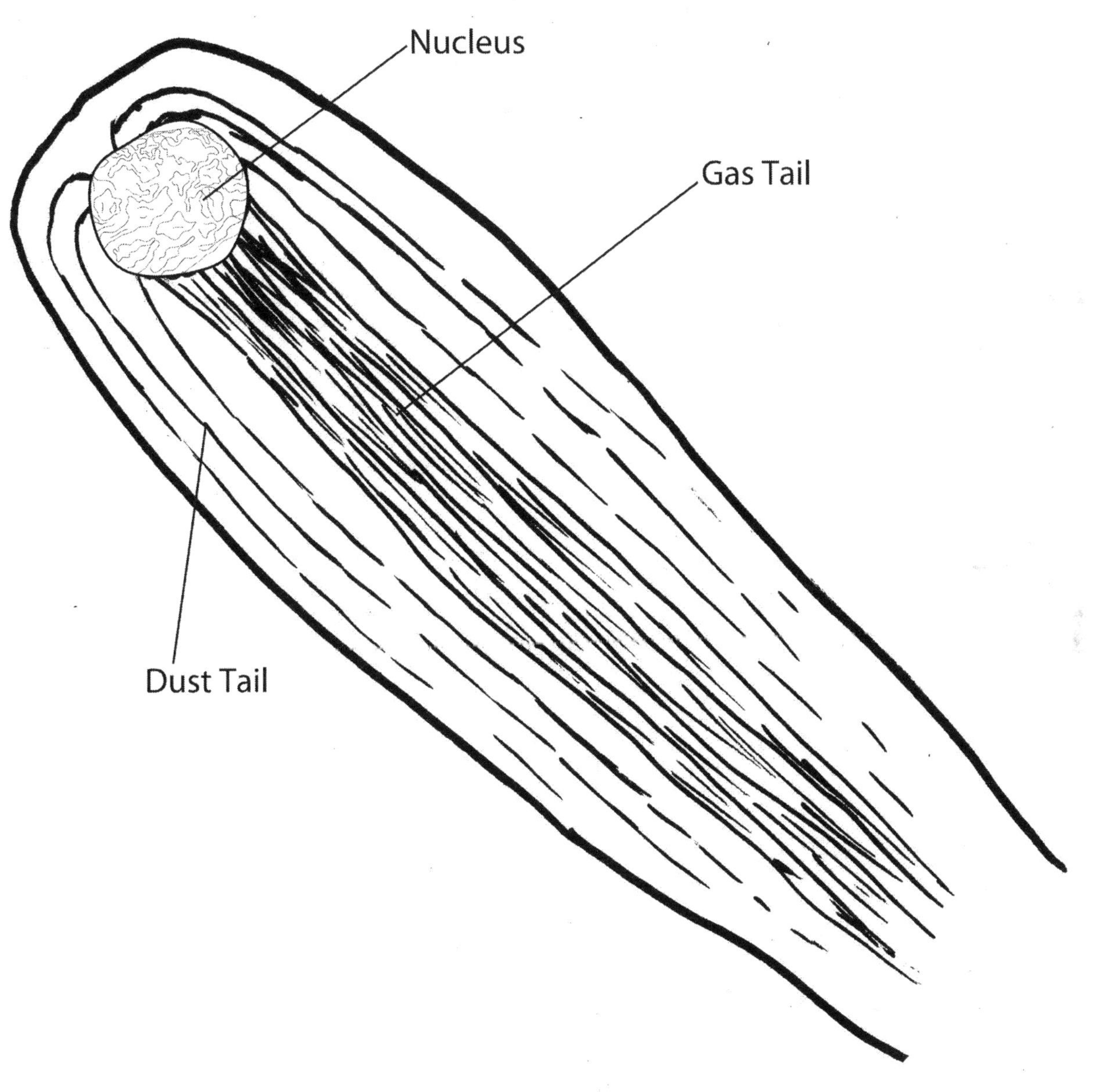

Astronomy Unit 2: Our Solar System
Discussion Questions

Week 6

1. What is the sun?
2. What causes sunspots?
3. What is the chromosphere of the sun composed of?
4. Briefly explain the expected life of the Sun.

Week 7

Mercury pg. 403

1. What is the surface of Mercury like?
2. What two factors contribute to the fact that a day on Mercury is longer than a year?

Venus pg. 404

1. Why does Venus appear as a bright star in our sky?
2. What are two reasons why humans could not survive on Venus?
3. What is the surface of Venus like?

Mars pg. 405

1. Why is Mars known as the Red Planet?
2. Has life been found on Mars? What have explorers found?
3. What is the surface of Mars like?

Week 8

Earth and the Moon pg. 400-401

1. What makes the Earth unique to our solar system?
2. How long does it take for the Earth to orbit the sun one time? How long does it take the Earth to complete one spin on its axis?
3. Why do we only see one side of the moon from the Earth?
4. What is a moon phase? How long does it take the moon to complete one cycle of its phases?

Eclipses pg. 402

1. What is the difference between a solar eclipse and a lunar eclipse?

Week 9

Jupiter pg. 406

1. Describe what Jupiter is like.
2. What are two factors that contribute to Jupiter's stormy atmosphere?

Saturn pg. 407

1. What is the outer surface of Saturn like?
2. What are Saturn's rings made from? Where are the largest pieces of Saturn's rings found?

Week 10

Uranus pg. 408

1. What are some key features of Uranus?

Neptune pg. 409

3. What are some key features of Neptune?
4. How was Neptune discovered?

The Solar System's Minor Members pg. 410-411

1. What are the four main groups of minor members in our solar system?
2. Why does Pluto's distance from the Sun vary?
3. Why are the asteroids in the asteroid belt called the minor planets?

Week 11

Comet pg. 412

1. What is common to all comets?
2. Why do comets grow a tail when they are closer to the sun?

Meteors & Meteorites pg. 413

1. What is a shooting star?
2. What are meteorites?

Astronomy Unit 2: Our Solar System
Unit Test

Vocabulary Matching

1. Photosphere ____
2. Prominence ____
3. Solar wind ____
4. Sunspot ____
5. Crater ____
6. Planet ____
7. Axis ____
8. Orbit ____
9. Moon ____
10. Eclipse ____
11. Galilean Moons ____
12. Gas Giant ____
13. Dwarf Planet ____
14. Asteroid ____
15. Comet ____
16. Meteor ____
17. Meteoroid ____

A. Dark, cooler areas of the Sun's photosphere.

B. The surface of the Sun.

C. The path of one celestial body around another.

D. A large globe composed of rock, liquid or gas that revolves around a star.

E. An imaginary line through the center of planet, around which it rotates.

F. A meteoroid that starts to burn as it enters the atmosphere.

G. The hole formed in a planet's surface by the impact of a meteorite.

H. A celestial body in orbit around a planet.

I. Large eruptions or loops of flaming gas from the Sun's surface.

J. Large chunks of rock and metal that orbit the sun in the region between Mars and Jupiter.

K. Jupiter's 4 largest moons, Io, Ganymede, Callisto and Europa, they are named after Galileo who discovered them.

L. A constant stream of particles that flow into space from the Sun.

M. A large planet that is mostly composed of gas.

N. A small piece of space debris.

O. A minor planet in the solar system.

P. A chunk of frozen gas and dirt that has an orbit.

Q. When one celestial body cast a shadow on another celestial body.

True or False

1. ______________________ The Sun is a giant ball of exploding gas.

2. ______________________ The chromosphere of the sun is composed of solid hydrogen and helium.

3. ______________________ Venus could support human life because of its atmosphere.

4. ______________________ Mars is known as the Red Planet due to the abundance of iron oxide on the planet's surface.

5. ______________________ It takes the Earth 365.25 days to orbit the sun one time.

6. ______________________ In a solar eclipse the moon blocks the sun and prevents its light from reaching Earth, while a lunar eclipse happens when the moon is in the Earth's shadow, preventing the moon from reflecting the Sun's light.

7. ______________________ Two factors that contribute to Jupiter's stormy atmosphere are its distance from the sun and the lack of pressure on the planet.

8. ______________________ Saturn's rings are made up of a variety of gases.

9. ______________________ The presence of methane gas in the atmosphere of Uranus gives the planet it's blue-green appearance.

10. ______________________ Neptune is a rocky planet with a lot of cobalt in the rock to give it its blue appearance.

11. ______________________ Some comets orbit the sun, some orbit other planets or stars.

12. ______________________ All meteorites completely burn in our atmosphere before hitting the surface.

Short Answer

1. What are the names of the planets in our solar system in order from the sun?

2. Briefly describe the surface of each of the 8 planets in our solar system.

3. What are the four main groups of minor members in our solar system?

4. Explain why comets grow a tail when their orbit gets closer to the sun.

Astronomy Unit 2: Our Solar System
Unit Test Answers

Vocabulary

1. B
2. I
3. L
4. A
5. G
6. D
7. E
8. C
9. H
10. Q
11. K
12. M
13. O
14. J
15. P
16. F
17. N

True or False

1. True
2. False *(The chromosphere is composed of hydrogen and helium gas.)*
3. False (*Venus cannot support human life.*)
4. True
5. True
6. True
7. False (*Two factors that contribute to Jupiter's storms are its rapid spin and interior heat.*)
8. False (*Saturn's rings are made of ice and rock.*)
9. True
10. False (*Neptune is composed of methane gas.*)
11. False (*All comets orbit the sun.*)
12. False (*Not all meteorites burn up completely before hitting the surface.)*

Short Answer

1. Mercury, Venus, Earth, Mars, Jupiter, Saturn, Uranus, Neptune
2. Answers should include most of the following information:
   - ✓ Mercury – The surface of Mercury is covered in craters and crossed by ridges and craters that can be up to a mile high. It is extremely hot during the day (842°F) and bitterly cold at night (-274°F).
   - ✓ Venus – The surface of Venus is very hot. It is a relatively smooth planet with volcanic craters and lava flows.
   - ✓ Earth – The Earth's surface has a lot of water and is full of life. It is a rocky planet.
   - ✓ Mars – The surface of Mars is a rock-filled desert. It has craters from meteors and dusty red dunes. Mars also has large mountains and deep canyons.
   - ✓ Jupiter – The surface of Jupiter is stormy and gaseous, with a liquid layer below the gas. The surface also contains the solar system's largest hurricane known as the Red Spot.
   - ✓ Saturn – The outer surface of Saturn is not solid. It is made of bands of ammonia, water and methane clouds. These clouds are colored by phosphorus and other elements.
   - ✓ Uranus – Uranus receives little heat and light, so it's cold and dark. Uranus's surface consists mostly of hydrogen and helium, plus a little methane which gives the planet its blue-green appearance.
   - ✓ Neptune – Neptune is a bright blue gas giant, due to higher concentrations of methane in its upper clouds. Neptune's surface is also dotted with dark spots and white clouds.
3. The first main group of minor members in our solar system is asteroids that can be found in the Asteroid Belt which is between Mars and Jupiter. The second main group of minor members in our solar system is asteroids that can be found in the Kuiper Belt which can be found after Neptune. The third main group of minor members in our solar system is comets which can be found in the Ort Cloud. The fourth main group of minor members in our solar system is dwarf planets.
4. As a comet's orbit gets close to the sun, the heat from the sun turns the surface of the comet's snowball nucleus to gas and this causes some of the dust to be released. The gas and dust are blown away to form the tail of the comet.

Astronomy Unit 3

Astronomers & Their Tools

Astronomy Unit 3: Astronomers & Their Tools

Overview of Study

Sequence of Study

Week 12: Astronomers
Week 13: Looking Into Space
Week 14: Exploring Space
Week 15: Satellites

Materials by Week

Week	Materials
12-14	Materials will vary depending on the Science Fair Project that your student has chosen to do

Vocabulary for the Unit

1. **Astronomer** – A scientist who studies the universe and the objects found in it.
2. **Telescope** – A device used to view objects in space.
3. **Radio telescope** – A telescope that detects radio waves from objects in space.
4. **Reflecting telescope** – A telescope that gathers light with a concave mirror.
5. **Refracting telescope** – A telescope that gathers light with a combination of lenses.
6. **Space probe** – An unmanned space craft that collects information about objects in space.
7. **Rocket** – A device capable of delivering objects into space, carries a small amount of cargo and lots of fuel.
8. **Space shuttle** – A reusable device capable of delivering objects into space, consists of an orbiter, a fuel tank and two booster rockets.
9. **Natural satellite** – A natural object that orbits a planet, such as a moon.
10. **Artificial satellite** – A man-made object that orbits a planet and is used to gather or relay information.

Memory Work for the Unit

Ten Nearest Galaxies and Their Type

1. Milky Way (spiral)
2. Sagittarius (elliptical)
3. Large Magellanic Cloud (irregular)
4. Small Magellanic Cloud (irregular)
5. Ursa Minor (elliptical)
6. Draco (elliptical)
7. Sculptor (elliptical)
8. Carina (elliptical)
9. Sextans (elliptical)
10. Fornax (elliptical)

Notes

Student Assignment Sheet Astronomy Week 12
Astronomers

Experiment: Science Fair Project

This week, you will complete step one and begin step two of your Science Fair Project. You will be choosing your topic, formulating a question, and doing some research about that topic.

1. **Choose your topic** – You should choose a topic in the field of earth science or astronomy that interests you, such as comets. Next, come up with several questions you have relating to that topic, (e.g. "How fast does a comet melt?" or "How does the tail of a comet form?"). Then, choose the one question you would like to answer and refine it (e.g. "Does the size of a comet affect how fast it melts?").
2. **Do Some Research** – Now that you have a topic and a question for your project, it is time to learn more about your topic so that you can make an educated guess (hypothesis) on the answer to your question. For the question stated above, you would need to research topics like comets and how their tails form. Begin by looking up the topic in the references you have at home. Then, make a trip to the library to search for more on the topic. As you do your research, write any relevant facts you have learned on index cards and be sure to record the sources you use.

Vocabulary & Memory Work

- ☐ Vocabulary: astronomer, telescope
- ☐ Memory Work – Begin to work on memorizing the Ten Nearest Galaxies and Their Types.

1. Milky Way (spiral)
2. Sagittarius (elliptical)
3. Large Magellanic Cloud (irregular)
4. Small Magellanic Cloud (irregular)
5. Ursa Minor (elliptical)
6. Draco (elliptical)
7. Sculptor (elliptical)
8. Carina (elliptical)
9. Sextans (elliptical)
10. Fornax (elliptical)

Sketch Assignment: Astronomers Through the Ages

Label the following:

- ➔Nicolaus Copernicus (1473-1543) – He said that the Earth revolved around the Sun.
- ➔Galileo Galilei (1564-1642) – He used the telescope to prove that the Earth and other planets move around the Sun.
- ➔Isaac Newton (1643-1727) – He built the first reflective telescope and showed that the gravity we have on Earth is also in the universe.
- ➔William Herschel (1738-1822) – He made a detailed catalog of nebulas and clusters, as well as discovered Uranus.
- ➔Fred Hoyle (1915-2001) – He showed that carbon and oxygen are created in stars.

Writing Assignment

- Reading Assignment: *Kingfisher Science Encyclopedia* pg. 414-415 Astronomers
- Additional Research Readings
  - Copernican Revolution: *DK Astro* pg. 18-19
  - The Astronomer: *DK Astro* pg. 28-29

Schedules for Week 12

Two Days a Week

Day 1	Day 2
☐ Define astronomer, telescope on SG pg. 85 ☐ Read pp. 414-415 from the *Kingfisher Science Encyclopedia*, then discuss what was read ☐ Color and label the "Astronomers Through the Ages" sketch on SG pg. 87 ☐ Prepare an outline or narrative summary, write it on SG pp. 90-91	☐ Decide on a Topic and State your Question for your Science Fair Project and record on SG pg. 88 ☐ Research for your Science Fair Project and record on SG pp. 88-89
Supplies I Need for the Week ✓ Index Cards	
Things I Need to Prepare	

Five Days a Week

Day 1	Day 2	Day 3	Day 4	Day 5
☐ Read pp. 414-415 from the *Kingfisher Science Encyclopedia*, then discuss what was read ☐ Write an outline or list of facts on SG pg. 90	☐ Define astronomer, telescope on SG pg. 85 ☐ Color and label the "Astronomers Through the Ages" sketch on SG pg. 87	☐ Read one or all of the additional reading assignments ☐ Prepare your report, write the report on SG pg. 91	☐ Decide on a Topic and State your Question for your Science Fair Project and record on SG pg. 88 ☐ Begin Research for your Science Fair Project	☐ Research for your Science Fair Project and record on SG pp. 88-89
Supplies I Need for the Week ✓ Index Cards				
Things I Need to Prepare				

Additional Information Astronomy Week 12

Notes

- **Science Fair Project** – If you choose not to have the students do a Science Fair Project, have them complete one of the Want More activities instead.

Science Fair Project

- Step 1: Choose the Topic – The students will be choosing a topic for their science fair project this week. Have them choose a topic in the field of earth science and astronomy that interests them. You can get ideas for projects from *Janice VanCleave's A+ Science Fair Projects*.
    1. **Key 1 ~ Decide on an area of earth science or astronomy.** The students should choose an area that fascinates them, something in earth science or astronomy that they want to know more about. You will begin by leading the students to brainstorm about things in earth science or astronomy that interest them. Have them rank these areas by degree of interest and then choose one area on which to focus. If their area is too broad, you will want them to narrow it down a bit. You can do this by asking them what they find interesting about the particular field.
    2. **Key 2 ~ Develop several questions about the area of earth science or astronomy.** Once the students have determined their area, they need to develop several questions about their topic that they can answer with their project. Good questions begin with how, what, when, who, which, why or where. At this point, you are just getting them to think of possible questions.
    3. **Key 3 ~ Choose a question to be the topic.** Now that the students have several options of questions that they can answer with their science fair project, you will need to have them choose one of those questions for their project. Some of their questions will be easy to develop into an experiment for their science fair project that will determine the answer' some will not.
- Step 2: Do Some Research– The students will also begin researching their topics. You may need to walk them through this process if they have not had much experience with doing research prior to this.
    1. **Key 1 ~ Brainstorm for research categories.** This is an important key, because developing relevant research categories before they begin to search for information will help the students to maintain a more focused approach. It will also help the students know where to begin their research and how to determine what information is important to their project and what is not. Keep in mind that some students may have a harder time coming up with categories that relate to their topic, so you may need to give them additional assistance. The students should have at least three categories and no more than five. This will help them to obtain relevant information as well as make it easier for them to write their report. Once the students have chosen their research categories, have them assign each category a number.
    2. **Key 2 ~ Research the categories.** Depending upon their experience with research, you may or may not have to walk the students through this entire process. Either way, have them begin by looking at the reference material that they have close at hand, such as encyclopedias that they own or that are in the classroom. Then, they can look to their local library or the

Internet for additional information. As the students uncover bits of relevant data, have them write each fact in their own words on a separate index card. They should number each card at the top left with the category in which it fits, which will make them easier to organize. We also recommend that they assign a letter for each reference they use, which they can write in the right-hand top corner of each card. This way, after they organize and sort their cards, they will know which references they need to include in their bibliography. See the following article for more information on the index card system:

- http://elementalblogging.com/the-index-card-system/

Discussion Questions

1. Who first studied the stars? (*The ancient Egyptians and the Greeks were the first to study the stars.*)
2. What was early astronomy used for? (*Early astronomy was mainly used for timekeeping and navigation.*)
3. What was the Ptolemaic theory? (*The Ptolemaic theory was the idea that everything revolved around the Earth or that the Earth was the center of the universe.*)
4. When did modern astronomy begin? (*Modern astronomy began with Copernicus's theory that the Earth revolves around the Sun.*)
5. What is the difference between practical and theoretical astronomy? (*Practical astronomy makes observations, while theoretical astronomy develops ideas using the laws of science.*)
6. Where can telescopes be placed? (*Telescopes can be placed at various spots around the Earth, in orbit around the Earth and on space probes.*)

Sketch Assignment Week 12

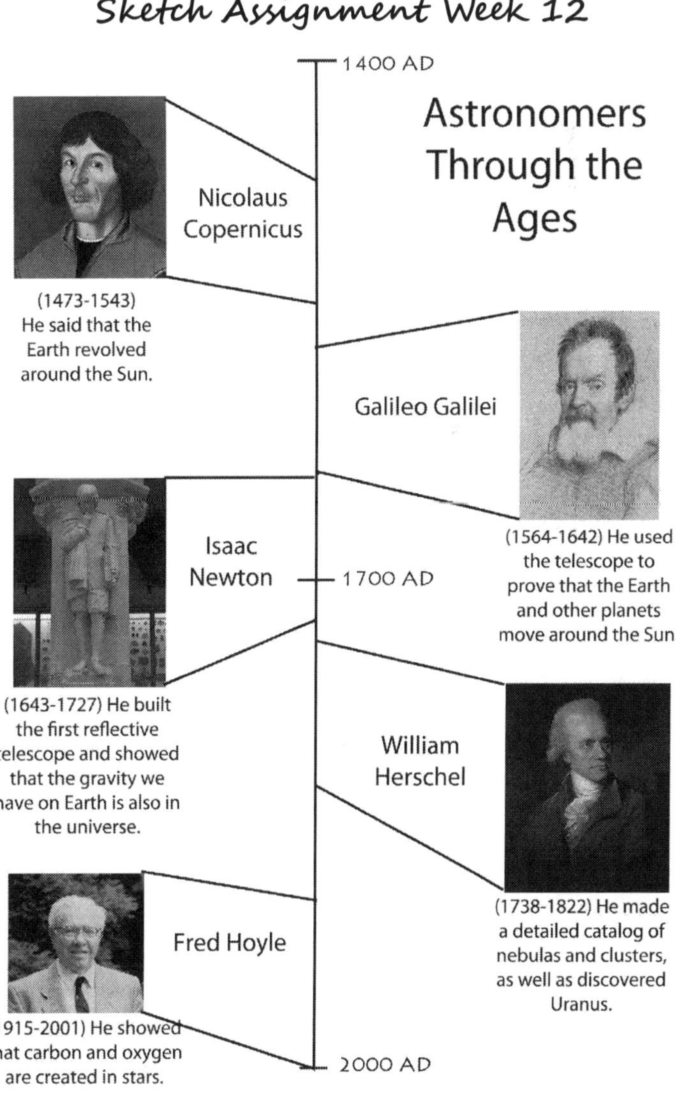

Want More

- **Biographical Sketch** – Have the students choose one of the astronomers from the sketch to write a biography about them. Have them research more about the scientist and then write a three to five paragraph report on the chosen astronomer.

Student Assignment Sheet Astronomy Week 13
Looking Into Space

Experiment: Science Fair Project

This week, you will complete steps two through four of your Science Fair Project. You will be finishing your research, formulating your hypothesis, and designing your experiment.

2. **Do Some Research** – This week, you will finish your research. Then, organize your research index cards and write a brief report on what you have found out.
3. **Formulate a Hypothesis** – A hypothesis is an educated guess. For this step, you need to review your research and make an educated guess about the answer to your question. A hypothesis for the question asked in step one would be, "The more a comet weighs, the quicker it will melt."
4. **Design an Experiment** – Your experiment will test the answer to your question. You need to have a control and several test groups. Your control will have nothing changed, while your test groups will change only one factor at a time. An experiment to test the hypothesis given above would be to fill three different sizes of balloons—large, medium, and small—with varying amounts of water. Make sure you have three of each size to make the test valid and then freeze each one. Once they are frozen, apply a heat source for a set amount of time. Each time, measure how much water has melted and record.

Vocabulary & Memory Work

- ☐ Vocabulary: radio telescope, reflecting telescope, refracting telescope
- ☐ Memory Work – Continue to work on memorizing the Ten Nearest Galaxies and Their Types.

Sketch Assignment: Refracting & Reflecting Telescopes

- Label the following: Refracting Telescope, eye, object lens, focus, eyepiece lens and draw the light rays; Reflecting Telescope, eye, eyepiece lens, focus, object mirror, secondary mirror and draw the light rays

Writing Assignment

- Reading Assignment: *Kingfisher Science Encyclopedia* pg. 416-417 Looking Into Space
- Additional Research Readings:
  - The Optical Telescope: *DK Astro* pg. 24-25
  - The Radio Telescope: *DK Astro* pg. 28-29
  - Exploring Space: *KSE* pg. 418-419

Dates to Enter

- 1609 – Galileo invents the first telescope.
- 1931 – American astronomer, Karl Janley, collects the first evidence of radio radiation coming from space.
- 1992 – *Keck I*, the first telescope to use a segmented mirror, is completed.

Schedules for Week 13

Two Days a Week

Day 1	Day 2
☐ Formulate a Hypothesis for your Science Fair Project and record on SG pg. 94 ☐ Design and begin your experiment for your Science Fair Project and record your observations on SG pp. 94-95 ☐ Enter the dates onto the date sheets on SG pp. 8-12	☐ Define radio telescope, reflecting telescope, refracting telescope on SG pg. 84 ☐ Read pp. 416-417 from the *Kingfisher Science Encyclopedia*, then discuss what was read ☐ Color and label the "Refracting & Reflecting Telescopes" sketch on SG pg. 93 ☐ Prepare an outline or narrative summary, write it on SG pp. 96-97
Supplies I Need for the Week	
Things I Need to Prepare	

Five Days a Week

Day 1	Day 2	Day 3	Day 4	Day 5
☐ Formulate a Hypothesis for your Science Fair Project and record on SG pg. 94 ☐ Design your experiment for your Science Fair Project and record on pp. 94-95	☐ Begin your experiment for your Science Fair Project ☐ Record your observations on SG pg. 95 ☐ Enter the dates onto the date sheets on SG pp. 8-12	☐ Read pp. 416-417 from the *Kingfisher Science Encyclopedia*, then discuss what was read ☐ Write an outline or list of facts on SG pg. 96	☐ Define radio telescope, reflecting telescope, refracting telescope on SG pg. 84 ☐ Color and label the "Refracting & Reflecting Telescopes"" sketch on SG pg. 93	☐ Read one or all of the additional reading assignments ☐ Prepare your report, write the report on SG pg. 97
Supplies I Need for the Week				
Things I Need to Prepare				

Additional Information Astronomy Week 13

Notes

- **Science Fair Project** — If you choose not to have the students do a Science Fair Project, have them complete the Want More activity instead.

Science Fair Project

- *Step 2: Do Some Research* — This week, the students will finish their research and write a brief report for their project board.
    1. **Key 3 ~ Organize the information.** Once the students have finished their research, you need to have them organize and sort through the information that they have found. Begin by having the students sort their cards into piles using the research categories which are in the top left hand of their index card. Then, have the student read through each fact and determine five to seven of the most relevant pieces of information from each pile. You will need to help them as they decide which facts are relevant to their project (i.e., useful for answering their topical question) and which ones are not. These facts will then form the basis of their report.
    2. **Key 4 ~ Write a brief report.** Have the students determine the order they want to share their research categories. Normally, they would go from broad information about their subject to more specific information for their project. After they do this, they need to take the five to seven facts from the first category and turn them into a three to four sentence paragraph by combining the facts into a coherent passage. They will repeat this process until they have a three to five paragraph paper. Then, the students will need to edit and revise their paper so that it becomes a cohesive report. Finally, they will need to add in a bibliography with the resources they used for their report.
- *Step 3: Formulate a Hypothesis* — The students need to review their research and apply what they have learned to help them determine the answer to their question.
    1. **Key 1 ~ Review the research.** The students will need to review their research, so that it is fresh in their minds. You can do this by having them read over their report, or by having them read over each of the index cards they made. The level of involvement for this key will depend on how much time goes by between step two and step three of the science fair project.
    2. **Key 2 ~ Formulate an answer.** After the students have reviewed their research, they should also read over their question one more time. Once all the information is fresh in their minds, they are ready to make an educated guess at the answer to their question. Guide them to craft a response in the form of an if-then statement that they will be able to design an experiment to test. However, keep in mind that not all questions can be answered easily with if-then statements. As they design their experiment in the next step, you can still have them make a few adjustments to their hypotheses, if necessary.
- *Step 4: Design an Experiment* — The students will also design their experiment this week. You may need to walk them through this process by suggesting ways they could test for the answer to their question.
    1. **Key 1 ~ Choose a test.** You can ask the students what kind of a test could you use that would answer your question and prove your hypothesis either true or false. Have them write down each idea they have, but keep in mind that the students may need a fair amount of help with this process. If they find that they cannot come up with any options for testing their

hypotheses, they may need to tweak their statements a bit. If they decide to do this, make sure they verify that the new versions still answer their original topical questions. Once the students have written down several ideas, have them review the options and choose one of the ideas for their projects.

2. **Key 2 ~ Determine the variables.** Now that the students have chosen a method to test their hypotheses, they need to determine the variables that will exist in their test. Here's a link to an article to help you understand the different types of variables:
   - http://elementalblogging.com/experiment-variables/

   Have them answer the questions found in the student guide to determine their independent, dependent and controlled variables.
3. **Key 3 ~ Plan the experiment.** Now that the students understand the variables that are at work, they are ready to use this information along with their testing idea to create an experiment design. You need to explain to them that they must have a control group as well as several test groups. The control group will have nothing changed, while each of the test groups will have only one change to the independent variable. The students should also plan on having several samples in each of their test groups. Once you have explained to the students the parameters of their experiment, they can begin formulating a plan by determining what their test groups will be. Then, they need to decide how long they have to run their tests. Once they have this information, they will write out their experiment design.

Discussion Questions

1. What do telescopes do for astronomers? (*They collect light, radio and other forms of energy waves from space that can provide astronomers with information.*)
2. How do telescopes work? (*Telescopes use one lens to collect and focus the light. They use another lens to magnify the image.*)
3. What two modern advances do astronomers use to help them view space? (*Astronomers now use electronic cameras to take pictures rather than viewing them with the naked eye. They also use computers to control the telescope and record the information collected.*)
4. Why are telescopes placed on mountain tops? (*Telescopes are placed on mountain tops because the air is thinner and clearer, so there is less interference from the atmosphere in the images they produce.*)
5. What can telescopes in space see that we cannot spot on Earth? (*Telescopes in space can see x-rays and other forms of energy that are reflected by the Earth's atmosphere.*)

Sketch Assignment Week 13

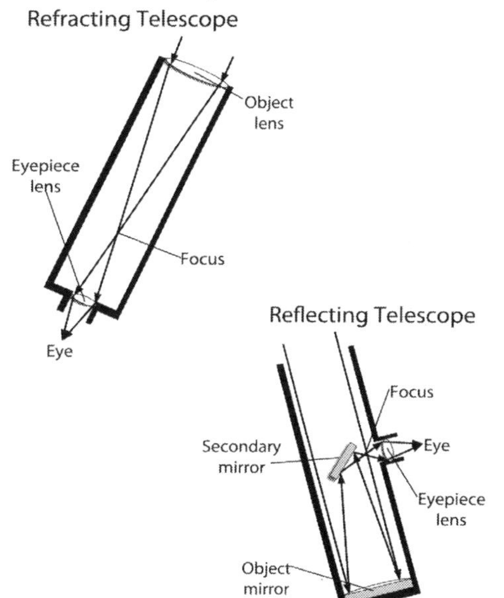

Want More

- **Go Spotting** – Have the students go out star spotting at night. Have them observe the differences between using their naked eye, binoculars, and a telescope.

Student Assignment Sheet Astronomy Week 14
Exploring Space

Experiment: Science Fair Project

This week, you will complete steps five and six of your Science Fair Project. You will carry out the experiment and record your observations and results.

5. **Perform the Experiment** – This week, you will perform the experiment you designed last week. Be sure to take pictures along the way as well as record your observations and results. (**Note**—*Observations are a record of the things you see happening in your experiment. An observation would be "the small comet melted completely, but the large one remained mostly intact." Results are specific and measureable. Results would be that you collected 40 mL of water from the small comet. Observations are generally recorded in journal form, while results can be compiled into tables, charts, and graphs or relayed in paragraph form.*)
6. **Analyze the Data** – Once you have compiled your observations and results, you can use them to answer your question. You need to look for trends in your data and make conclusions from that. A possible conclusion to the electrolysis experiment would be, "Grass needs light to grow. The more light that grass is exposed to the better it will grow." If your hypothesis does not match your conclusion or your were not able to answer your question using the results from your experiment, you may need to go back and do some additional experimentation.

Vocabulary & Memory Work

- ☐ Vocabulary: space probe, rocket, space shuttle
- ☐ Memory Work – Continue to work on memorizing the Ten Nearest Galaxies and Their Types.

Sketch Assignment: Space Traveling Vehicles

- Label the following: *Saturn V, Titan III, Ariane V, Long March, Soyuz, H-IIA, US Space Shuttle*

Writing Assignment

- Reading Assignment: *Kingfisher Science Encyclopedia* pp. 420-421 Rockets and Space Planes
- Additional Research Readings
  - Venturing Into Space: *DK Astro* pp. 34-35
  - Humans in Space: *KSE* pp. 422-423

Dates to Enter

- 1926 – Robert Goddard launches the first liquid fuel rocket.
- 1942 – The first rocket, launched by Germany, reaches space.
- 1981 – NASA launches the first reusable space shuttle.
- 2011 – NASA's four reusable space shuttles are retired.

Schedules for Week 14

Two Days a Week

Day 1	Day 2
☐ Continue your experiment for your Science Fair Project and record your observations and results on SG pp. 100-101 ☐ Define space probe, rocket, space shuttle on SG pg. 84 ☐ Enter the dates onto the date sheets on SG pp. 8-12	☐ Read pp. 420-421 from the *Kingfisher Science Encyclopedia*, then discuss what was read ☐ Color and label "The Space Shuttle" sketch on SG pg. 99 ☐ Prepare an outline or narrative summary, write it on SG pp. 102-103
Supplies I Need for the Week	
Things I Need to Prepare	

Five Days a Week

Day 1	Day 2	Day 3	Day 4	Day 5
☐ Continue your experiment for your Science Fair Project ☐ Record your observations and results on SG pp. 100-101	☐ Read pp. 420-421 from the *Kingfisher Science Encyclopedia*, then discuss what was read ☐ Write an outline or list of facts on SG pg. 102	☐ Define space probe, rocket, space shuttle on SG pg. 84 ☐ Enter the dates onto the date sheets on SG pp. 8-12 ☐ Color and label "The Space Shuttle" sketch on SG pg. 99	☐ Read one or all of the additional reading assignments ☐ Prepare your report, write the report on SG pg. 103	☐ Continue your experiment for your Science Fair Project ☐ Record your observations & results on SG pp. 100-101
Supplies I Need for the Week				
Things I Need to Prepare				

Additional Information Astronomy Week 14

Notes

- **Science Fair Project** — If you choose not to have the students do a Science Fair Project, have them complete the Want More activity instead.

Science Fair Project

- *Step 5: Perform the Experiment* — The students will be performing the experiment and recording their observations and results. Be sure to check in with them to see how they are doing.
    1. **Key 1 ~ Get ready for the experiment.** The students already have a plan in place, but there are still a few things they need to do before beginning their experiment. They need to look at a calendar and make sure that they will be home for the duration of the trial because they will need to be there to make observations and record results on each day of testing. The students also need to gather and prep any materials that they will be using during their experiment.
    2. **Key 2 ~ Run the experiment.** The students have done a lot of work to reach this point, but that preparation has paved a smooth road for their experiment. At this point, they are familiar with their research and their design, so they should be able to carry out their testing with little to no help. You want to make sure that the students write down a list of things they need to check each day during the experiment. Be sure that they include taking pictures of what they see on their list as they will need these images for their project board.
    3. **Key 3 ~ Record any observations and results.** As the students run their experiment, they need to compile their observations and results. Observations are the record of the things the scientist sees happening in an experiment, while results are specific and measurable. Observations are generally recorded in journal form, while results can be compiled into tables, charts or graphs. You will need to help the students create a table to record their results as well as provide them with a journal for their observations. Once they finish their experiment, you may need to help them chart or graph their data.
- *Step 6: Analyze the Data* — The students will now analyze their observations and results to draw conclusions from their experiment.
    1. **Key 1 ~ Review and organize the data.** The students need to analyze their observations and results to determine if their hypotheses are true or false. To do this, you need to have them read over each of their journal entries and note any trends in their observations. You also need to have the students interpret the charts or graphs they created in the last step and write down the information that they can glean from them.
    2. **Key 2 ~ State the answer.** Now that the students have noted trends from their observations and interpreted information from their results, they can use this data to answer their question. They need to first determine if they have proved their hypotheses true or false. Once the students have decided if their hypotheses statements were true or false, they can craft a one sentence answer to their original topical questions from step one. Their statements should begin with, "I found that ___" or "I discovered that ___." In the rare case that the students are unable to state an answer to their question, they need to take what they have learned, go back to the drawing table and redesign their experiment.

3. **Key 3 ~ Draw several conclusions.** When the students draw conclusions, they are putting into words what they have learned from their project. Their conclusion should include the following information:
   - ☑ The answer to their question;
   - ☑ Whether or not their hypotheses were proven true (**Note**—*If their hypotheses were proven false, they should state why.*);
   - ☑ Any problems or difficulties they ran into while performing their experiment;
   - ☑ Anything interesting they discovered that they would like to share;
   - ☑ Ways that they would like to expand their experiment in the future.

   It should be one paragraph, or about four to six sentences in length. Have the students begin their concluding paragraph with the statement they wrote for the previous key.

Discussion Questions

1. What is escape velocity? (*Escape velocity is the speed at which something must travel to break free from Earth's gravity, which is 7 miles per second.*)
2. What are two downsides of using a rocket? (*Two downsides of using a rocket are that only a small part of it can be set aside for cargo and that it is not reusable.) (Students may also answer that rockets are expensive.*)
3. What is the main difference between a rocket and the space shuttle? (*The space shuttle is a reusable system, while a rocket can only be used once.*)
4. What have space planes been used for? (*Space planes have been used to launch and repair satellites, to build the International Space States, and to ferry astronauts to and from space.*)

Want More

- **Field Trip** – If you live close by to one of the space stations, this is a good week to visit one. If not, take a virtual tour from this website:
  - http://imedia.ksc.nasa.gov/index1.html

Sketch Assignment Week 14

Space Traveling Vehicles

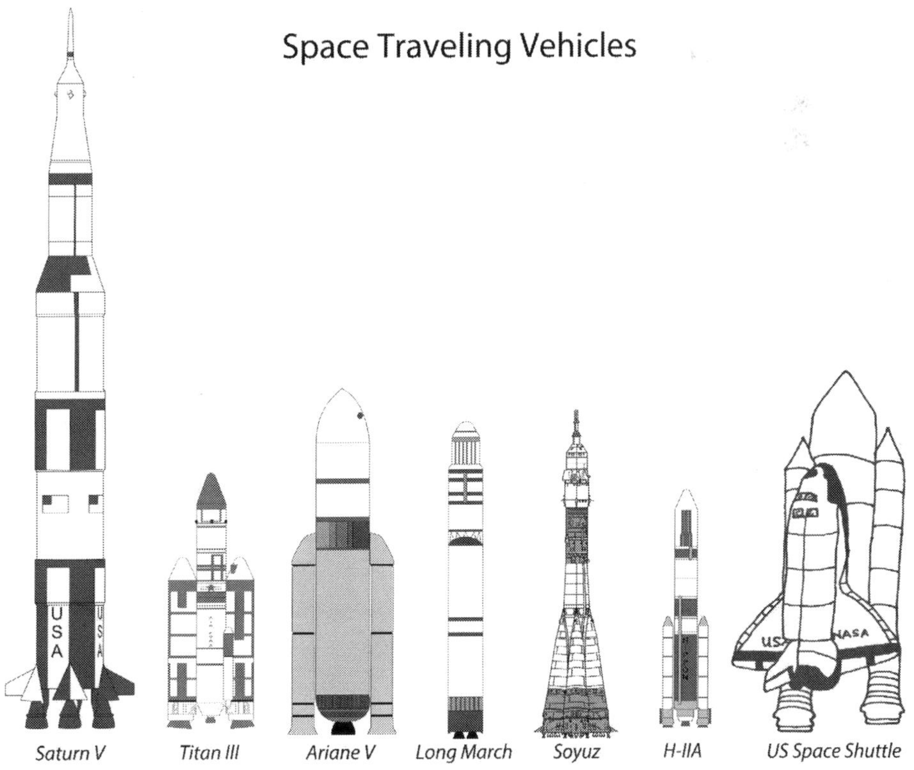

Saturn V | Titan III | Ariane V | Long March | Soyuz | H-IIA | US Space Shuttle

Student Assignment Sheet Astronomy Week 15
Satellites

Experiment: Science Fair Project

This week, you will complete steps seven and eight of your Science Fair Project. You will be writing and preparing a presentation of your Science Fair Project.

7. **Create a Board** — This week, you will be creating a visual representation of your science fair project that will serve as the centerpiece of your presentation. You will begin by planning the look of your board, then, move onto preparing the information, and finally, you will pull it all together.
8. **Give a Presentation** — After you have completed your presentation board, determine if you would like to include part of your experiment in your presentation. Then, prepare a 5 minute talk about your project. Be sure to include the question you tried to answer, your hypothesis, a brief explanation of your experiment, and the results plus the conclusion to your project. Be sure to arrive on time for your presentation. Set up your project board and any other additional materials. Give your talk and then ask if there are any questions. Answer the questions and end your time by thanking whoever has come to listen to your presentation.

Vocabulary & Memory Work

- ☐ Vocabulary: natural satellite, artificial satellite
- ☐ Memory Work – Continue to work on memorizing the Ten Nearest Galaxies and Their Types.

Sketch Assignment

- ☒ There is no sketch assignment this week.

Writing Assignment

- Reading Assignment: *Kingfisher Science Encyclopedia* pg. 424-425 Satellites
- Additional Research Readings
  - Space Exploration: *USE* pg. 174-177

Dates to Enter

- 1957 – A rocket delivers the first Russian satellite, *Sputnik*, into space.
- 1989 – The satellite *Hipparcos* is launched. Its job is to map the night sky.

Schedules for Week 15

Two Days a Week

Day 1	Day 2
☐ Write your conclusions for your Science Fair Project and record on SG pg. 106 ☐ Prepare and present your Science Fair Project Report, see SG pg. 107 for details	☐ Define natural satellite, artificial satellite on SG pg. 85 ☐ Read pp. 424-425 from the *Kingfisher Science Encyclopedia*, then discuss what was read ☐ Prepare an outline or narrative summary, write it on SG pp. 105 ☐ Enter the dates onto the date sheets on SG pp. 8-12
Supplies I Need for the Week	
Things I Need to Prepare	

Five Days a Week

Day 1	Day 2	Day 3	Day 4	Day 5
☐ Write your conclusion for your Science Fair Project and record on SG pg. 106 ☐ Begin working on your Science Fair Project Report, see SG pg. 107 for details	☐ Read pp. 424-425 from the *Kingfisher Science Encyclopedia*, then discuss what was read ☐ Write an outline or list of facts on SG pg. 105	☐ Define natural satellite, artificial satellite on SG pg. 85 ☐ Enter the dates onto the date sheets on SG pp. 8-12 ☐ Continue working on your Science Fair Project Report	☐ Read one or all of the additional reading assignments ☐ Prepare a short report, write the report on SG pg. 105	☐ Present your Science Fair Project, see SG pg. 107 for details ☐ Take the Unit 3 Test
Supplies I Need for the Week				
Things I Need to Prepare				

Additional Information Astronomy Week 15

Notes

- **Science Fair Project** — If you choose not to have the students do a Science Fair Project, have them complete one of the Want More activities instead.

Science Fair Project

- *Step 7: Create a Board* — In this step, the students will pull together all the information they have learned to create a presentation board.
  1. **Key 1 ~ Plan out the board.** The science fair project board is the visual representation of the students' hard work, so you definitely want them to put as much effort into this step as they have into the others. The board will have specific sections that are set, but they should personalize the look with color and graphics that suit their tastes and match their projects. Please see the Appendix pg. 238 for a more detailed explanation of the science fair project board layout.
  2. **Key 2 ~ Prepare the information.** The students have put in a lot of effort until this point, but the work they have done in the previous steps will make it easier for them to prepare the information for their board. The students need to type the information up and choose a font and font size for their board. Please see the Appendix pg. 238 for a more detailed explanation of what each section should include.
  3. **Key 3 ~ Put the board together.** Now that the students have planned out their science fair project board and prepared the information, they are ready to pull it all together. They need to cut out the decorative elements and glue them to the backboard. Then, they need to print and cut out their informational paragraphs. For added depth, they can glue the paragraphs onto a foam board before adding the information. Finally, the students should add their title and the finishing touches to their board.
- *Step 8: Give a Presentation* — This step gives the students a chance to communicate with an audience what they have learned from their project. The best way to achieve this is to have the students participate in a Science Fair where their projects will be judged, but if that's not possible, don't skip this key. The students can still present their project to their family or to a group of their peers.
  1. **Key 1 ~ Prepare the presentation.** Once the students have finished their project board, they can begin to work on their presentation. They should prepare a brief five minute talk about their science fair project. This talk should include the question they tried to answer, their hypotheses, a brief explanation of their experiment, the results, and the conclusion to their project. You will need to guide the students as they turn their information paragraphs into an outline for their presentation. This outline should highlight the main points that they want to cover for their presentation.
  2. **Key 2 ~ Practice the presentation.** Once the students have finished preparing the outline for their talk, have them practice in front of a mirror. They should practice looking at the audience while pointing to the different sections on their project board as they present. Once they feel confident with their presentation, have them give a practice talk to you. Be sure to give them feedback, so that they can make the necessary changes before they present their science fair project to a group.

3. **Key 3 ~ Share the presentation.** It is important to have the students present their work to an audience and answer related questions from the group. This will reinforce what they have learned as well as help them to discern how to communicate what they know.

Discussion Questions

1. Once an artificial satellite is placed into orbit, what happens? (*Once a satellite is placed in orbit, it's activated, works for several years, dies and then returns to Earth.*)
2. What are the four main types of orbits for artificial satellites? (*The four main types of orbits for artificial satellites are polar, geostationary, eccentric and circular.*)
3. How do artificial satellites get power? (*Artificial satellites get power from solar panels that convert sunlight into electricity.*)
4. What are the purposes of artificial satellites? (*The main purposes of artificial satellites are navigation, communication, collecting scientific data, military purposes and monitoring the Earth.*)
5. How do communication satellites work? (*The signal is beamed to a satellite above where the signal begins. Then it's relayed around the Earth by satellites in space, till it reaches the one above where it needs to be delivered. Finally, the signal is sent down to a receiver where it is processed.*)

Want More

- **A Satellite's Centrifugal Force** – Do the experiment from this website:
  - http://www.proteacher.com/redirect.php?goto=459

Astronomy Unit 3: Astronomers & Their Tools
Discussion Questions

Week 12
1. Who first studied the stars?
2. What was early astronomy used for?
3. What was the Ptolemaic theory?
4. When did modern astronomy begin?
5. What is the difference between practical and theoretical astronomy?
6. Where can telescopes be placed?

Week 13
1. What do telescopes do for astronomers?
2. How do telescopes work?
3. What two modern advances do astronomers use to help them view space?
4. Why are telescopes placed on mountain tops?
5. What can telescopes in space see that we cannot spot on Earth?

Week 14
1. What is escape velocity?
2. What are two downsides of using a rocket?
3. What is the main difference between a rocket and the space shuttle?
4. What have space planes been used for?

Week 15
1. Once an artificial satellite is placed into orbit, what happens?
2. What are the four main types of orbits for artificial satellites?
3. How do artificial satellites get power?
4. What are the purposes of artificial satellites?
5. How do communication satellites work?

Astronomy Unit 3: Astronomers & Their Tools
Unit Test Answers

Vocabulary

1. B
2. G
3. A
4. C
5. E
6. J
7. I
8. D
9. H
10. F

True or False

1. True
2. False (*The Ptolematic theory states that the planets revolve around the Earth.*)
3. False (*Telescopes are place on mountain tops because there is less interference.*)
4. True
5. True
6. False (*Space shuttles are reusable systems capable of delivering material into space.*)
7. True
8. False (*Artificial satellites get power from solar panels.*)

Short Answer

1. Modern astronomy began with Copernicus's theory that the Earth revolved around the Sun.
2. Telescopes use one lens to collect and focus the light. They use another lens to magnify the image.
3. Space planes have been used to launch and repair satellites, to build the International Space States, and to ferry astronauts to and from space.
4. The signal is beamed to a satellite above where the signal begins. Then it's relayed around the Earth by satellites in space, till it reaches the one above where it needs to be delivered. Finally, the signal is sent down to a receiver where it is processed.
5. Answers will vary.

Astronomy Unit 3 Astronomers & Their Tools: Space
Unit Test

Vocabulary Matching

1. Astronomer
2. Telescope
3. Radio telescope
4. Reflecting telescope
5. Refracting telescope
6. Space probe
7. Rocket
8. Space shuttle
9. Natural satellite
10. Artificial satellite

A. A telescope that detects radio waves from objects in space.

B. A scientist who studies the universe and the objects found in it.

C. A telescope that gathers light with a concave mirror.

D. A reusable device capable of delivering objects into space, consists of an orbiter, a fuel tank and two booster rockets.

E. A telescope that gathers light with a combination of lenses.

F. A man-made object that orbits a planet and is used to gather or relay information.

G. A device used to view objects in space.

H. A natural object that orbits a planet, such as a moon.

I. A device capable of delivering objects into space, carries a small amount of cargo and lots of fuel.

J. An unmanned space craft that collects information about objects in space.

True or False

1. ____________________ The ancient Egyptians and the Greeks were the first to study the stars.

2. ____________________ The Ptolemaic theory states that the planets revolve around the Sun.

3. ____________________ Telescopes are placed in a valley because the air is clearer.

4. ____________________ Telescopes are placed on mountain tops because the air is thinner and clearer, so the interference from the atmosphere is less.

5. ____________________ Escape velocity is seven miles per second.

6. ______________________ Rockets are reusable systems capable of delivering material into space.

7. ______________________ The four main types of orbits of artificial satellites are polar, geostationary, eccentric and circular.

8. ______________________ Artificial satellites get power from the Earth.

Short Answer

1. What theory was the basis for modern astronomy?

2. How do telescopes work?

3. What have space planes been used for?

4. How do communication satellites work?

5. Share several facts about two of the key astronomers you studied this unit.

Earth Science Unit 4

Our Planet

Earth Science Unit 4: Our Planet
Overview of Study

Sequence of Study

Week 16: Inside the Earth
Week 17: Maps and Mapping
Week 18: Rivers
Week 19: Oceans
Week 20: Glaciers
Week 21: Natural Cycles
Week 22: Biomes and Habitats

Materials by Week

Week	Materials
16	Modeling clay (you will need yellow, orange, red, blue, and green), Ruler
17	Blue balloon (with the continents drawn or printed on it), Flat map, Pin
18	Pitcher for water, Water, Cookie sheet, Paper cup, Straw, Dirt or sand, Small rocks, Clay or play dough, Books, Tape
19	Aluminum bread pan or Plastic bin, Air dry clay, Water, Sand (1 cup), 2 Straws
20	Glacier Melt Model (make using cup, water, pebbles, sand), Large cutting board with a handle, Large rubber band
21	Cup, Baggie, Water, Rubber band
22	Paper towels, Wax paper, Rubber band, Water

Vocabulary for the Unit

1. **Mantle** – The mostly solid part of the Earth that lies between its crust and its core.
2. **Cartographer** – A person who makes maps.
3. **Lines of Latitude** (parallels) – Lines that run parallel around the globe, dividing the globe into flat slices; they never meet.
4. **Lines of Longitude** (meridians) – Lines that run from the North to the South pole, dividing the globe into segments; they all meet at the poles.
5. **Delta** – A fan-shaped system of streams that is created when a river splits into many smaller branches before it enters the sea.
6. **Estuary** – A wide channel that forms where a river joins the sea.
7. **Source** – The beginning of a river.
8. **Coast** – The stretch of land that meets the sea.
9. **Oceanic ridge** – A raised ridge on the seabed caused by the movement of the Earth's crustal plates.
10. **Oceanic trench** – A deep trench in the seabed formed when one place of the Earth's crust

moves under another.

11. **Tides** – The daily movements of the sea up and down the shore; they are caused by the gravitational pull of the moon.
12. **Deposition** – The dropping or leaving behind of rock and other debris by a glacier.
13. **Erratics** – Large boulders that have been deposited away from their source by a glacier.
14. **Glacier** – A mass of ice that gathers at the top of a land mass and slowly flows downhill.
15. **Moraine** – Rock, clay, sand, and other debris left by a glacier at the valley floor.
16. **Natural cycle** – The exchanging of essential elements, such as nitrogen, carbon, and oxygen.
17. **Greenhouse gas** – Any gas that traps heat from the Sun, such as carbon dioxide.
18. **Biome** – A region of the Earth that contains unique plants and animals and is characterized by a distinct climate.

Memory Work for the Unit

Major Lines of Longitude & Latitude

1. Prime Meridian
2. Equator
3. Tropic of Cancer
4. Tropic of Capricorn

The World's Major Seas & Oceans

1. Arctic Ocean
2. Pacific Ocean
3. Atlantic Ocean
4. Indian Ocean
5. Southern Ocean
6. Mediterranean Sea
7. Red Sea
8. Black Sea
9. Caribbean Sea
10. Gulf of Mexico
11. Hudson Bay
12. Bering Sea
13. Tasman Sea
14. Coral Sea
15. Bay of Bengal
16. Arabian Sea
17. North Sea

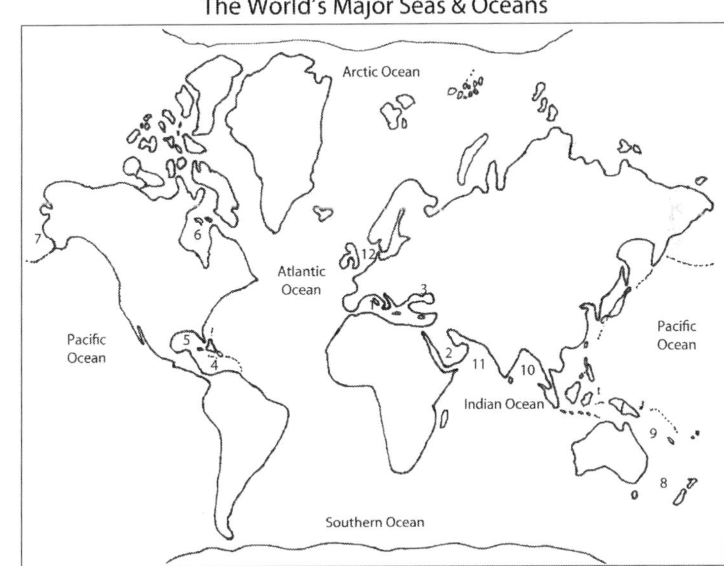

Notes

Student Assignment Sheet Week 16
Inside the Earth

Experiment: Model Earth

Materials

- ✓ Modeling clay (you will need yellow, orange, red, blue, and green)
- ✓ Ruler

Procedure

1. Read the introduction to this experiment.
2. Begin by making a ball about 1.2 cm across out of the yellow clay. This represents the Earth's inner core.
3. Then make another layer about 3 cm across out of the red clay around the ball. This layer represents the Earth's outer core.
4. Then you make another layer about 6 cm across out of the orange clay around the ball. This layer represents the Earth's mantle.
5. Finally, make some flattened pieces of blue and green clay to represent the Earth's crust and layer them over your ball.
6. Cut your ball in half and observe the layers of the Earth that were created.
7. Take a picture and complete your experiment sheet.

Vocabulary & Memory Work

- ☐ Vocabulary: mantle
- ☐ Memory Work – Work on memorizing the Major Lines of Longitude & Latitude.
    1. Prime Meridian
    2. Equator
    3. Tropic of Cancer
    4. Tropic of Capricorn

Sketch Assignment: Inside the Earth

- Label the following: inner core, outer core, mantle, crust, ocean, and continent

Writing Assignment

- Reading Assignment: *The Kingfisher Science Encyclopedia* pp. 8-9 Earth's Structure
- Additional Research Readings
    - Earth's Structure: *USE* pp. 180-181
    - Structure of the Earth: *DKEOS* pp. 212-213

Dates

- 1965 – Tuzo Wilson, a Canadian geophysicist, explains how the plates on the ocean floor move.

Schedules for Week 16

Two Days a Week

Day 1	Day 2
☐ Define mantle on SG pg. 110 ☐ Do the "Model Earth" experiment, then fill out the experiment sheet on SG pp. 114-115 ☐ Enter the dates onto the date sheets on SG pp. 8-12	☐ Read pp. 8-9 from the *Kingfisher Science Encyclopedia,* then discuss what was read ☐ Prepare an outline or narrative summary, write it on SG pp. 116-117 ☐ Color and label the "Inside the Earth" sketch on SG pg. 113

Supplies I Need for the Week

✓ Modeling clay (you will need yellow, orange, red, blue, and green)
✓ Ruler

Things I Need to Prepare

Five Days a Week

Day 1	Day 2	Day 3	Day 4	Day 5
☐ Do the "Model Earth" experiment, then fill out the experiment sheet on SG pp. 114-115	☐ Read pp. 8-9 from the *Kingfisher Science Encyclopedia,* then discuss what was read ☐ Write an outline or list of facts on SG pg. 116	☐ Define mantle on SG pg. 110 ☐ Enter the dates onto the date sheets on SG pp. 8-12 ☐ Color and label the "Inside the Earth" sketch on SG pg. 113	☐ Read one or all of the additional reading assignments ☐ Prepare your report, write the report on SG pg. 117	☐ Complete one of the Want More Activities listed **OR** ☐ Study a scientist from the field of Earth Science

Supplies I Need for the Week

✓ Modeling clay (you will need yellow, orange, red, blue, and green)
✓ Ruler

Things I Need to Prepare

Additional Information Week 16

Experiment Information

☞ **Introduction** – (*from the Student Guide*) The Earth consists of three main layers, the crust, the mantle and the core. Some of these layers are solid, some of them are molten. Each layer varies in thickness and consists of different elements. In this experiment, you are going to use modeling clay to create a model of the Earth and its internal layers.

☞ **Explanation** – This activity was designed to help the students learn the layers of the Earth in a memorable way. The goal of this activity was to enable the students to see the various layers when they cut their ball in half and to tell you what each layer represented. If the students are able to do so, you have accomplished the goal of this experiment.

Discussion Questions

1. What are the three main layers of the Earth? (Be sure to include a detail or two about each.) (*The three main layers of the Earth are the crust, the mantle, and the core. The crust is the thinnest layer, which floats over the layers below. The mantle has a solid upper layer, which consists mostly of dense silicate rock. The core is extremely hot and consists of molten rock made from iron and nickel.*)
2. How is the Earth's magnetic field created and why is it important? (*The Earth's magnetic field is created by the electrical currents generated by the circulating molten iron in the core. The magnetic field protects the Earth from harmful radiation and particles from the sun.*)
3. What causes seismic activity on the Earth? (*Seismic activity on the Earth is caused by the heat escaping from the core.*)
4. What have seismic scans of the Earth revealed about the mantle? (*Seismic scans have revealed that there are probably two layers of circulating rock within the mantle.*)

Want More

Edible Earth – Make an edible Earth to demonstrate its layers. Place one spice drop into a large marshmallow. Cover the spice drop completely and set aside. This will be the Earth's core. Then, combine 1 tbsp. of butter with 12 more large marshmallows and melt in a microwave for 1 minute. Mix the marshmallow mixture thoroughly with 2 cups of rice cereal and let cool to touch. With moistened hands, roll the cereal/marshmallow mixture around the core and pack it tightly into a ball. Chill the ball for 15 minutes in the freezer, and then cover with a bottle of chocolate shell. Once hardened, cut open, observe, and eat. The spice drop comprises the Earth's inner core, the marshmallow represents the Earth's outer core, the cereal/marshmallow mixture represents the Earth's mantle, and the chocolate shell represents the Earth's crust.

Sketch Assignment Week 16

Inside the Earth

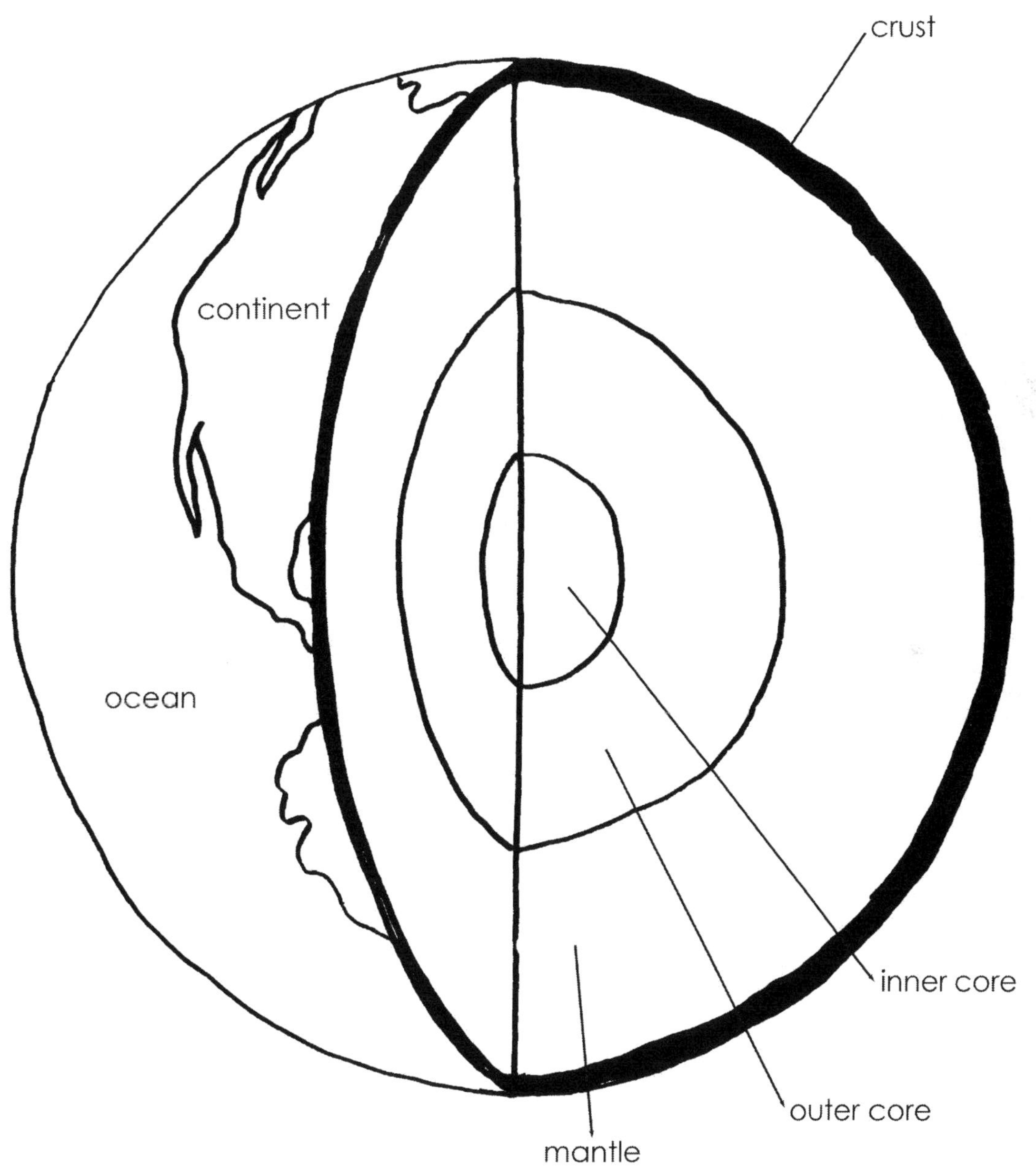

Student Assignment Sheet Week 17
Maps and Mapping

Experiment: Is a flat representation the same as a spherical representation of the Earth?

Materials
- ✓ Blue balloon (with the continents drawn or printed on it)
- ✓ Flat map
- ✓ Pin

Procedure
1. Read the introduction to this experiment and answer the question.
2. Blow up your balloon so that it looks like a globe. (If your balloon did not have the continents already printed on it, now is the time to draw them.)
3. Take your flat map and wrap it around the balloon, while attempting to match the continents up. Record your observations.
4. Take the pin, pop your balloon and then cut it between The Americans and Asia. Try to stretch your balloon to match the map. Record your observations.
5. Draw conclusions and complete your experiment sheet.

Vocabulary & Memory Work
- ☐ Vocabulary: cartographer, lines of longitude, lines of latitude
- ☐ Memory Work – Work on memorizing the Major Lines of Longitude & Latitude.
  1. Prime Meridian
  2. Equator
  3. Tropic of Cancer
  4. Tropic of Capricorn

Sketch: Lines on the Globe
- Label the following: Lines of longitude, Lines of latitude, Arctic Circle, Antarctic Circle, Prime Meridian, Equator, Tropic of Cancer, Tropic of Capricorn, North Pole, South Pole

Writing
- Reading Assignment: *The Kingfisher Science Encyclopedia* pp. 46-47 Maps and Mapping
- Additional Research Readings
  - Mapping the Earth: *DKEOS* pg. 240

Dates
- 1538 – Gerhard Mercator, a Flemish cartographer, devises a fairly accurate way to represent the Earth's surface on a map.

Schedules for Week 17

Two Days a Week

Day 1	Day 2
☐ Define cartographer, lines of longitude, lines of latitude on SG pg. 110 ☐ Do the "Is a flat representation the same as a spherical representation of the Earth?" experiment, then fill out the experiment sheet on SG pp. 120-121 ☐ Enter the dates onto the date sheets on SG pp. 8-12	☐ Read pp. 46-47 from *The Kingfisher Science Encyclopedia,* then discuss what was read ☐ Color and label the "Lines on the Globe" sketch on SG pg. 119 ☐ Prepare an outline or narrative summary, write it on SG pp. 122-123
Supplies I Need for the Week ✓ Blue balloon (with the continents drawn or printed on it) ✓ Flat map ✓ Pin	
Things I Need to Prepare	

Five Days a Week

Day 1	Day 2	Day 3	Day 4	Day 5
☐ Do the "Is a flat representation the same as a spherical representation of the Earth?" experiment, then fill out the experiment sheet on SG pp. 120-121	☐ Read pp. 46-47 from *The Kingfisher Science Encyclopedia,* then discuss what was read ☐ Write an outline or list of facts on SG pg. 122	☐ Define cartographer, lines of longitude, lines of latitude on SG pg. 110 ☐ Enter the dates onto the date sheets on SG pp. 8-12 ☐ Color and label the "Lines on the Globe" sketch on SG pg. 119	☐ Read one or all of the additional reading assignments ☐ Prepare your report, write the report on SG pg. 123	☐ Complete one of the Want More Activities listed **OR** ☐ Study a scientist from the field of Earth Science
Supplies I Need for the Week ✓ Blue balloon (with the continents drawn or printed on it) ✓ Flat map ✓ Pin				
Things I Need to Prepare				

Additional Information Week 17

Experiment Information

- **NOTE** – I have provided a copy of a flat map for you to use in the Appendix on pg. 258.
- **Introduction** – *(from the Student Guide)* Maps are graphical representations of the Earth. There are several different types of maps, such as world maps, relief maps, topographical maps, and street maps, but they all have one thing in common. All maps share information that helps the user to determine position, so it is very important that they are accurate. The Earth is a spherical object, but most maps are flat representations. In this experiment, you are going to examine if flat representations of the Earth are the same as spherical representations.
- **Results** – The students should find that it was very difficult, if not impossible, to perfectly match the flat map to the balloon globe without cutting the map. They should also see that it was very difficult, if not impossible, to perfectly match the popped balloon globe to the flat map.
- **Explanation** – It is virtually impossible to make a perfect representation of a spherical object on a flat surface. Either some of the object will be distorted or sections of the flat map will be missing. This is the reason that cartographers have come up with so many different projections or methods of representing the Earth on a flat surface.

Discussion Questions

1. What is the purpose of a map? (*The purpose of a map is to give geographical information about an area.*)
2. What is the purpose of the lines that you find on a globe? (*The purpose of the lines that can be found on a globe is to help us measure distances and find places on the globe.*)
3. How are lines of latitude measured? (*Lines of latitude are measured at angles north or south of the central latitude line, the equator.*)
4. How do lines of longitude differ from lines of latitude? (*Lines of longitude divide the globe in segments from pole to pole. Lines of longitude do not have an obvious reference point, like the equator, so one was arbitrarily chosen.*)
5. How do cartographers represent a round Earth on a flat surface? (*Cartographers represent a round Earth on flat surface by using projections.*)
6. How are satellites used in mapping? (*Satellites produce images of the Earth's surface that cartographers can use to produce more accurate maps of the Earth.*)

Want More

- **Create a Map** – Have the students create a street level map of your town, showing your home and various landmarks. Be sure they label the streets and landmarks. If you want to challenge them further, have them draw a grid with coordinate blocks and a scale for their map.
- **Pumpkin Map** – Have the students mark a pumpkin with the longitude and latitude lines. A pumpkin has natural longitude lines as well as a North and South Pole. Choose one of the longitude lines to be the Prime Meridian and the measure halfway in between the stem and bottom of the pumpkin to mark the Equator. Measure a third of the distance from the Equator and the stem and draw the Tropic of Cancer. Then, measure a quarter of the distance from the

stem to the Equator and draw the Arctic Circle. Repeat for the bottom half of the pumpkin, labeling the Tropic of Capricorn and the Antarctic Circle. Then have the students add several more lines of longitude and latitude.

Sketch Assignment Week 17

Note – The information for this sketch is not all in the reading.
The students will need to use a map, globe, or atlas to complete the sketch.

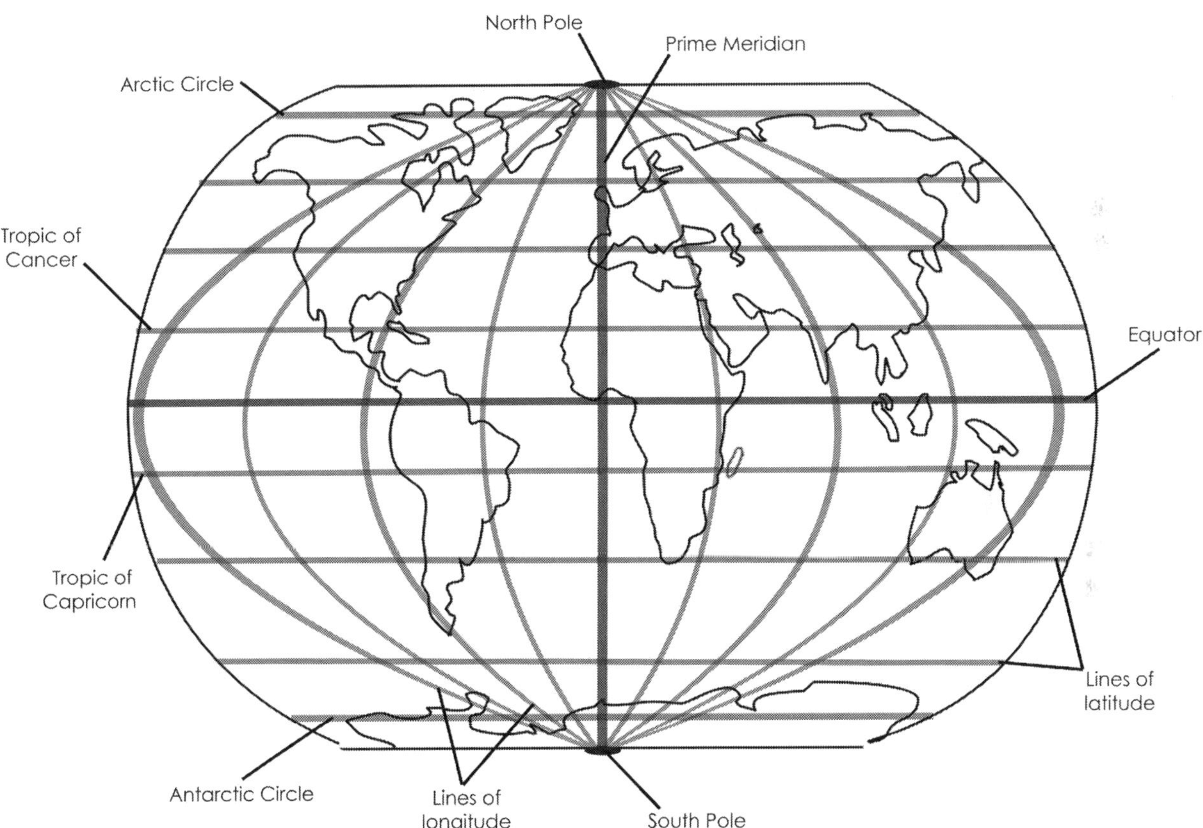

Student Assignment Sheet Week 18
Rivers

Experiment: How is the course of a river determined?

Materials

- ✓ Pitcher for water
- ✓ Water
- ✓ Cookie sheet
- ✓ Paper cup
- ✓ Straw
- ✓ Dirt or sand
- ✓ Small rocks
- ✓ Books
- ✓ Tape

Procedure

1. Read the introduction to this experiment and answer the question.
2. Poke a hole in the base of the cup, just large enough for the straw to fit tightly, using a pencil. Insert the straw and place the cup in the sink. Fill the cup halfway with water and watch what happens. If the water comes out of the straw like a stream, the cup is ready to use. If not, make the necessary adjustments.
3. Using several books, prop your cookie sheet up at an angle, so that water will flow down easily. Tape the cup to the top of the cookie sheet and fill it three quarters full with water. Observe what happens and record where the water went.
4. Dry the cookie sheet off and then sprinkle some dirt or sand all over the sheet. Refill the cup three quarters full with water, observe what happens and record where the water went.
5. Clean the cookie sheet off, sprinkle some dirt or sand all over the sheet, and place a few rocks in various places. Refill the cup three quarters full with water, observe what happens and record where the water went.
6. Draw conclusions and complete your experiment sheet.

Vocabulary & Memory Work

- ☐ Vocabulary: delta, estuary, source
- ☐ Memory Work – Begin to work on the World's Major Seas & Oceans (*See the unit overview sheet for a complete list.*)

Sketch Assignment: A River's Course

- Label the following: source, upper stage, middle stage, tributary, lower stage, delta

Writing Assignment

- Reading Assignment: *The Usborne Science Encyclopedia* pp. 190-191 Rivers
- Additional Research Readings
  - Rivers: *DKEOS* pg. 233

Dates

- 3300 BC – The Indus Valley Civilization uses rivers for navigation.

Schedules for Week 18

Two Days a Week

Day 1	Day 2
☐ Define delta, drainage basin, estuary, source on SG pg. 110 ☐ Do the "How is the course of a river determined?" experiment, then fill out the experiment sheet on SG pp. 126-127 ☐ Enter the dates onto the date sheets on SG pp. 8-12	☐ Read pp. 190-191 from the *The Usborne Science Encyclopedia,* then discuss what was read ☐ Color and label the "The World's Major Seas & Oceans" sketch on SG pg. 125 ☐ Prepare an outline or narrative summary, write it on SG pp. 128-129

Supplies I Need for the Week

✓ Pitcher for water, Water, Cookie sheet, Paper cup , Straw, Dirt or sand, Small rocks, Books, Tape

Things I Need to Prepare

Five Days a Week

Day 1	Day 2	Day 3	Day 4	Day 5
☐ Do the "How is the course of a river determined?" experiment, then fill out the experiment sheet on SG pp. 126-127	☐ Read pp. 190-191 from the *The Usborne Science Encyclopedia,* then discuss what was read ☐ Write an outline or list of facts on SG pg. 128	☐ Define delta, drainage basin, estuary, source on SG pg. 110 ☐ Enter the dates onto the date sheets on SG pp. 8-12 ☐ Color and label the "The World's Major Seas & Oceans" sketch on SG pg. 125	☐ Read one or all of the additional reading assignments ☐ Prepare your report, write the report on SG pg. 129	☐ Complete one of the Want More Activities listed **OR** ☐ Study a scientist from the field of Earth Science

Supplies I Need for the Week

✓ Pitcher for water, Water, Cookie sheet, Paper cup , Straw, Dirt or sand, Small rocks, Books, Tape

Things I Need to Prepare

Additional Information Week 18

- ☞ **Introduction** – (*from the Student Guide*) A river is a natural flow of water from one area to a lake, sea, or ocean. Rivers typically contain fresh water and they are a very important part of the water cycle. Rivers are also home to a variety of wildlife and plant species. In this experiment, you are going to examine how a river's course is determined.
- ☞ **Results** – The students should see that the plain stream (step 3) flowed straight down the sheet. The stream with the dirt (step 4) meandered a bit as it made its way down the sheet. The stream with the dirt and rocks (step 5) meandered even more as it avoided the rocks in its way.
- ☞ **Explanation** – A river's course can be altered. As water makes its way down the mountain from the source, it encounters obstacles. The water can move some of these hindrances, but some of these impediments cannot be moved by the force of the water. Either way, these obstacles slow down and possibly alter the river's course. Other factors that contribute to how a river is formed are the amount of water and the angle of descent.
- ☞ **Troubleshooting** – If your straw does not seal tightly, you may need to use some silicone sealant or air dry clay around the hole to prevent water from leaking out.
- ☞ **Take it Further** – Have the students take the experiment one step further by changing the angle of the cookie sheet. Have them choose an angle that is lower and one that is higher to see if their previous results are changed.

Discussion Questions

1. Where does the water in a river come from? (*The water in a river comes from rainwater runoff, springs, or glacier flows.*)
2. Describe a river's course. (*A river begins in the mountains and flows downhill, where smaller streams or tributaries joint it. As it grows and the land levels out, the river meanders through the landscape, forming large loops. Finally, it widens out into an estuary or delta before it reaches the sea.*)
3. How do rivers erode the landscape around them? (*Rivers erode by sweeping away any loose soil, sand, or rocks. As they sweep those away, they tear at the remaining rocks and chip away at the riverbed. The force of the river can also cause rocks to fracture and chemicals in the water can slowly dissolve the rocks as the river passes by.*)
4. How is a load deposited by a river? (*As a river slows down, it deposits the heavier material first. This is followed by the smaller, lighter particles, which creates layers.*)
5. Where is a river delta found and what happens at this point in the river? (*A river delta is found at the end of the river where it meets the sea. At this point in the river, fresh water mixes with salt water and the remaining sediment is deposited, creating narrower channels.*)

Want More

- **River Deposition** – Have the students complete the activity suggested on pg. 191 of *The Usborne Science Encyclopedia* to see how material carried by rivers is deposited in layers.
- **Explore a river** – Follow the directions from this website:
  - http://tlc.howstuffworks.com/family/easy-outdoor-science-activities-for-kids1.htm

Sketch Assignment Week 18

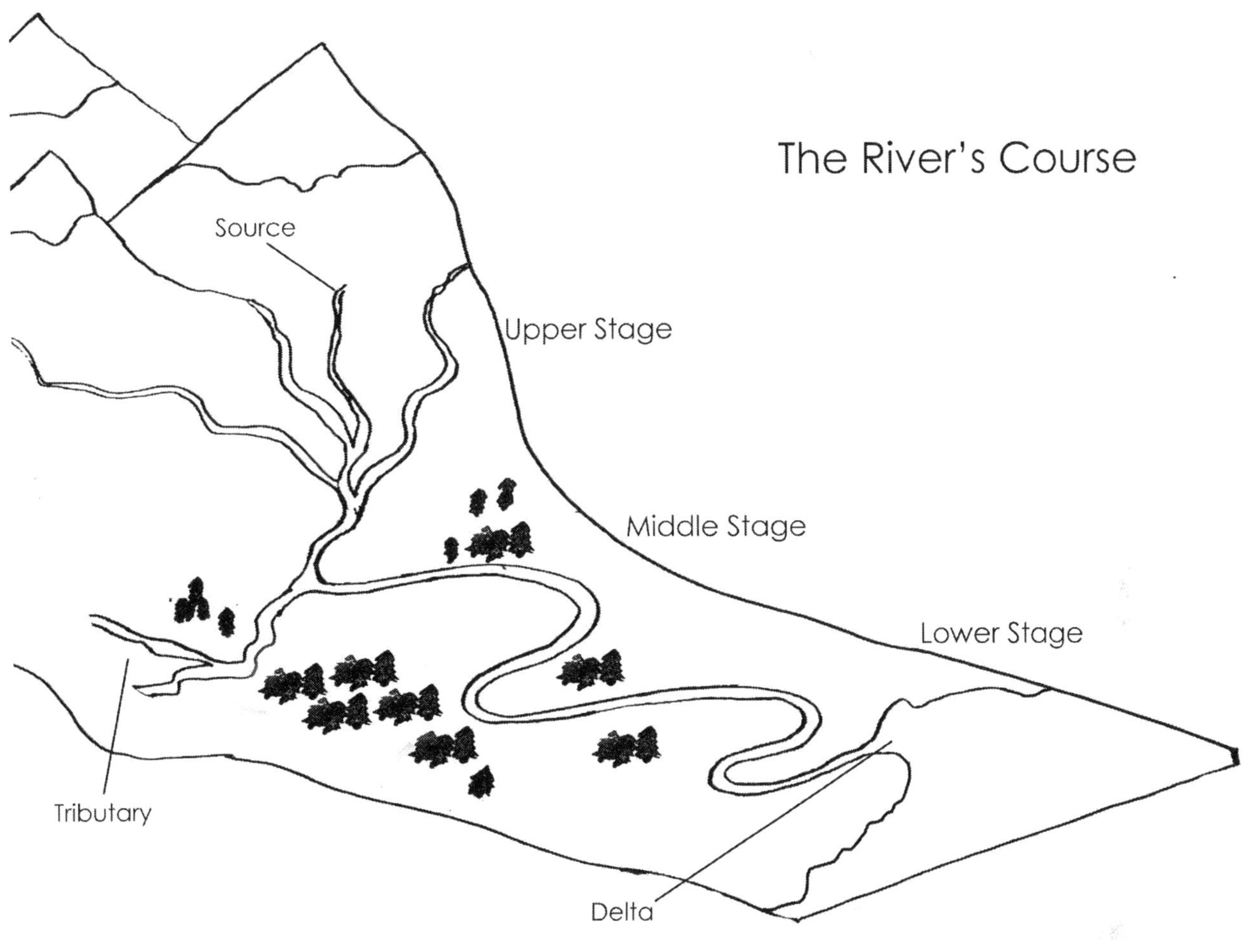

Student Assignment Sheet Week 19
Oceans

Experiment: Can surface currents affect the ocean floor the same way that deep water currents do?

Materials

- ✓ Aluminum bread pan or Plastic bin
- ✓ Air dry clay
- ✓ Water
- ✓ Sand (1 cup)
- ✓ 2 Straws

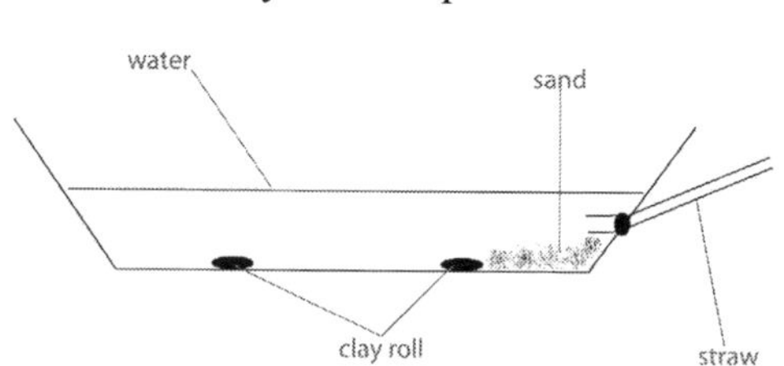

Procedure

1. Read the introduction to this experiment and answer the question.
2. Have your teacher cut a small hole at the center of one end of your pan that is 1½ inches from the bottom. Insert your straw into the hole, so that when you blow through it the air skips over the bottom of the pan. Use some of the air dry clay to hold the straw in place and prevent water from coming out of the hole.
3. Next, roll out two lengths of air dry clay that are the exact width of the pan and place them 2 inches from the each end of the pan. (*See diagram above for a visual reference.*)
4. Fill your pan two-thirds of the way with water and add ½ cup of sand to the end of the pan that has the straw. Make sure that the sand stays between the air dry clay roll and the end of the pan.
5. Make some deep water currents by blowing air through the straw at the end of the pan intermittently over one minute. Observe what happens and record your results.
6. Empty the pan, clean it out, refill it one third of the way with water and add ½ cup of sand in the same way you did in step # 4.
7. Make some surface currents by blowing air through the a straw onto the surface of the water in the pan intermittently over one minute. Observe what happens and record your results.
8. Draw conclusions and complete your experiment sheet.

Vocabulary & Memory Work

- ☐ Vocabulary: coast, oceanic ridge, oceanic trench, tides
- ☐ Memory Work – Continue to work on memorizing the World's Major Seas and Oceans.

Sketch Assignment: The World's Major Seas & Oceans

- Label the following: Arctic Ocean, Pacific Ocean, Atlantic Ocean, Indian Ocean, Southern Ocean, Mediterranean Sea, Red Sea, Black Sea, Caribbean Sea, Gulf of Mexico, Hudson Bay, Bering Sea, Tasman Sea, Coral Sea, Bay of Bengal, Arabian Sea, and North Sea

Writing Assignment

- Reading Assignment: *The Kingfisher Science Encyclopedia* pp. 12-13 The Oceans
- Additional Research Readings
  - Seas and Oceans: *USE* pp. 188-189, *DKEOS* pg. 234
  - The Shoreline: *DKEOS* pp. 236-237
  - The Ocean Floor: *KSE* pp. 14-15

Dates

- 1800 BC – Egyptians begin using very simple techniques to measure water depths.
- 1620 – Dutch physician, Cornelis Drebbel, builds the world's first submarine and makes several trips in the River Thames near London at a depth of about 12 or 15 feet.
- 1960 – A two-manned submarine, named *Trieste*, dives to what was believed to be the deepest point in the Mariana Trench, which was 10,915 meters.

Schedules for Week 19

Two Days a Week

Day 1	Day 2
☐ Define coast, oceanic ridge, oceanic trench, tides on SG pp. 110-111 ☐ Do the "Can surface currents affect the ocean floor the same way that deep water current do?" experiment, then fill out the experiment sheet on SG pp. 132-133 ☐ Enter the dates onto the date sheets on SG pp. 8-12	☐ Read pp. 12-13 from the *The Kingfisher Science Encyclopedia,* then discuss what was read ☐ Prepare an outline or narrative summary, write it on SG pp. 134-135 ☐ Create the "The World's Major Seas and Oceans" sketch on SG pg. 131
Supplies I Need for the Week ✓ Aluminum bread pan or Plastic bin ✓ Air dry clay, Water ✓ Sand (1 cup), 2 Straws	
Things I Need to Prepare	

Five Days a Week

Day 1	Day 2	Day 3	Day 4	Day 5
☐ Do the "Can surface currents affect the ocean floor the same way that deep water current do?" experiment, then fill out the experiment sheet on SG pp. 132-133	☐ Read pp. 12-13 from the *The Kingfisher Science Encyclopedia,* then discuss what was read ☐ Write an outline or list of facts on SG pg. 134	☐ Define coast, oceanic ridge, oceanic trench, tides on SG pp. 110-111 ☐ Enter the dates onto the date sheets on SG pg. 8-12 ☐ Create the "The World's Major Seas and Oceans" sketch on SG pg. 131	☐ Read one or all of the additional reading assignments ☐ Prepare your report, write the report on SG pg. 135	☐ Complete one of the Want More Activities listed **OR** ☐ Study a scientist from the field of Earth Science
Supplies I Need for the Week ✓ Aluminum bread pan or Plastic bin ✓ Air dry clay, Water ✓ Sand (1 cup), 2 Straws				
Things I Need to Prepare				

Additional Information Week 19

Experiment Information

- **Introduction** – (*from the Student Guide*) The ocean is constantly in motion due to several currents that affect it. These currents are caused by several factors, such as wind, density, and temperature. Surface currents are caused by the wind blowing over the surface of the ocean, which then forms waves. Deep water currents are caused by cold water sinking and warm water rising. Deep water currents can also cause underwater waves. In this experiment, you are going to examine how these two different currents can affect the ocean floor.
- **Results** – The students should see that both times the sand moved past the first barrier and possibly the second one as well. However, the students may see that when they create surface currents, the sand barely moves. This is because the water was too deep for the surface currents to be able to affect the bottom.
- **Explanation** – Surface currents are caused by the wind blowing over the surface of the ocean, which then forms waves. They affect the ocean floor, but mostly when they are close to the shore, as the waves they create don't reach great depths. Deep water currents are caused by cold water sinking while warm water is rising. Deep water currents can also cause underwater waves, which can affect the ocean floor at great depths. In other words, both surface and deep water currents can move the ocean floor, but their effects are felt at different depths of the ocean.

Discussion Questions

1. How much of the Earth's surface is covered with water? (*Over two thirds of the Earth's surface is covered with water.*)
2. How do currents work in the ocean? (*In the ocean, as warm water around the tropics moves northward, it cools and sinks. The cooler water circulates back towards the south, creating a circular pattern.*)
3. Why are the ocean depths so difficult to explore? (*The ocean depths are difficult to explore because the underwater pressure is so great.*)
4. Where do waves form and why do they crash on the shore? (*Waves are formed in the open sea and are pushed by the wind. When they reach the shore, the lower part of the motion is slowed, causing the top of the wave to crest and crash on the coast.*)

Want More

- **Ocean Zones** – Have the students make a poster depicting the different zones of the ocean. Have them include the depth ranges, a brief description of the conditions in the zones (i.e., temperature and pressure), and the typical animals found in that zone.
- **Tide Pools** – If you live near tide pools, take a field trip to explore them this week. If you do not, then visit the following websites for virtual tour:
  - http://montereybay.noaa.gov/visitor/TidePool/VRTidepool/welcome.html

Sketch Assignment Week 19

The World's Major Seas & Oceans

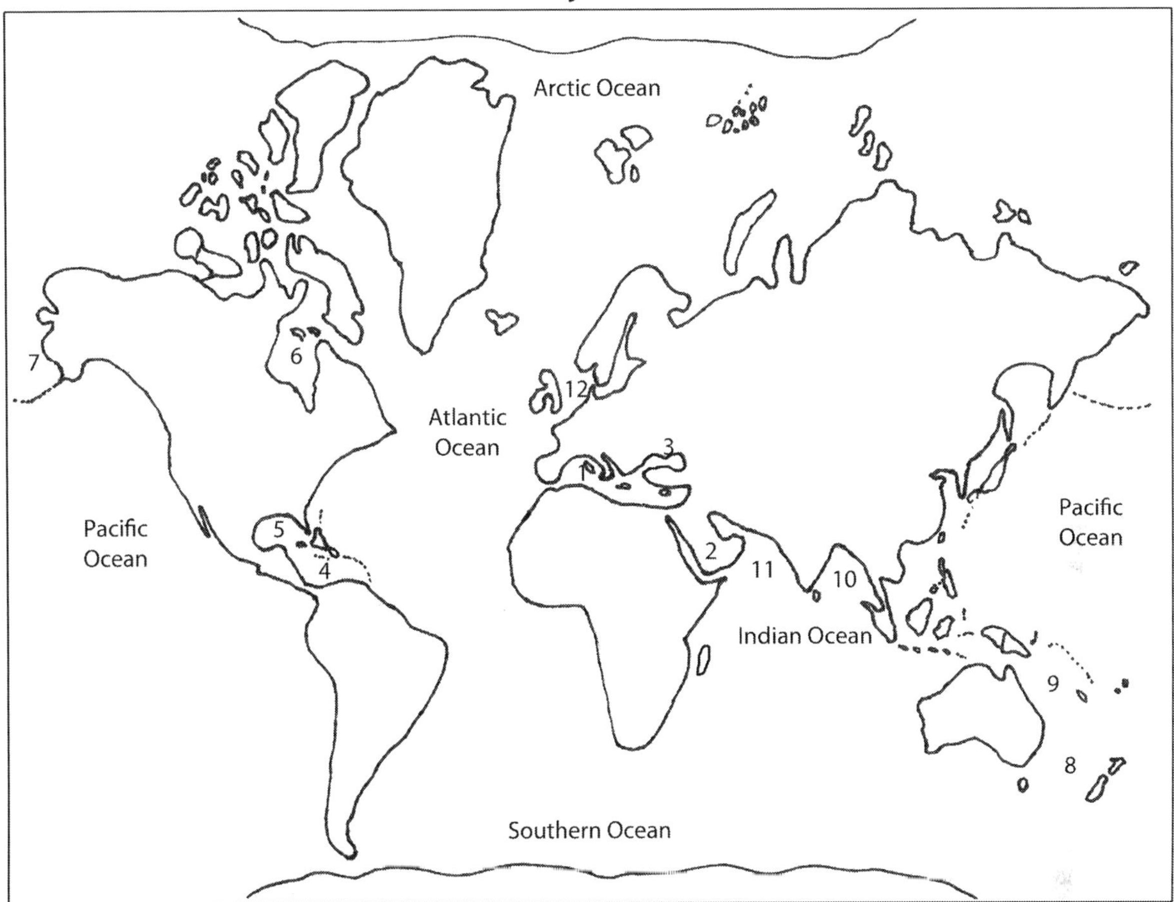

1. Mediterranean Sea
2. Red Sea
3. Black Sea
4. Caribbean Sea
5. Gulf of Mexico
6. Hudson Bay
7. Bering Sea
8. Tasman Sea
9. Coral Sea
10. Bay of Bengal
11. Arabian Sea
12. North Sea

Student Assignment Sheet Week 20
Glaciers

Experiment: What happens when glaciers melt?

Materials

- ✓ Glacier Melt Model (*See note below for how to make using cup, water, pebbles, and sand.*)
- ✓ Large cutting board with a handle
- ✓ Large rubber band

Procedure

NOTE *– The day before you do this experiment, you will need to make your Glacier Melt Model. Begin by pouring a layer of both pebbles and sand on the bottom of your cup, then cover with water and place in the freezer. Once the water has frozen, repeat the process again until the cup has been filled. You should have at least three layers.*

1. Read the introduction to this experiment and answer the question.
2. Prop your cutting board up in the sink, handle-side up, so that the board is at about a 45 degree angle.
3. Remove your Glacier Melt Model from the cup using a little warm water. Use the rubber band to secure it pebble/sand side down to the top of the cutting board. Observe what happens as the ice melts.
4. Record your observations and the time it takes for the model to melt.
5. Draw conclusions and complete your experiment sheet.

Vocabulary & Memory Work

- ☐ Vocabulary: deposition, erratics, glacier, moraine
- ☐ Memory Work – Continue to work on memorizing the World's Major Seas & Oceans.

Sketch Assignment: Anatomy of a Glacier

- Label the following: Cirque, Crevasses, Glacier's Snout, Meltwater, Movement of the Glacier (including arrows)

Writing Assignment

- Reading Assignment: *The Kingfisher Science Encyclopedia* pp. 34-35 Glaciers and Ice Sheets
- Additional Research Readings
  - Ice and Glaciers: *DKEOS* pp. 34-35

Dates

- No dates to be entered this week.

Schedules for Week 20

Two Days a Week

Day 1	Day 2
☐ Define deposition, erratics, glacier, moraine on SG pg. 111 ☐ Do the "What happens when glaciers melt?" experiment, then fill out the experiment sheet on SG pp. 138-139	☐ Read pp. 34-35 from the *The Kingfisher Science Encyclopedia,* then discuss what was read ☐ Prepare an outline or narrative summary, write it on SG pp. 140-141 ☐ Color and label the "Anatomy of a Glacier" sketch on SG pg. 137

Supplies I Need for the Week

- ✓ Glacier Melt Model (You will need a cup, water, pebbles, and sand to make this.)
- ✓ Large cutting board with a handle
- ✓ Large rubber band

Things I Need to Prepare

Five Days a Week

Day 1	Day 2	Day 3	Day 4	Day 5
☐ Do the "What happens when glaciers melt?" experiment, then fill out the experiment sheet on SG pp. 138-139	☐ Read pp. 34-35 from the *The Kingfisher Science Encyclopedia,* then discuss what was read ☐ Write an outline or list of facts on SG pg. 140	☐ Define deposition, erratics, glacicr, moraine on SG pg. 111 ☐ Color and label the "Anatomy of a Glacier" sketch on SG pg. 137	☐ Read one or all of the additional reading assignments ☐ Prepare your report, write the report on SG pg. 141	☐ Complete one of the Want More Activities listed **OR** ☐ Study a scientist from the field of Earth Science

Supplies I Need for the Week

- ✓ Glacier Melt Model (You will need a cup, water, pebbles, and sand to make this.)
- ✓ Large cutting board with a handle
- ✓ Large rubber band

Things I Need to Prepare

Additional Information Week 20

Experiment Information

- **Introduction** – (*from the Student Guide*) Glaciers are huge masses of ice that flow downhill. Glaciers are solid, powerful forces that can cut through the landscape, picking up rocks and soil along the way. In this experiment, you are going to look at what happens when those glaciers begin to melt.
- **Results** – The students should see that as the model melts, the pebbles and sand will slide down the board. Some will slide off in clumps and other will slide off in streams that form strange patterns.
- **Explanation** – As a glacier melts, it affect the terrain. When a glacier melts and moves, it picks up rocks and dirt along the way. Then, as it melts, the glacier deposits the matter further down the hill. The valley just below a glacier will usually have a thick deposit of debris, called moraine, on the basin floor.
- **Take it Further** – Repeat the experiment with several variations to see if there are any differences. One variation would be to use a hair dryer to melt the model more quickly. Another variation would be to put the whole set-up in the refrigerator so that it melts slowly. The students could also vary the materials added to the ice, such using only sand or using larger rocks. Have the students play a part in determining the variations they would like to test.

Discussion Questions

1. Where are glaciers found? (*Glaciers can be found on the highest mountains and near the poles.*)
2. How do glaciers form? (*Glaciers begin in high, cold places, such as mountains. Layers of fallen snow compact into hard ice. As more snow falls on top of the ice, the ice mass gets heavier and begins to move down the mountain. As it moves down the mountain, it slowly melts.*)
3. What are some clues that let you know a glacier was once present in a valley? (*You can know a valley once had a glacier by its deep, rounded, U-shape and by the moraine hills and other debris markers found in it.*)

Want More

- **Edible Glacier** – Make an edible glacier with the students. You can find the directions for this project here:
  - http://elementalblogging.com/glacier-study/
- **Research Project** – Have the students research the changes in glaciers over the past twenty years. When they are done, have them write a one to three paragraph report about their findings.

Sketch Assignment Week 20

Anatomy of a Glacier

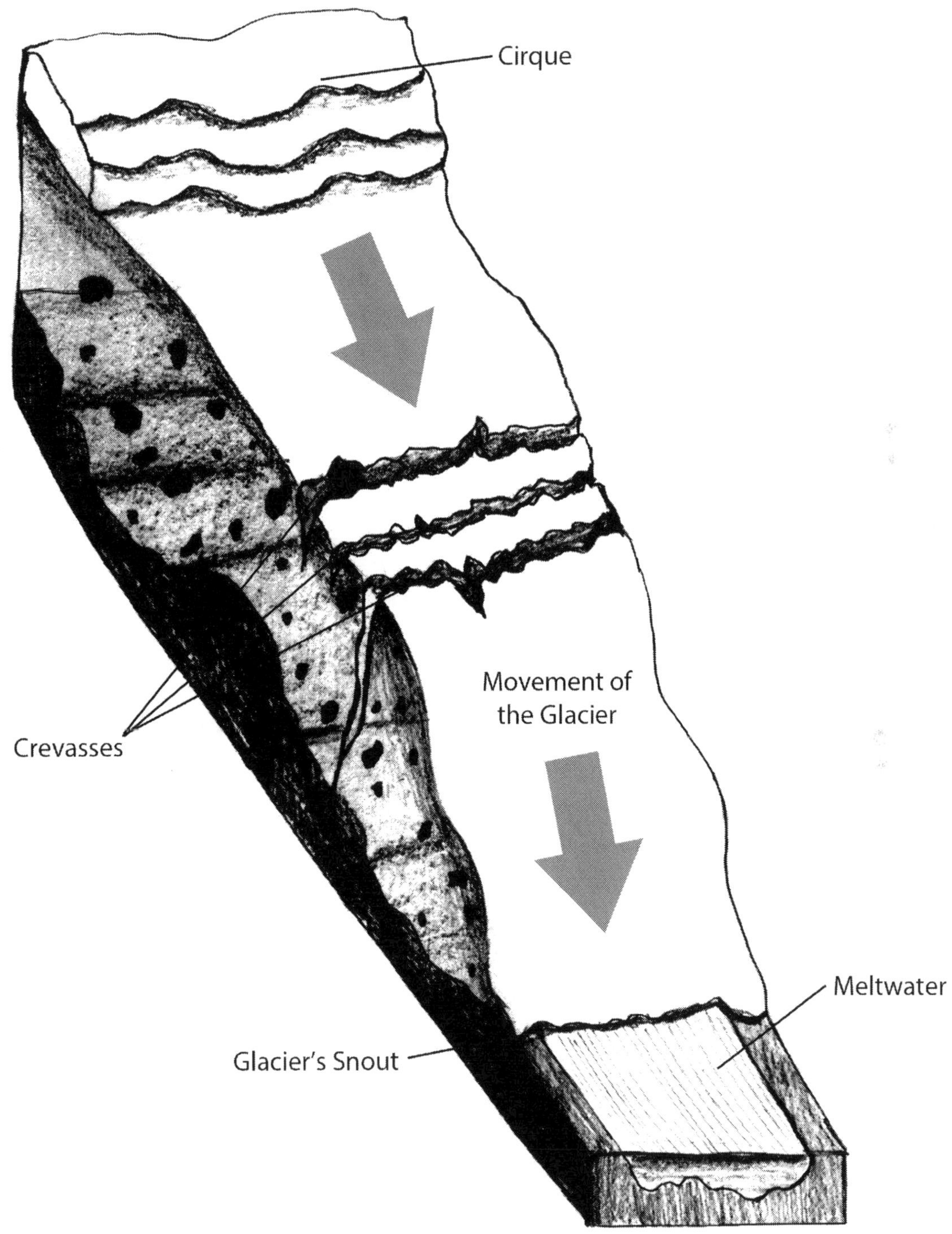

Student Assignment Sheet Week 21
Natural Cycles

Experiment: Can I recreate the water cycle?

Materials:
- ✓ Cup
- ✓ Water
- ✓ Plastic Baggie
- ✓ Rubber Band

Procedure:
1. Read the introduction to this experiment and answer the question.
2. Pour a little warm water into the bottom of your cup. Cover it with the plastic baggie and use the rubber band to secure it in place.
3. Set the cup in a place where it will receive direct sunlight for the next two hours. (***NOTE*** *– If you do not have a sunny place to set your cup, set it under a desk lamp instead.*)
4. Check the glass after 2 hours; observe and record what has happened.
5. Draw conclusions and complete your experiment sheet.

Vocabulary & Memory Work
- ☐ Vocabulary: natural cycle, greenhouse gas
- ☐ Memory Work – Continue to work on memorizing the World's Major Seas & Oceans.

Sketch Assignment: The Nitrogen Cycle & The Carbon Cycle
- The Nitrogen Cycle – Label the following: Bacteria convert ammonia in the soil into nitrate, which is taken up by plants; plants also take up nitrogen from the air; plants are eaten by animals; as dead plants and animals decay, nitrogen is released into the soil.
- The Carbon Cycle – Label the following: When fossil fuels are burned, carbon dioxide is released into the air; plants take in carbon dioxide from the air to make food; animals take in carbon when they eat plants and release carbon dioxide when they breathe; as dead plants and animal decay, they release carbon dioxide into the air.

Writing Assignment
- Reading Assignment: *The Usborne Science Encyclopedia* pp. 292-293 Natural Cycles
- Additional Research Readings
  - Nutrient Cycles: *USE* pp. 334-335

Dates
- 1896 – Svante Arrhenius, a Swedish chemist, shows that CO_2 helps to trap heat in the atmosphere.

Schedules for Week 21

Two Days a Week

Day 1	Day 2
☐ Define natural cycle, greenhouse gas on SG pg. 111 ☐ Do the "Can I recreate the water cycle?" experiment, then fill out the experiment sheet on SG pp. 144-145 ☐ Enter the dates onto the date sheets on SG pp. 8-12	☐ Read pp. 292-293 from the *The Usborne Science Encyclopedia,* then discuss what was read ☐ Prepare an outline or narrative summary, write it on SG pp. 146-147 ☐ Color and label the "The Nitrogen Cycle & The Carbon Cycle" sketch on SG pg. 143

Supplies I Need for the Week
- ✓ Cup
- ✓ Water
- ✓ Plastic Baggie
- ✓ Rubber Band

Things I Need to Prepare

Five Days a Week

Day 1	Day 2	Day 3	Day 4	Day 5
☐ Do the "Can I recreate the water cycle?" experiment, then fill out the experiment sheet on SG pp. 144-145	☐ Read pp. 292-293 from the *The Usborne Science Encyclopedia,* then discuss what was read ☐ Write an outline or list of facts on SG pg. 146	☐ Define natural cycle, greenhouse gas on SG pg. 111 ☐ Enter the dates onto the date sheets on SG pp. 8-12 ☐ Color and label the "The Nitrogen Cycle & The Carbon Cycle" sketch on SG pg. 143	☐ Read one or all of the additional reading assignments ☐ Prepare your report, write the report on SG pg. 147	☐ Complete one of the Want More Activities listed **OR** ☐ Study a scientist from the field of Earth Science

Supplies I Need for the Week
- ✓ Cup
- ✓ Water
- ✓ Plastic Baggie
- ✓ Rubber Band

Things I Need to Prepare

Additional Information Week 21

Experiment Information

- **Introduction** – (*from the Student Guide*) The water cycle shows how water changes forms on the Earth.

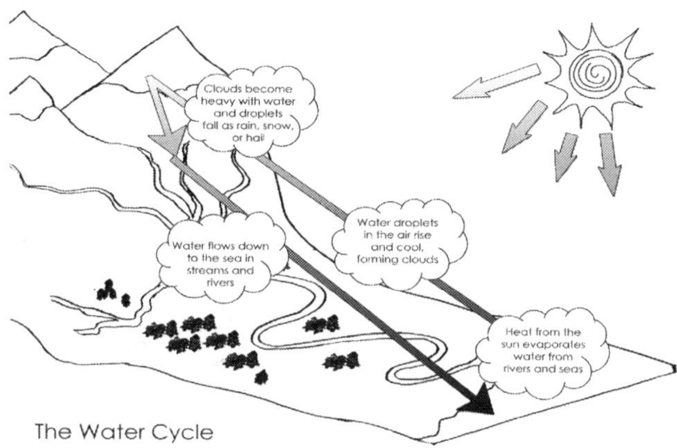

The Water Cycle

In today's experiment, you are going to try to create your very own mini-version of the water cycle.

- **Results** – The students should see that the plastic baggie has many droplets of water on it. They should also see that several of these droplets have come together to form bigger droplets, which then fall to the bottom of the cup.
- **Explanation** – Water from the oceans and rivers is being evaporated by the Sun. The water vapors cool and come together to form clouds. When enough water vapor is in the clouds, they become heavy and rain begins to fall. The rain fills the rivers and oceans on the Earth once again.

Discussion Questions

1. Briefly describe the nitrogen cycle. (*Lightning forms nitrates in the air and bacteria form other nitrates in the soil. These nitrates are taken up by plants, which are then eaten by animals. When these plants and animals die, they release nitrogen back into the environment and the cycle begins again.*)
2. Briefly describe the carbon cycle. (*Plants take in carbon dioxide from the air and use it to make carbohydrates. Living things, like animals, ingest those carbohydrates and break them down for energy. This process produces carbon dioxide, which is released into the air and the cycle begins again.*)
3. Briefly describe the water cycle. (*Water falls as rain. It drains into the rivers and out to the sea. Then, the sun heats up the water, forming vapor, which rises to form clouds. Once the clouds become heavy with water, the cycle begins again.*)
4. How are the natural cycles being upset? (*The natural cycles are being upset by the presence of pollution and additional wastes and chemicals used by humans. This is creating more carbon dioxide in the air and more nitrogen in the soil than is needed.*)

Want More

- **Create a Poster** – Have the students make a poster detailing the water cycle.
- **Make a Greenhouse** – Use a 2 liter bottle or a large glass jar to make a terrarium or mini-greenhouse. Fill the bottom of your container with moist soil and plant several small plants in it. Cover and set it in the sun. You should see that the water follows through the water cycle as the plants grow over time.

Sketch Assignment Week 21

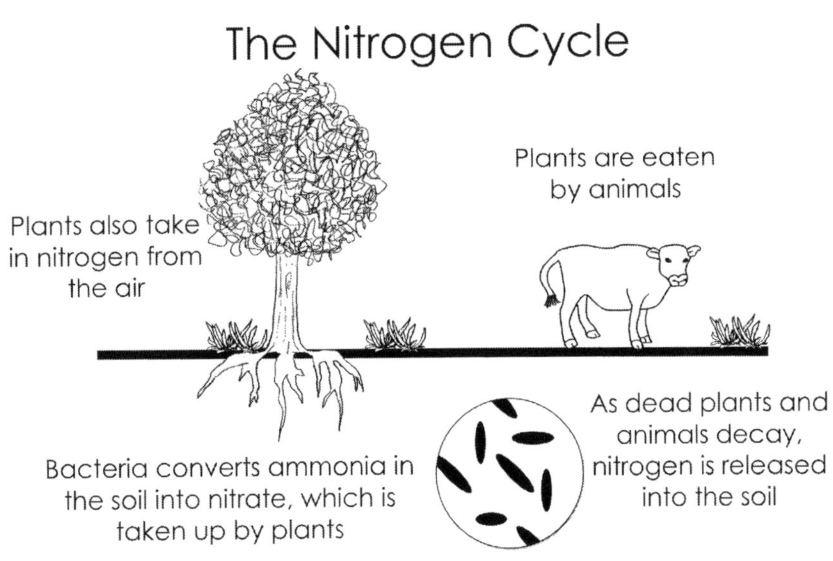

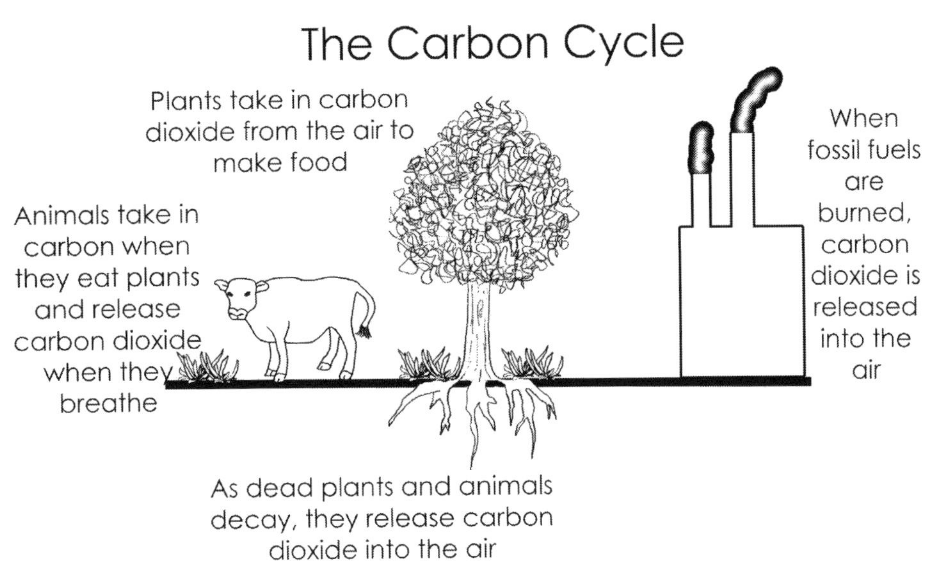

Student Assignment Sheet Week 22
Biomes and Habitats

Experiment: How do desert plants live with so little water?

Materials
- ✓ Paper towels
- ✓ Cookie sheet
- ✓ Wax paper
- ✓ Rubber band
- ✓ Water

Procedure
1. Read the introduction to this experiment and answer the question.
2. Moisten three paper towels with water until they are soaked, but not dripping, with water.
3. Lay one of the paper towels flat on the cookie sheet.
4. Roll the second paper towel up, secure it with the paper clips and lay it next to the flat paper towel on the cookie sheet.
5. Place the third paper towel flat on a piece of wax paper that is slightly larger, roll the two up together and secure with paper clips. Then, lay the roll next to the other papers towels on the cookie sheet and set the sheet in a place where it will not be disturbed.
6. Check your paper towels the next day, make observations, and record the results.
7. Draw conclusions and complete your experiment sheet.

Vocabulary & Memory Work
- ☐ Vocabulary: biome
- ☐ Memory Work – Continue to work on memorizing the World's Major Seas & Oceans.

Sketch Assignment: Biomes around the World
- Choose one of the following biomes—arctic, desert, grasslands, rainforest, taiga, or tundra. Find where the particular biome is on the globe and label that region on the globe.

Writing Assignment
- Reading Assignment: *The Kingfisher Science Encyclopedia* pp. 68-69 Biomes and Habitats
- Additional Research Readings
  - Plants and People: *USE* pp. 290-291
  - Major Biomes: *DKEOS* pp. 382-396

Dates
- 20th century – Tropical and temperate rainforests experience heavy logging, which leads to a reduction of the forests' sizes.

Schedules for Week 22

Two Days a Week

Day 1	Day 2
☐ Define biome on SG pg. 111 ☐ Do the "How do desert plants live with so little water?" experiment, then fill out the experiment sheet on SG pp. 150-151 ☐ Enter the dates onto the date sheets on SG pg. 8-12	☐ Read pp. 68-69 from the *The Kingfisher Science Encyclopedia,* then discuss what was read ☐ Prepare an outline or narrative summary, write it on SG pp. 152-153 ☐ Color and label the "Biomes around the world" sketch on SG pg. 149

Supplies I Need for the Week
- ✓ Paper towels
- ✓ Cookie sheet
- ✓ Wax paper
- ✓ Rubber band
- ✓ Water

Things I Need to Prepare

Five Days a Week

Day 1	Day 2	Day 3	Day 4	Day 5
☐ Do the "How do desert plants live with so little water?" experiment, then fill out the experiment sheet on SG pp. 150-151	☐ Read pp. 68-69 from the *The Kingfisher Science Encyclopedia,* then discuss what was read ☐ Write an outline or list of facts on SG pg. 152	☐ Define biome on SG pg. 111 ☐ Enter the dates onto the date sheets on SG pp. 8-12 ☐ Color and label the "Biomes around the world" sketch on SG pg. 149	☐ Read one or all of the additional reading assignments ☐ Prepare your report, write the report on SG pg. 153	☐ Complete one of the Want More Activities listed **OR** ☐ Study a scientist from the field of Earth Science ☐ Take the Unit 4 Test

Supplies I Need for the Week
- ✓ Paper towels
- ✓ Cookie sheet
- ✓ Wax paper
- ✓ Rubber band, Water

Things I Need to Prepare

Additional Information Week 22

Experiment Information

- **Introduction** – (*from the Student Guide*) The desert is a harsh environment in which only the hardiest plants and animals can survive. It is extremely hot during the day and very cold at night. The desert also receives very little rainfall. The plants and animals living there are well adapted to these conditions, like the camel, which can go for months without drinking water because its digestive system is extremely effective at extracting water. In this experiment, you are going to test how desert plants have adapted to survive with so little water.
- **Results** – The students should see that the flat paper towel was completely dry and that the rolled paper towel was almost completely dry. The rolled paper towel plus the wax paper should still have been damp.
- **Explanation** – Desert plants conserve water. The wax paper in the experiment simulated the waxy coating that most desert plants have. The rolled paper towel in the experiment represented the reduced number of stomata that are also found in a desert plant. Stomata are small pores in the leaves of plants that take in carbon dioxide and release water vapor. The cactus, a typical desert plant, has a thick waxy coating and a reduced number of stomata, both of which help it to live in an environment with very little water.

Discussion Questions

1. What determines the boundaries between biomes? (*The boundaries of the different biomes are determined by variations in climate.*)
2. What is the difference between a habitat and a biome? (*A biome is a larger region with a distinct climate, which includes several smaller habitats. A habitat is an area where a given organism lives.*)
3. What is a community? (*A community is a group of plants and animals that live together in mutually beneficial relationships.*)

Want More

- **Habitat Diorama** – Have the students choose to make a diorama of either the arctic or the deciduous forests. Then have them create that environment inside a shoebox and add the necessary plants and animals to it.

Sketch Assignment Week 22

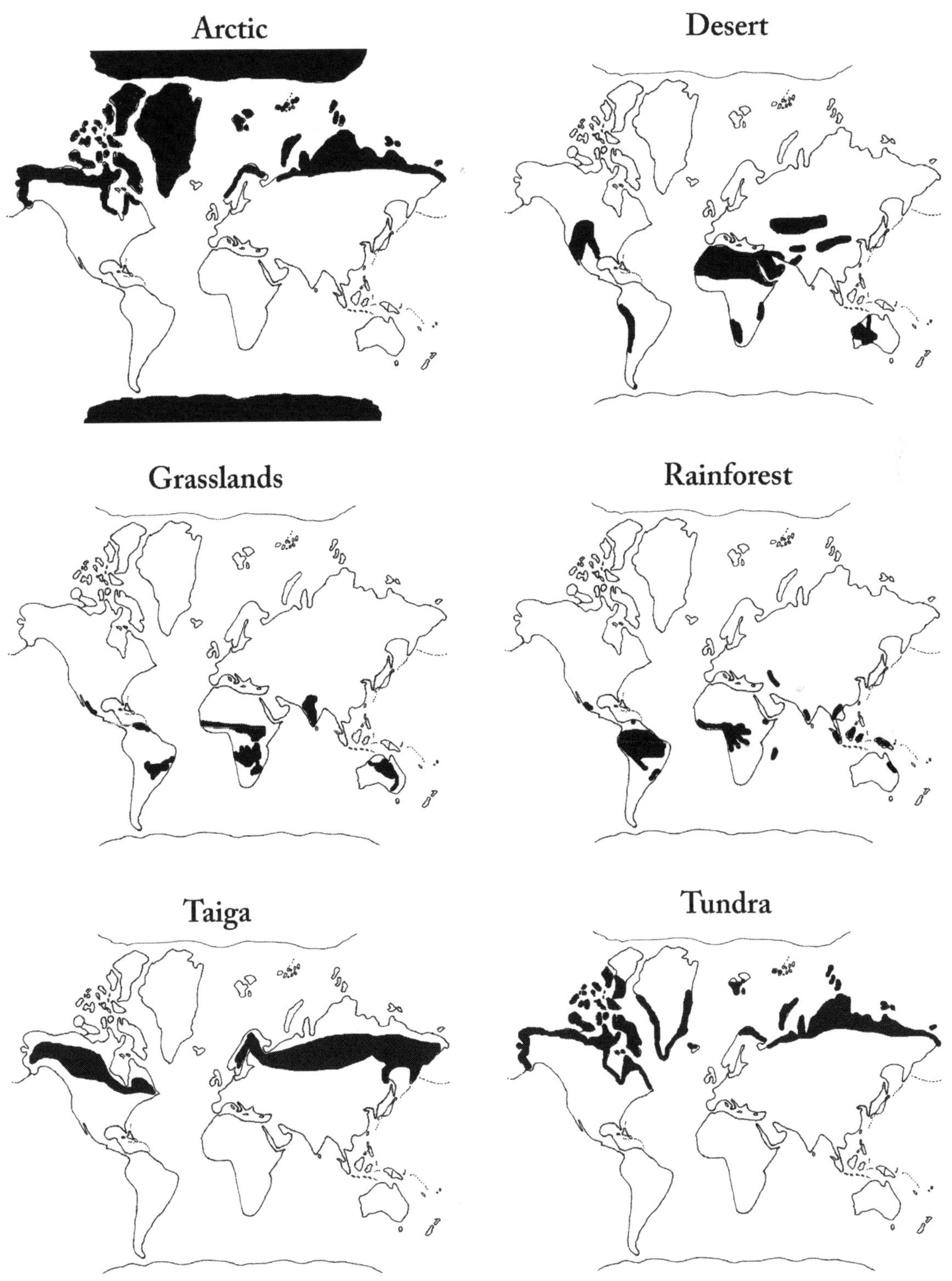

Earth Science Unit 4: Our Planet
Discussion Questions

Week 16

1. What are the three main layers of the Earth? (*Be sure to include a detail or two about each.*)
2. How is the Earth's magnetic field created and why is it important?
3. What causes seismic activity on the Earth?
4. What have seismic scans of the Earth revealed about the mantle?

Week 17

1. What is the purpose of a map?
2. What is the purpose of the lines that you find on a globe?
3. How are lines of latitude measured?
4. How do lines of longitude differ from lines of latitude?
5. How do cartographers represent a round Earth on a flat surface?
6. How are satellites used in mapping?

Week 18

1. Where does the water in a river come from?
2. Describe a river's course.
3. How do rivers erode the landscape around them?
4. How is a load deposited by a river?
5. Where is a river delta found and what happens at this point in the river?

Week 19

1. How much of the Earth's surface is covered with water?
2. How do currents work in the ocean?
3. Why are the ocean depths so difficult to explore?
4. Where do waves form and why do they crash on the shore?

Week 20

1. Where are glaciers found?
2. How do glaciers form?
3. What are some clues that let you know a glacier was once present in a valley?

Week 21

1. Briefly describe the nitrogen cycle.
2. Briefly describe the carbon cycle.
3. Briefly describe the water cycle.
4. How are the natural cycles being upset?

Week 22

1. What determines the boundaries between biomes?
2. What is the difference between a habitat and a biome?
3. What is a community?

Earth Science Unit 4: Our Planet
Unit Test Answers

Vocabulary

1. C
2. F
3. H
4. A
5. D
6. K
7. J
8. O
9. Q
10. N
11. P
12. G
13. R
14. I
15. M
16. B
17. E
18. L

True or False

1. True
2. True
3. False (*Satellites do help cartographers to produce more accurate maps.*)
4. True
5. False (*A river begins inland and flows into a lake, sea, or ocean.*)
6. True
7. False (*Over two-third's of the Earth's surface is covered with salt water.*)
8. False (*The gravitational pull of the Moon affects the oceans on the Earth, creating tides.*)
9. False (*Glaciers can also be found in the arctic regions, near the poles.*)
10. True
11. True
12. False (*Pollution has had an effect on the natural cycles.*)
13. True
14. True

Short Answer

1. The three main layers of the Earth are the crust, the mantle, and the core. The crust is the thinnest layer, which floats over the layers below. The mantle has a solid upper layer, which consists mostly of dense silicate rock. The core is extremely hot and consists of molten rock made from iron and nickel.
2. See the week 17 sketch for the answers.
3. A river begins in the mountains and flows downhill, where smaller streams or tributaries join it. As it grows and the land levels out, the river meanders through the landscape, forming large loops. Finally, the river widens out into an estuary or delta before it reaches the sea.
4. In the ocean, as warm water around the tropics moves northward, it cools and sinks. The cooler water circulates back towards the south, creating circular pattern.
5. Glaciers begin in high, cold places, such as mountains. Layers of fallen snow compact into hard ice. As more snow falls on top of the ice, the ice mass gets heavier and begins to move down the mountain. As it moves down the mountain, the ice slowly melts.
6. Water falls as rain. It drains into the rivers and out to the sea. Then, the sun heats up the water, forming vapor, which rises to form clouds. Once the clouds become heavy with water, the cycle begins again.
7. A biome is a larger region with a distinct climate, which includes several smaller habitats. A habitat is an area where a given organism lives.

Earth Science Unit 4: Our Planet
Unit Test

Vocabulary Matching

1. Mantle ____
2. Cartographer ____
3. Lines of Latitude ____
4. Lines of Longitude ____
5. Delta ___
6. Estuary ___
7. Source ___
8. Coast ___
9. Oceanic ridge ___
10. Oceanic trench ___
11. Tides ___
12. Deposition ___
13. Erratics ___
14. Glacier ___
15. Moraine ___
16. Natural cycle ____
17. Greenhouse gas ____
18. Biome ___

A. Lines that run from the North to the South pole, dividing the globe into segments; the lines all meet at the poles.

B. The exchanging of essential elements, such as nitrogen, carbon, and oxygen.

C. The mostly solid part of the Earth that lies between its crust and its core.

D. A fan-shaped system of streams that is created when a river splits into many smaller branches before it enters the sea.

E. Any gas that traps heat from the Sun, such as carbon dioxide.

F. A person who makes maps.

G. The dropping or leaving behind of rock and other debris by a glacier.

H. Lines that run parallel around the globe, dividing the globe into flat slices; the lines never meet.

I. A mass of ice that gathers at the top of a land mass and slowly flows downhill.

J. The beginning of a river.

K. A wide channel that forms where a river joins the sea.

L. A region of the Earth that contains unique plants and animals and is characterized by a distinct climate.

M. Rock, clay, sand, and other debris left by a glacier at the valley floor.

N. A deep trench in the seabed formed when one place of the Earth's crust moves under another.

O. The stretch of land that meets the sea.

P. The daily movement of the sea up and down the shore; they are caused by the gravitational pull of the moon.

Q. A raised ridge on the seabed caused by the movement of the Earth's crustal plates.

R. Large boulders that have been deposited away from their source by a glacier.

True or False

1. ____________________ The Earth is magnetic due to the molten iron in its core.

2. ____________________ The plates move because they float on top of the mantle.

3. ____________________ Satellites do not help cartographers produce more accurate maps of the Earth.

4. ____________________ Cartographers use projections to make flat maps of the Earth.

5. ____________________ A river begins at the sea or ocean and flows inland to the mountains.

6. ____________________ As a river slows, it deposits the heavier material it has picked up first.

7. ____________________ Only one quarter of the Earth's surface is covered with salt water.

8. ____________________ The gravitational pull of the Moon does not affect the oceans on Earth.

9. ____________________ Glaciers can only be found on mountains.

10. ____________________ The presence of a deep, rounded, U-shaped valley and moraine hills let you know that a glacier was once present in the valley.

11. ____________________ In the carbon cycle, plants take in carbon dioxide and animals produce it.

12. ____________________ Pollution has no effect on the natural cycles.

13. ____________________ The boundaries of the different biomes are determined by variations in climate.

14. ____________________ A community is a group of plants and animals that live together in mutually beneficial relationships.

Short Answer

1. What are the 3 main layers of the Earth? (Be sure to include a detail or two about each.)

2. Label the globe below with the Arctic Circle, Prime Meridian, Equator, Tropic of Cancer & Tropic of Capricorn, North & South Pole.

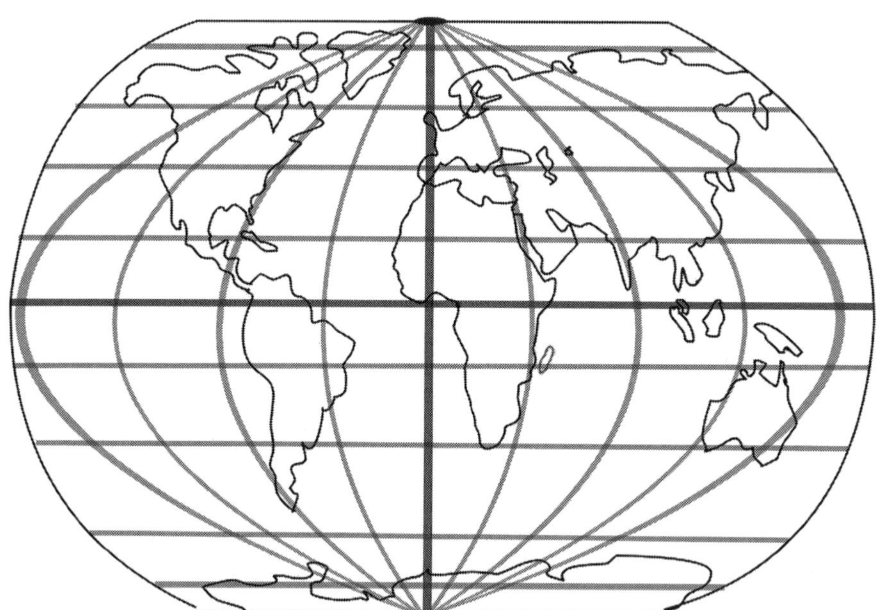

3. Describe the course of a river.

4. How do currents work in the ocean?

5. How do glaciers form?

6. Briefly describe the water cycle.

7. What is the difference between a habitat and a biome?

Earth Science
Unit 5

Geology

Earth Science Unit 5: Geology
Overview of Study

Sequence of Study

Week 23: Continents
Week 24: Volcanoes
Week 25: Earthquakes
Week 26: Mountains
Week 27: Rocks
Week 28: Ores and Gems
Week 29: Erosion and Weathering

Materials by Week

Week	Materials
23	Marshmallow creme (or whipping cream), Graham crackers, 3 Plates, Bowl with water
24	Mentos™, Cardboard cereal box, 1-Liter bottle of cola (or orange soda), 1 Can of Great Stuff™ Foam, Paints, Aluminum oil
25	Partner, Slinky, Rope
26	Several different colors of crayons, Grater, Butter knife, Pencil sharpener, Foil, Bowl, Warm water, Foil muffin cups
27	7 to 10 Rocks collected from outside, Rock & Mineral field guide, Plastic baggie, Sharpie Marker, White-out
28	5 to 8 More rocks collected from outside, Rock & Mineral field guide, Foam board, Sharpie Marker, White-out
29	Dirt or sand, Grass seed, Water, Pitcher, 2 Aluminum Pans ***NOTE:*** *You will need to plant your grass seed mountain at least 7 days before doing this experiment so that it will grow in time to do the experiment.*

Vocabulary for the Unit

1. **Continent** – Any of the seven large landmasses into which the Earth is divided.
2. **Faults** – Cracks in the Earth caused by the movement of its plates.
3. **Magma** – Molten rock inside the Earth.
4. **Lava** – Molten rock at and on the surface of the Earth.
5. **Spreading ridge** – A ridge under the ocean that spreads out sideways as magma wells up along its center.
6. **Subduction zone** – An area where two plates collide and one slips under the other, forming volcanoes & deep trenches.
7. **Seismic wave** – An underground shockwave that travels outward from the focus of an earthquake.
8. **Richter scale** – A scale that rates earthquakes from 1 to 10, based on the power of the vibrations that travel through the ground when the earthquake occurs.

9. **Mercalli scale** – A scale that rates earthquakes from I to XII based on the effects of the shaking and the damage caused.
10. **Mountain range** – A chain, or line, of mountains connected together.
11. **Fossil** – The impression or remains of an ancient plant or animal that has been hardened and preserved in a rock.
12. **Strata** – The layers of rock found in the Earth's crust.
13. **Gem** – A mineral or organic stone that is chosen to be cut, polished, and used, typically in jewelry.
14. **Ore** – A mineral from which we can extract a useful substance, such as a metal.
15. **Erosion** – The movement of particles of soil, sand, or rock by wind or water to a new location.
16. **Weathering** – The gradual wearing down of rock by wind or water.

Memory Work for the Unit

The Tectonic Plates

1. Juan de Fuco
2. North American
3. Cocos
4. Caribbean
5. South American
6. Nazca
7. Scotia
8. Antarctic
9. African
10. Arabian
11. Eurasian
12. Indo-Australian
13. Philippine
14. Carolina
15. Bismarc
16. Fiji
17. Pacific

Types of Rock

1. Metamorphic – Rock that has been changed by heat or pressure
2. Sedimentary – Rock made from particles of sand, mud, and other debris that have settled on the seabed and been squashed down to form hardened rock
3. Igneous – Rock that is formed when magma escapes from inside the Earth, cools, and hardens

Notes

Student Assignment Sheet Week 23
Continents

Experiment: What type of plate movement is responsible for making mountains?

Materials

- ✓ Marshmallow creme (or whipping cream)
- ✓ Graham crackers
- ✓ 3 Plates
- ✓ Bowl with about an inch of water

Procedure

1. Read the introduction to this experiment and fill in the hypothesis blank.
2. On each of the plates, add about half a cup of marshmallow creme and label the plates with #1, #2, and #3.
3. On the plate #1, you will recreate a divergent plate movement. Begin by heating the plate up for 10 seconds so that the fluff is a bit warm. Then, break one of the graham crackers in half and quickly dip both of the cracked edges into the bowl of water. Place both crackers on the marshmallow creme with the dipped ends next to each other. Gently push the two ends away from each other and observe what happens.
4. On the plate #2, you will recreate a convergent plate movement. Begin by heating the plate up for 10 seconds so that the fluff is a bit warm. Then, break one of the graham crackers in half and quickly dip both cracked edges into the bowl of water. Place both crackers on the marshmallow creme with the dipped ends next to each other. Gently push the two ends towards each other and observe what happens.
5. On the plate #3, you will recreate a transforming plate movement. Begin by heating the plate up for 10 seconds so that the fluff is a bit warm. Then, break one of the graham crackers in half and quickly dip both cracked edges into the bowl of water. Place both crackers on the marshmallow creme with the dipped ends next to each other. Gently push one cracker up and the other cracker down, so that the ends slide past each other. Observe what happens.
6. Write down your observations, draw conclusions, and complete your experiment sheet.

Vocabulary & Memory Work

- ☐ Vocabulary: continents, faults
- ☐ Memory Work – Work on memorizing the Tectonic Plates.

Sketch: The Seven Continents

- Label the following: North America, South America, Europe, Asia, Africa, Australia (or Oceania), Antarctica

Writing

- Reading Assignment: *The Kingfisher Science Encyclopedia* pp. 16-17 Continental Drift
- Additional Research Readings
  - Moving Continents: *DKEOS* pp. 214-215

Dates

- c. 30 AD – Prominent geographer, Strabo, suggests that there might be continents that are not yet known to the Greeks.

Schedules for Week 23

Two Days a Week

Day 1	Day 2
❐ Define continent, faults on SG pg. 156 ❐ Do the "Which type of plate movement is responsible for forming mountains?" experiment, then fill out the experiment sheet on SG pp. 160-161 ❐ Enter the dates onto the date sheets on SG pp. 8-12	❐ Read pp. 16-17 *The Kingfisher Science Encyclopedia,* then discuss what was read ❐ Color and label the "7 Continents" sketch on SG pg. 159 ❐ Prepare an outline or narrative summary, write it on SG pp. 162-163
Supplies I Need for the Week ✓ Marshmallow creme (or whipping cream) ✓ Graham crackers ✓ 3 Plates ✓ Bowl with water	
Things I Need to Prepare	

Five Days a Week

Day 1	Day 2	Day 3	Day 4	Day 5
❐ Do the "Which type of plate movement is responsible for forming mountains?" experiment, then fill out the experiment sheet on SG pp. 160-161	❐ Read pp. 16-17 *The Kingfisher Science Encyclopedia,* then discuss what was read ❐ Write an outline or list of facts on SG pg. 162	❐ Define continent, faults on SG pg. 156 ❐ Enter the dates onto the date sheets on SG pp. 8-12 ❐ Color and label the "7 Continents" sketch on SG pg. 159	❐ Read one or all of the additional reading assignments ❐ Prepare your report, write the report on SG pg. 163	❐ Complete one of the Want More Activities listed **OR** ❐ Study a scientist from the field of Earth Science
Supplies I Need for the Week ✓ Marshmallow creme (or whipping cream) ✓ Graham crackers ✓ 3 Plates ✓ Bowl with water				
Things I Need to Prepare				

Additional Information Week 23

Experiment Information

☞ **Introduction** – (*from the Student Guide*) There are three main types of plate movements—divergent, convergent, and transforming. Each of these types of plate movements explain how the pieces of the Earth's crust interact with each other at the points at which they meet. In divergent plate movements, the two plates move away from each other. In convergent plate movements, the two plates move towards each other. In transforming plate movements, the two plates slide past each other. In this experiment, you are going to look at models of the three plate movements and see the results of their interactions.

☞ **Results** – The students should see on plate #1 that there was no changes to the crackers, on plate #2 a ridge of buckled up crackers should have been created, and on plate #3 chunks of the crackers should have broken off as the two crackers slid past each other. They should have also seen that the water softened the crackers just a bit, allowing them to replicate the plate movements.

☞ **Explanation** – As the plates move extremely slowly over the mantle, they interact with each other along the borders. Heat and pressure soften the rock and allow changes to the Earth's crust. In divergent plate movements, the two plates separate, leaving a gap, which allows molten rock from the mantle to rise up, cool, and create new crust. The results of this type of plate movement typically create new oceanic crust. In convergent plate movements, the two plates collide, which causes the plates to buckle or forces one plate to bend under the other. The results of this type of plate movement typically creates mountain ranges and volcanos or the destruction of the crust that has been bent under the plate it met. In transforming plate movements, the two plates slide past each other, which forces pieces to be broken off. The results of this type of plate movement does not create or destroy the crust, but it does form fault lines.

☞ **Take it Further** – Have the students repeat the experiment with several crackers stacked on top of each other to see how the movement of the plates affects the different levels of layers of rock found in the crust.

Discussion Questions

1. What creates the Earth's solid surface? (*The Earth's solid surface is formed by the oceanic and continental crust.*)
2. What causes the movement of the tectonic plates of the Earth's crust? (*The crustal plates float on top of the liquid mantle. Heat from the Earth's core causes the liquid rock in the mantle to swirl around, which is known as convection. This movement causes the surface plates to slowly move around.*)
3. What is one difference between oceanic and continental crust? (*Oceanic crust is constantly being destroyed and created, while continental crust is much thicker and older.*)
4. What happens as the tectonic plates stretch? Collide? (*When the tectonic plates stretch, they become thinner and can break, allowing new crust to form. When the tectonic plates collide, they buckle at the edges, causing a chain of mountains to form.*)
5. How can geologists track the movement of the tectonic plates? (*Geologists can use lasers and satellites to track the subtle continental drift.*)

Want More

- **Continent Profile** – Have the students create a continent profile page. They will begin by choosing one of the seven continents that interests them or one that they want to learn more about. The students can use the internet and the resources they have in their home or at their library to find out more about their chosen continent. As they complete their research. have them write down any interesting facts and answer the following questions:
  - ✓ Is the continent in the western or eastern hemisphere?
  - ✓ What are the geographic borders of the continent?
  - ✓ What are the geographic regions on the continent?
  - ✓ What countries are included in the continent?
  - ✓ What are the major geographical features (i.e., major rivers, mountains, etc.)?

  Once the research is done, have the students each write create a continent profile page. Their pages should include the answers to the questions above, along with at least one or two cultural facts about the continent.

Sketch Assignment Week 23

Note – The information for this sketch is not all in the reading.
The students will need to use a map, globe, or atlas to complete the sketch.

Student Assignment Sheet Week 24
Volcanoes

Experiment: Exploding Volcano

Materials
- ✓ Mentos™
- ✓ Cardboard cereal box
- ✓ 1-Liter bottle of cola (or orange soda)
- ✓ 1 Can of Great Stuff™ Foam
- ✓ Paints
- ✓ Aluminum Foil

CAUTION

Please follow all the safety instructions on the bottle of Great Stuff™ when forming the volcano.

Procedure
1. Read the introduction to this experiment.
2. Cover your bottle with aluminum foil so that it fits snugly over the bottle. Then, have an adult spray Great Stuff™ around the bottle, starting at the bottom to make a cone volcano.
3. Let the foam dry for the recommended amount of time, remove the bottle (leaving the foil behind), and paint the foam to look like a volcano. Let the paint dry.
4. Meanwhile, cut a rectangle and a square out of your cereal box. Roll one of the rectangles into a tube that will fit three Mentos™ and tape it.
5. Take your supplies outside, remove the top from your soda bottle, and place the foam volcano over it. Cover the opening with the flat cardboard square, place your cardboard tube on top of that, and load three Mentos™ into it.
6. Quickly remove the flat cardboard square so the Mentos™ drop in the soda, step back, and observe what happens.
7. Take a picture and complete your experiment sheet.

Vocabulary & Memory Work
- ☐ Vocabulary: magma, lava, spreading ridge, subduction zone
- ☐ Memory Work – Continue to work on memorizing the Tectonic Plates.

Sketch Assignment: Cross-section of a Cone Volcano
- Label the following: dust, ash, and gases, crater, lava flow, main vent, side vents, magma chamber

Writing Assignment
- Reading Assignment: *The Kingfisher Science Encyclopedia* pp. 18-19 Volcanoes
- Additional Research Readings:
  - Volcanoes: *DKEOS* pp. 216-217
  - Volcano Section: *USE* pp. 182-183

Dates
- 79 AD – Mount Vesuvius, in Italy, erupts and destroys Pompeii.
- May 18, 1980 – Mount St. Helens, in Washington, erupts.

Schedules for Week 24

Two Days a Week

Day 1	Day 2
❒ Define magma, lava, spreading ridge, subduction zone on SG pg. 156 ❒ Do the "Exploding Volcano" experiment, then fill out the experiment sheet on SG pp. 166-167 ❒ Enter the dates onto the date sheets on SG pp. 8-12	❒ Read pp. 18-19 *The Kingfisher Science Encyclopedia,* then discuss what was read ❒ Prepare an outline or narrative summary, write it on SG pp. 168-169 ❒ Color and label the "Cross-section of a Cone Volcano" sketch on SG pg. 165

Supplies I Need for the Week

- ✓ Mentos
- ✓ Cardboard cereal box
- ✓ 2-liter bottle of Cola (can also use orange soda)
- ✓ 1 Can of Great Stuff™ Foam
- ✓ Paints and Aluminum Foil

Things I Need to Prepare

Five Days a Week

Day 1	Day 2	Day 3	Day 4	Day 5
❒ Do the "Exploding Volcano" experiment, then fill out the experiment sheet on SG pp. 166-167	❒ Read pp. 18-19 *The Kingfisher Science Encyclopedia,* then discuss what was read ❒ Write an outline or list of facts on SG pg. 168	❒ Define magma, lava, spreading ridge, subduction zone on SG pg. 156 ❒ Enter the dates onto the date sheets on SG pp. 8-12 ❒ Color and label the "Cross-section of a Cone Volcano" sketch on SG pg. 165	❒ Read one or all of the additional reading assignments ❒ Prepare your report, write the report on SG pg. 169	❒ Complete one of the Want More Activities listed **OR** ❒ Study a scientist from the field of Earth Science

Supplies I Need for the Week

- ✓ Mentos & a Cardboard cereal box
- ✓ 2-liter bottle of Cola (can also use orange soda)
- ✓ 1 Can of Great Stuff™ Foam, Paint, and Aluminum Foil

Things I Need to Prepare

Additional Information Week 24

Notes

- **Magma vs. Lava** – For your knowledge, both magma and lava are composed of molten rock. The difference is where they are found. Magma is molten rock found inside the Earth. Lava is molten rock found at or above the Earth's surface.

Experiment Information

- **NOTE** – This volcano is reusable; the students just need to pull the soda bottle out from underneath and replace it with a new one so that they can erupt it another time.
- **Introduction** – (*from the Student Guide*) Volcanoes are openings in the Earth's surface that are formed by magma bursting out. When they erupt, lava and ash are thrown out and build up along the sides. Eventually, the lava and ash set up and form a solid layer of volcanic rock. In this experiment, you are going to create your own volcanic eruption.
- **Results** – The students should see an eruption about three to seven feet in the air.
- **Explanation** – This experiment was designed to be a fun look at a volcanic eruption. If the students enjoyed the project, you have accomplished the goal of this experiment.
- **Take it Further** – Have the students repeat the experiment with a greater or a fewer number of Mentos™ to see how this affects the resulting explosion.
- **Troubleshooting** – The following tips will help you as you create your volcano:
  - *When making the volcano, you need to start at the bottom and slowly work your way up in concentric circles. Here is a mid-action shot from our Instagram account to give you an idea of how this works:*
    - https://www.instagram.com/p/jiMo0NwHXu/
  - *The Great Stuff™ will adhere as it dries, so don't mess with it once you spray it on or it will slide down the foil.*
  - *If you use a 2-Liter bottle, you may need two cans of Great Stuff™ Foam to make your volcano.*

Discussion Questions

1. What is a volcano? (*A volcano is an opening in the Earth's crust where molten rock, known as magma, from the mantle can escape in the form of lava, ash, or gas.*)
2. What does the behavior of a volcano depend on? (*The behavior of a volcano is dependent upon the type of magma that feeds it.*)
3. Name three different types of volcanos and share a characteristic about each. (*The student's answer should include three of the following volcano types—A fissure volcano, which erupts from a narrow slit. A shield volcano, which oozes molten rock over a large area. A dome volcano, which is created by sticky molten rock. A conical volcano, which is formed by volcanic ash. A composite volcano, which can have several side vents. A caldera, which is created by an explosive eruption.*)
4. What happens during a volcanic eruption? (*During a volcanic eruption, the pressure drops, causing lava, ash, and gas to escape. The escape can be a violent explosion or a slow ooze*

that cools quickly, depending on where the volcano is located and what type of volcano it is.)

Want More

- **Research Report** – Have the students research a famous volcanic eruption. Pompeii and Mount St. Helens are good examples to choose from. Be sure to have them include the location of the volcano, whether it was a shield or cone volcano, whether the volcano is at a spreading ridge or at a subduction zone, how long the eruption lasted, and what were the results after the eruption.
- **Volcano Model** – Have the students create a clay cross-section model of a cone or shield volcano. Have them use different colors of clay for the different layers. You can also have them add in dirt or small rocks for the layers of volcanic ash. Have them cover the outside with natural materials, such as moss, grass and twigs, to make a realistic looking volcano.

Sketch Assignment Week 24

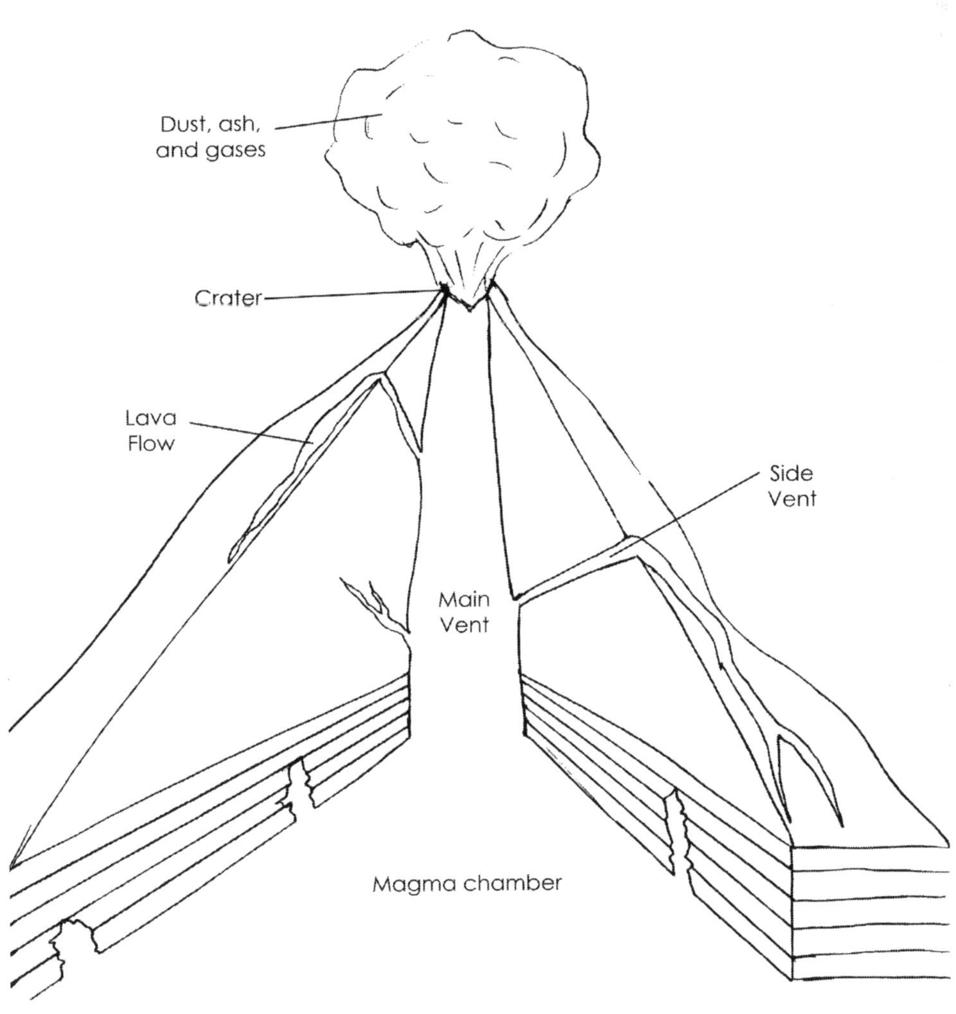

Student Assignment Sheet Week 25
Earthquakes

Experiment: Do seismic p-waves travel in the same way as seismic s-waves?

Materials
- ✓ Partner
- ✓ Slinky
- ✓ Rope

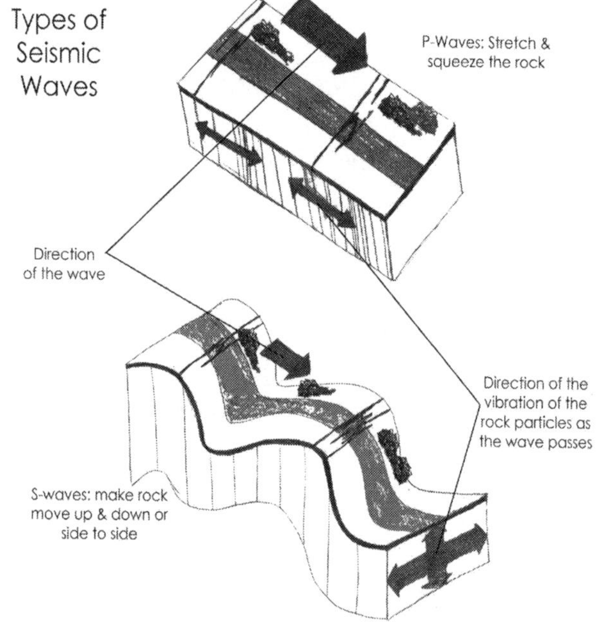

Procedure
1. Read the introduction to this experiment and answer the question.
2. Sit down at a table across from your partner, set the slinky on the table, and stretch it gently between the two of you. Gently push your end of the slinky towards your partner several times and observe what happens. Record how the slinky moved on your experiment sheet and set the slinky aside.
3. Set the rope on the table and stretch it gently between the two of you. Move your end of the rope side to side several times and observe what happens. Record how the rope moved on your experiment sheet.
4. Draw conclusions and complete your experiment sheet.

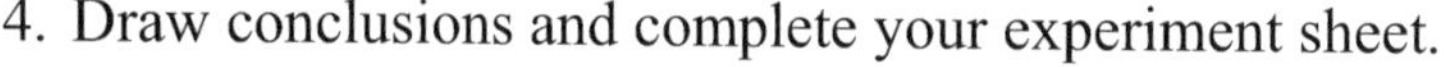

Vocabulary & Memory Work
- ☐ Vocabulary: seismic wave, Richter Scale, Mercalli Scale
- ☐ Memory Work – Continue to work on memorizing the Tectonic Plates.

Sketch Assignment: Tectonic Plates Around the Globe
- Label the following: Juan de Fuco, North American, Cocos, Caribbean, South American, Nazca, Scotia, Antarctic, African, Arabian, Eurasian, Indo-Australian, Philippine, Carolina, Bismarc, Fiji, Pacific

Writing Assignment
- Reading Assignment: *The Kingfisher Science Encyclopedia* pp. 20-21 Earthquakes
- Additional Research Readings
  - Earthquakes: *USE* pg. 220

Dates
- 132 – The Chinese invent the first seismograph, in which precisely balanced metal balls fall if the ground shakes.
- 1935 – Charles Richter, a US seismologist, develops a scale for reporting the strength of earthquakes.

Schedules for Week 25

Two Days a Week

Day 1	Day 2
☐ Define seismic wave, Richter Scale, Mercalli Scale on SG pp. 156-157 ☐ Do the "Do seismic p-waves travel in the same way as seismic s-waves?" experiment, then fill out the experiment sheet on SG pp. 172-173 ☐ Enter the dates onto the date sheets on SG pp. 8-12	☐ Read pp 20-21 *The Kingfisher Science Encyclopedia,* then discuss what was read ☐ Prepare an outline or narrative summary, write it on SG pp. 174-175 ☐ Color and label the "Tectonic Plates Around the World" sketch on SG pg. 171

Supplies I Need for the Week

- ✓ Partner
- ✓ Slinky
- ✓ Rope

Things I Need to Prepare

Five Days a Week

Day 1	Day 2	Day 3	Day 4	Day 5
☐ Do the "Do seismic p-waves travel in the same way as seismic s-waves?" experiment, then fill out the experiment sheet on SG pp. 172-173	☐ Read pp 20-21 *The Kingfisher Science Encyclopedia,* then discuss what was read ☐ Write an outline or list of facts on SG pg. 174	☐ Define seismic wave, Richter Scale, Mercalli Scale on SG pp. 156-157 ☐ Enter the dates onto the date sheets on SG pp. 8-12 ☐ Color and label the "Tectonic Plates Around the World" sketch on SG pg. 171	☐ Read one or all of the additional reading assignments ☐ Prepare your report, write the report on SG pg. 175	☐ Complete one of the Want More Activities listed **OR** ☐ Study a scientist from the field of Earth Science

Supplies I Need for the Week

- ✓ Partner
- ✓ Slinky
- ✓ Rope

Things I Need to Prepare

Additional Information Week 25

Experiment Information

☞ **Introduction** – (*from the Student Guide*) Earthquakes happen when plates slide along each other and cause the rock to be twisted, stretched or squeezed. The movement of the rock is caused by seismic waves that are sent out from the focus of the earthquake. In this experiment, you are going to look at two types of seismic waves, p-waves (using a slinky) and s-waves (using a rope.) They will also examine the differences and similarities of the two waves.

☞ **Results** – The students should see the slinky travel towards their partners and then back towards them, making a stretching and squeezing type movement. The students should see the rope travel side to side between them and their partners, making a horizontal movement.

☞ **Explanation** – P-waves are also known as primary seismic waves. They travel deep below the ground and can either push or pull. This causes the rock particles to stretch or squeeze. The way the slinky moves back & forth is a good example of the motion caused by a p-wave. S-waves are also known as secondary seismic waves. They travel deep underground and cause the rock to move up and down or side to side. The way the rope moves side to side is a good example of the motion caused by an s-wave.

Discussion Questions

1. What is an earthquake? (*An earthquake is a sudden release of energy that makes the ground tremble.*)
2. Where do earthquakes most commonly occur? (*Earthquakes commonly occur near the plate boundaries along the fault lines.*)
3. What causes the destruction in a earthquake? (*The destruction in an earthquake is caused by shock waves that radiate from the hypocenter of the earthquake.*)
4. What are the two scales used to measure earthquakes? (*The two scales used to measure earthquakes are the Richter and Mercalli scale.*)
5. Why is it so difficult to create a warning system for earthquakes? (*It is difficult to create a warning system for when an earthquake will occur as there are not always warning signs and it is very challenging to predict when a fault line will release pressure.*)
6. What is a seismograph? (*A seismograph is an instrument that can record the shaking of the ground.*)

Want More

✎ **Shake Table** – Make your own shake table to test out the strength of various building designs in an earthquake. Follow the directions from the following website:

💻 http://jclahr.com/science/earth_science/shake/index.html

Sketch Assignment Week 245

Note – The information for this sketch is not in the reading.
The students will need to use a map, globe, or atlas to complete the sketch.

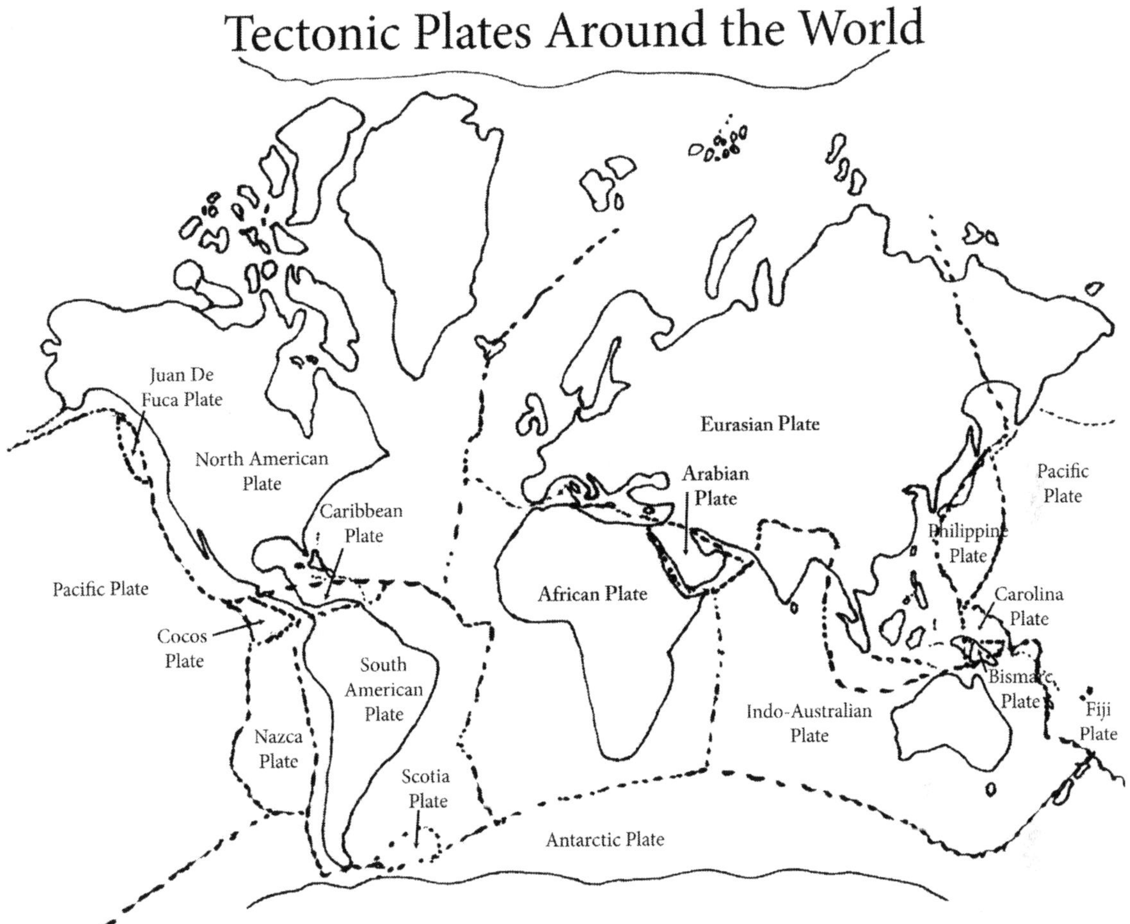

Student Assignment Sheet Week 26
Mountains

Experiment: How does the rock cycle work?

Materials

- ✓ Several different colors of crayons
- ✓ Grater
- ✓ Butter knife
- ✓ Pencil sharpener
- ✓ Foil
- ✓ Bowl
- ✓ Warm water
- ✓ Foil muffin cups

Procedure

1. Read the introduction to this experiment.
2. Begin by using the grater, butter knife, and pencil sharpener to break apart, or "weather," a crayon. Catch the shavings, or "sediments," on a piece of aluminum foil. Once you have enough, gather up the "sediments" and fold the foil to create a pocket around them. Then, use a hand or a foot to compress the sediment shavings. Open up the foil packet and observe the changes.
3. Next, wrap the rock you created in the previous step in foil and place the packet in a bowl filled with warm water for one to two minutes or until the contents are soft. Take the foil packet out of the water and use a hand to massage and squeeze the rock into a ball. Open up the foil packet and observe the changes.
4. Finally, place the rock you created in the previous step in a foil muffin cup. Put the muffin cup in a tin and place it in an oven set to 300°F for 15 minutes. Take the tin out and allow the rocks to cool. Remove the rock from the foil cup and observe the changes.
5. Write down your observations, draw conclusions, and complete your experiment sheet.

Vocabulary & Memory Work

- ☐ Vocabulary: mountain range
- ☐ Memory Work – Begin to work on memorizing the Types of Rock.

Sketch Assignment: Mountain Features

- Label the following: nappe, recumbent fold, anticline, syncline, valley, fault, horst, rift valley

Writing Assignment

- Reading Assignment: *The Kingfisher Science Encyclopedia* pp. 22-23 Building Mountains
- Additional Research Readings
  - Mountain Building: *DKEOS* pp. 218-219

Dates

- 1785 – James Hutton, a Scottish geologist, says that moutains are formed by hot rock erupted from volcanoes.

Schedules for Week 26

Two Days a Week

Day 1	Day 2
☐ Define mountain range on SG pg. 157 ☐ Do the "How does the rock cycle work?" experiment, then fill out the experiment sheet on SG pp. 178-179 ☐ Enter the dates onto the date sheets on SG pp. 8-12	☐ Read pp. 22-23 *The Kingfisher Science Encyclopedia,* then discuss what was read ☐ Color and label the "Mountain Features" sketch on SG pg. 177 ☐ Prepare an outline or narrative summary, write it on SG pp. 180-181
Supplies I Need for the Week ✓ Several different colors of crayons ✓ Grater, Butter knife, Pencil sharpener ✓ Foil, Bowl, Warm water ✓ Foil muffin cups	
Things I Need to Prepare	

Five Days a Week

Day 1	Day 2	Day 3	Day 4	Day 5
☐ Do the "How does the rock cycle work?" experiment, then fill out the experiment sheet on SG pp. 178-179	☐ Read pp. 22-23 *The Kingfisher Science Encyclopedia,* then discuss what was read ☐ Write an outline or list of facts on SG pg. 180	☐ Define mountain range on SG pg. 157 ☐ Enter the dates onto the date sheets on SG pp. 8-12 ☐ Color and label the "Mountain Features" sketch on SG pg. 177	☐ Read one or all of the additional reading assignments ☐ Prepare your report, write the report on SG pg. 181	☐ Complete one of the Want More Activities listed **OR** ☐ Study a scientist from the field of Earth Science
Supplies I Need for the Week ✓ Several different colors of crayons ✓ Grater, Butter knife, Pencil sharpener ✓ Foil, Bowl, Warm water ✓ Foil muffin cups				
Things I Need to Prepare				

Additional Information Week 26

Experiment Information

☞ **Introduction** – (*from the Student Guide*) The rock cycle is a process that explains the changes rocks go through. It is summed up in the graphic below:

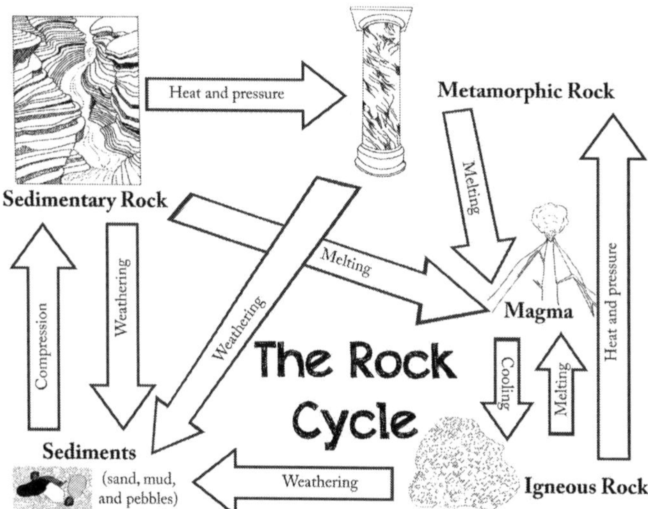

In today's experiment, you are going use crayons to see how the rock cycle works.

☞ **Results and Explanation** – In the first step, the different sized chunks represent the sand, mud, and pebbles that form sedimentary rock. After compressing these chunks together, the students should have seen a compacted hard mass with recognizable flecks of different colored crayons that resembled a sedimentary rock. In the second step, the warm water provided the heat and the hand provided the pressure need to change the sedimentary rock into metamorphic rock. The students should have see a compacted hard mass with the flecks less visible and more flowing, similar to a metamorphic rock. In the third step, the heat from the oven represented the heat found in the Earth's interior, which can melt and mix rock. In the cooled rock, the students should have seen only one discernible color in a smooth rock that is similar to an igneous rock, obsidian.

☞ **Take it Further** – Have the students create crayon igneous rock similar to pumice. Use hot mitts, goggles, and tongs to pour the melted, boiling crayon quickly into a bowl filled with ice water. The result is a light crayon rock with holes and pockets similar to pumice.

Discussion Questions

1. What four factors contribute to the formation and destruction of mountains? (*The four factors that contribute to the formation and destruction of mountains are volcanoes, earthquakes, continental collisions, and weathering.*)
2. What are some of the newer mountain chains around the globe? (*Some of the newer mountain chains around the globe are the Himalayans and the Alps.*) Older ones? (*Some of the older mountain chains around the globe are the Appalachians and the Highlands of northern Scandinavia.*)
3. What can the Earth's crust tell us about mountains? (*The Earth's crust records the history of*

the uplift of mountains and the erosional forces that destroy them.)

4. Explain how the Himalayan Mountains were formed. (*The Himalayan Mountains were formed when the Indo-Australian plate and the Eurasian plate collided and forced rock up to form the mountain chain.*)

Want More

- **Towel Mountains** – Have the students see how mountains are formed using dish towels and two shoeboxes. Begin by laying out eight to ten layers of dish towels. Place the two shoeboxes at the two long ends of the dish towels. Gently push the two boxes towards each other and observe what happens.

Sketch Assignment Week 26

Mountain Features

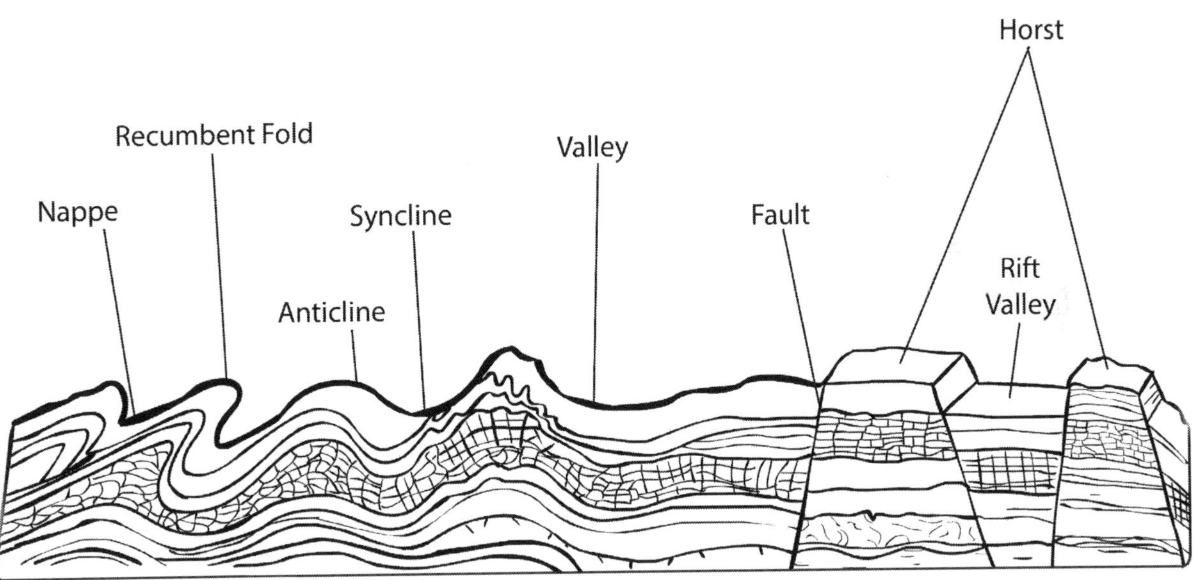

Student Assignment Sheet Week 27
Rocks

Experiment: Rock Collection (week 1)

Materials

- ✓ 10 to 12 rocks collected from outside
- ✓ Rock & Mineral field guide
- ✓ Plastic baggie
- ✓ Sharpie Marker
- ✓ White-out

Procedure

1. Go outside and collect seven to ten different rocks.
2. Once inside, paint a small section of each rock, assign each one a number, and write that number on the painted section of the rock.
3. Then, use your field guide to identify the rocks you have collected. Write the identification of each rock, along with a fact or two about the rock, on the experiment sheet.
4. Place your rock samples in a plastic baggie. You will finish this project next week.

Vocabulary & Memory Work

- ☐ Vocabulary: fossil, strata
- ☐ Memory Work – Continue to work on memorizing the Types of Rock.

Sketch Assignment: Types of Rock

- Label the following: igneous rock, metamorphic rock, sedimentary rock, mineral, fossil

Writing Assignment

- Reading Assignment: *The Kingfisher Science Encyclopedia* pg. 28 Igneous Rock, pg. 29 Metamorphic Rock, and pp. 30-31 Sedimentary Rock
- Additional Research Readings
  - Igneous Rock: *DKEOS* pg. 222
  - Sedimentary Rock: *DKEOS* pg. 223
  - Metamorphic Rock: *DKEOS* pg. 224
  - Fossils: *DKEOS* pg. 225

Dates

- 1546 – Georgius Agricola, a German metallurgist, first uses the term "fossil" when referring to the rock-like remains of animals and plants.

Schedules for Week 27

Two Days a Week

Day 1	Day 2
☐ Define fossil, strata on SG pg. 157 ☐ Begin the rock collection project, then fill out the experiment sheet on SG pp. 184-185	☐ Read pp. 28-31 from *The Kingfisher Science Encyclopedia,* then discuss what was read ☐ Prepare an outline or narrative summary, write it on SG pp. 186-187 ☐ Color and label the "Types of Rock" sketch on SG pg. 183

Supplies I Need for the Week

- ✓ Glass cup
- ✓ 7 to 10 rocks collected from outside
- ✓ Rock & Mineral field guide
- ✓ Plastic baggie
- ✓ Sharpie Marker, White-out

Things I Need to Prepare

Five Days a Week

Day 1	Day 2	Day 3	Day 4	Day 5
☐ Begin the rock collection project, then fill out the experiment sheet on SG pp. 184-185	☐ Read pp. 28-31 from *The Kingfisher Science Encyclopedia,* then discuss what was read ☐ Write an outline or list of facts on SG pg. 186	☐ Define fossil, strata on SG pg. 157 ☐ Color and label the "Types of Rock" sketch on SG pg. 183	☐ Read one or all of the additional reading assignments ☐ Prepare your report, write the report on SG pg. 187	☐ Complete one of the Want More Activities listed **OR** ☐ Study a scientist from the field of Earth Science

Supplies I Need for the Week

- ✓ 7 to 10 rocks collected from outside
- ✓ Rock & Mineral field guide
- ✓ Plastic baggie
- ✓ Sharpie Marker
- ✓ White-out

Things I Need to Prepare

Additional Information Week 27

Experiment Information

☞ **Tip** – You can check out a rock field guide from your library or purchase one if you have a real rock hound! When looking for a field guide for this project, search for one that meets the following criteria:

1. **Local Guide** – Use a field guide that contains information about your area. For example, if you live on the East Coast of the United States, you will want a guide that contains rocks found in the eastern part of the United States, not one for the western part.
2. **Highly Visual** – Use a field guide that has lots of pictures so that you can compare your sample to these images. This will greatly help in the students in their identification of the sample. We really like the National Audubon guides, but the guides from the Smithsonian, Peterson, and National Geographic are also good options.

Discussion Questions

Pg. 28 Igneous Rock

1. Describe igneous rock and how it is classified. *(Igneous rock is rock made from fire, meaning that it forms when hot molten rock cools. Igneous rock is classified according to texture, composition, and origin.)*
2. What are the two ways that igneous rock can form? (*Igneous rock forms by intrusion and extrusion. Extrusive igneous rocks form during volcanic eruptions. Intrusive igneous rocks are pushed up beneath overlying rocks.*)

Pg. 29 Metamorphic Rock

1. What is metamorphic rock and how does it form? (*Metamorphic rock is rock that has been changed by heat or pressure. It can be formed from igneous and sedimentary or other metamorphic rocks.*)
2. Describe the two types of metamorphic rock. (*The first type of metamorphic rock is contact. These rocks are formed when the rock is literally baked by surrounding rocks. The second type of metamorphic rock is regional. These rocks are formed when an area of rock is squeezed and heated.*)

Pp. 30-31 Sedimentary Rock (Note—Weathering will also be addressed in week 28.)

1. What is sedimentary rock? (*Sedimentary rock is made from tiny pieces of rock and dead organic matter that have been compressed into solid layers.*)
2. What are the three types of sedimentary rock? (*The three types of sedimentary rock are clastic, chemical, and biogenic.*)
3. What are the two main ways of weathering rock (explain both)? (*The two main ways of weathering a rock are chemical weathering and physical weathering. Chemical weathering happens when rocks are changed by water, carbon dioxide, or by organic acids. Physical weathering happens when rocks are fractured or broken apart.*)

Want More

✐ **Fossils** – Have the students learn more about the three different types of fossils from the following post:

http://elementalblogging.com/3-types-of-fossils/

Sketch Assignment Week 27

Types of Rock

Sedimentary Rock

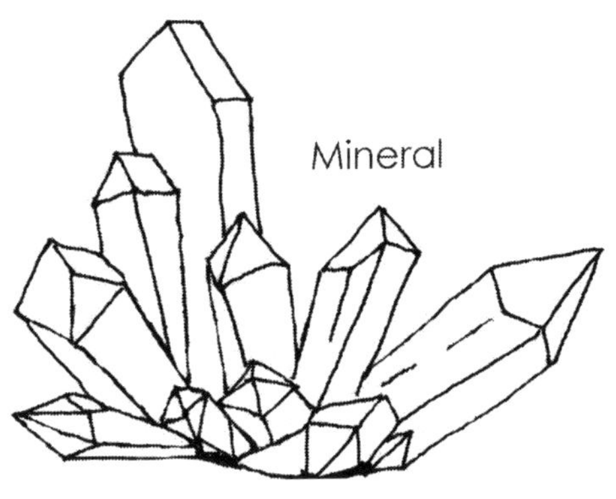

Mineral

Igneous Rock

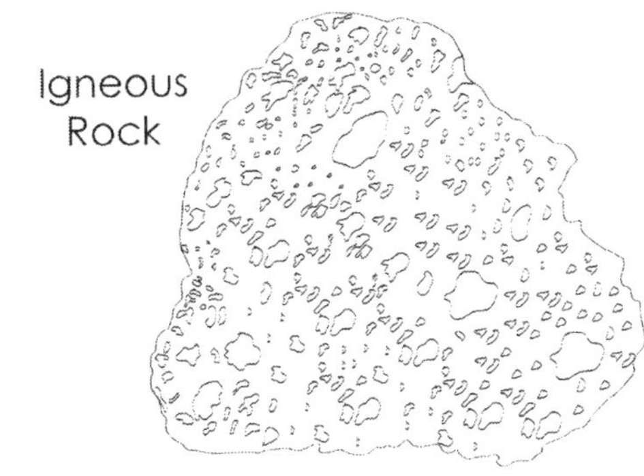

Metamorphic Rock

Fossil

Student Assignment Sheet Week 28
Ores and Gems

Experiment: Rock Collection (week 2)

Materials

- ✓ 10 to 12 rocks more collected from outside
- ✓ Rock & Mineral field guide
- ✓ Foam board
- ✓ Sharpie Marker
- ✓ White-out

Procedure

1. Go outside and collect five to eight more rocks.
2. Once inside, paint a small section of each rock, assign each one a number, and write that number on the painted section of the rock, just like you did for the previous week.
3. Then, use your field guide to identify the rocks you have collected. Write the identification of each rock, along with a fact or two about the rock on the experiment sheet.
4. Mount each rock, in order, on your foam board. You should have a total of 15 samples on your board. Once you have mounted the rocks, create a key somewhere on your board that identifies each type of rock.

Vocabulary & Memory Work

- ☐ Vocabulary: gem, ore
- ☐ Memory Work – Continue to work on memorizing the Types of Rocks.

Sketch Assignment: Rock Research Project

This week for the sketch, you will choose a rock, research that rock, and create a profile page for the rock. You can do this by completing the following steps:

1. ***Choose a rock*** – Choose a rock that you want to learn more about.
2. ***Do some research about the rock*** – Use the internet and the resources you have in your home or at your library to find out more about your chosen rock. As you do your research, write down any interesting facts and answer the following questions:
   - ✓ What group is your rock from? What is its composition or chemical formula? What is the typical crystal system for your rock? What is the typical color of your rock? What is the hardness rating for your rock? Does your rock cleave?
3. ***Complete the profile page for your rock*** – Write the name for your rock on the blank at the top of the page. Then fill out the remaining information. Your summary of interesting facts should include five to seven facts about the rock. Finally, draw your rock or glue a picture of it in the box.

Writing Assignment

- Reading Assignment: *The Kingfisher Science Encyclopedia* pp. 26-27 Ores and Gems
- Additional Research Readings
  - Rocks and Minerals: *DKEOS* pg. 221

Dates

- 1822 – Friedrich Mohs, a German mineralogist, creates the first hardness scale based on 10 common minerals to use as a reference.

Schedules for Week 28

Two Days a Week

Day 1	Day 2
☐ Define gem, ore on SG pg. 157 ☐ Do the Rock Research Project for the sketch, then fill out the Rock Profile Page on SG pg. 189	☐ Read pp. 26-27 from *The Kingfisher Science Encyclopedia,* then discuss what was read ☐ Prepare an outline or narrative summary, write it on SG pp. 192-193 ☐ Finish the rock collection project, then fill out the experiment sheet on SG pp. 190-191

Supplies I Need for the Week
- ✓ 5 to 8 more rocks collected from outside
- ✓ Rock & Mineral field guide
- ✓ Foam board
- ✓ Sharpie Marker
- ✓ White-out

Things I Need to Prepare

Five Days a Week

Day 1	Day 2	Day 3	Day 4	Day 5
☐ Finish the rock collection project, then fill out the experiment sheet on SG pp. 190-191 ☐ Define gem, ore on SG pg. 157	☐ Read pp. 26-27 from *The Kingfisher Science Encyclopedia,* then discuss what was read ☐ Write an outline or list of facts on SG pg. 192	☐ Do the Rock Research Project for the sketch, then fill out the Rock Profile Page on SG pg. 189	☐ Read one or all of the additional reading assignments ☐ Prepare your report, write the report on SG pg. 193	☐ Complete one of the Want More Activities listed **OR** ☐ Study a scientist from the field of Earth Science

Supplies I Need for the Week
- ✓ 5 to 8 more rocks collected from outside
- ✓ Rock & Mineral field guide
- ✓ Foam board
- ✓ Sharpie Marker
- ✓ White-out

Things I Need to Prepare

Additional Information Week 28

Notes

- **Prep for next week** – Next week, the students will be performing an experiment that will require a dirt mountain with grass growing on it. Be sure to have the students read ahead to week twenty-nine's experiment this week.

Experiment Information

- **Take it Further** – Have the students give a presentation of their rock collections to a group of people. As part of the presentation, the students should include the names of the samples, what type of rock each sample is, and a fact or two about each sample.

Discussion Questions

1. Describe three ways that mineral deposits can be formed. (*One way that mineral deposits form occurs when molten rock cools, the denser crystals fall to the bottom, causing a concentration of minerals. Another way that mineral deposits form occurs when mineral-rich water is forced through fissures and the minerals are deposited along the way. Another way that mineral deposits form occurs when the other components of a rock are dissolved, leaving behind only the minerals from the rock.*)
2. What is the purpose of smelting? (*Smelting is a process used to extract metal from an ore.*)
3. What are types of minerals make up gemstones? (*Gemstones can be organic in origin, made from silicate minerals, or fromed from pure carbon.*)

Want More

- **Crystals** – Have the students grow their own crystals. The quickest way to grow crystals at home is to use Borax. They will need a glass jar, a pipe cleaner, a pencil, and some Borax, which can be found in the laundry detergent aisle. Have the students shape the pipe cleaners into their desired shapes. This can be as simple or as complex as they wish, but make sure it will fit through the opening of their jar. Next, attach the shape to the pencil using another pipe cleaner—the pencil to be able to rest on the edge of the jar without having the shape touch the sides or bottom of the jar. Now, add hot water until it almost fills the jar, noting how many cups of water it takes to fill the jar. Then, add the Borax, one tablespoon at a time, taking care each time to stir until the Borax is dissolved. They will want to add about 3 tablespoons of Borax for every cup of water added. Finally, hang the shape in the jar so that it is completely covered by the liquid and allow the jar to sit undisturbed overnight. The next morning, the students should see crystals forming on the pipe cleaner.

Sketch Assignment Week 28

This week, the students will be doing a mini-research project for their sketch assignment in which they will be choosing a type of rock to profile. All the instructions they need are on the Student Assignment Page, but they may need you to walk them through the process, depending on how much experience they have with doing research prior to this assignment. You can have the students simply list facts about the rock they have chosen or they can choose to write several paragraphs. Below is a sample profile page from one of my students, for your reference:

Rock Profile Page

Amethyst

Group: Silicates

Composition (Chemical Formula): SiO_2 (silicone dioxide)

Crystal System: hexagonal / trigonal

Color: violet

Hardness: 7

Cleavage: none

Interesting Facts:

- Amethyst crystals grow in groups.
- Amethyst are usually used in jewelry.
- If an amethyst gets heat-treated, it can turn yellow or brown.
- Amethyst are typically found in Colorado.
- Amethyst crystals can grow straight up.

Student Assignment Sheet Week 29
Erosion and Weathering

Experiment: Do plants help to prevent erosion?

> ***NOTE*** *– You will need to plant your grass seed mountain (steps two and three) at least 7 days before doing this experiment so that the grass will have the time to grow.*

Materials
- ✓ Dirt or sand
- ✓ Grass seed
- ✓ Water
- ✓ Pitcher
- ✓ 2 Aluminum Pans

Procedure
1. Read the introduction to this experiment and answer the question.
2. Build up a mountain of dirt in each of your pans. Be sure that both of your mountains are of equal height. Record the height on your experiment sheet.
3. Set one mountain aside. Plant the other mountain with grass seed and water it frequently until the grass begins to grow. Once the grass has grown at least an inch, you are ready to continue the experiment.
4. Add water to your pitcher, one cup at a time, until it is almost full. Record how many cups you added and then pour the water over the top of your dirt mountain. Record the height of the mountain.
5. Refill the pitcher with the same amount of water and then pour the water over the top of your grass seed mountain. Record the height of the mountain.
6. Repeat steps four and five two more times and record your results.
7. Make observations, draw conclusions, and complete your experiment sheet.

Vocabulary & Memory Work
- ☐ Vocabulary: erosion, weathering
- ☐ Memory Work – Continue to work on memorizing the Types of Rock.

Sketch Assignment: Freeze-thaw Weathering
- Label the following: water from rain seeps into a small crack in the rock; the water freezes and expands, causing the crack to widen and allowing more water in the next time; the temperature rises and falls, causing the crack to grow until part of the rock breaks off

Writing Assignment
- Reading Assignment: The *Kingfisher Science Encyclopedia* pp. 32-33 Erosion and Weathering, *Freeze-thaw Weathering* pg. 251 in the SG Appendix
- Additional Research Readings
  - Weathering and Erosion: *DKEOS* pp. 230-231

Dates
- No dates to be entered this week.

Schedules for Week 29

Two Days a Week

Day 1	Day 2
☐ Define erosion, weathering on SG pg. 157 ☐ Do the "Do plants help to prevent erosion?" experiment, then fill out the experiment sheet on SG pp. 196-197	☐ Read pp. 32-33 from *The Kingfisher Science Encyclopedia* and the *Freeze-thaw Weathering* article, then discuss what was read ☐ Prepare an outline or narrative summary, write it on SG pp. 198-199 ☐ Color and label the "Freeze-thaw Weathering" sketch on SG pg. 195

Supplies I Need for the Week

- ✓ Dirt or sand
- ✓ Grass seed
- ✓ Water
- ✓ Pitcher
- ✓ 2 Aluminum Pans

Things I Need to Prepare

Five Days a Week

Day 1	Day 2	Day 3	Day 4	Day 5
☐ Do the "Do plants help to prevent erosion?" experiment, then fill out the experiment sheet on SG pp. 196-197	☐ Read pp. 32-33 from *The Kingfisher Science Encyclopedia* and the *Freeze-thaw Weathering* article, then discuss what was read ☐ Write an outline or list of facts on SG pg. 198	☐ Define erosion, weathering on SG pg. 157 ☐ Color and label the "Freeze-thaw Weathering" sketch on SG pg. 195	☐ Read one or all of the additional reading assignments ☐ Prepare your report, write the report on SG pg. 199	☐ Complete one of the Want More Activities listed **OR** ☐ Study a scientist from the field of Earth Science ☐ Take the Unit 5 Test

Supplies I Need for the Week

- ✓ Dirt or sand
- ✓ Grass seed
- ✓ Water
- ✓ Pitcher
- ✓ 2 Aluminum Pans

Things I Need to Prepare

Additional Information Week 29

Experiment Information

- ☞ **Introduction** – (*from the Student Guide*) Soil is the substance that covers most of the land surface of the Earth. It is composed of rocks, minerals, dead organic matter, tiny living organisms, gases, and water. It is important to life on Earth because it provides the environment and food in which plants can grow. Water and wind can cause the soil to be washed or blown away, which is known as erosion. In this experiment, you are going to see if plants can help to prevent soil erosion.
- ☞ **Results** – The students should see that their dirt mountain decreases in height much more than the mountain with the grass growing on it.
- ☞ **Explanation** – Plants help to prevent erosion because their roots that hold the soil together. So, when it rains heavily or the wind blows, the soil will not move much. However, if all the trees & plants have been removed from a mountain, there is nothing to hold the soil in place. When there is a storm, a good bit of the soil will be washed or blown away.
- ☞ **Take it Further** – Have the students repeat the experiment using oil to see how the viscosity of the liquid affects the amount of material that is eroded.

Discussion Questions

1. What cycle drives erosion and weathering? (*The water cycle drives erosion and weathering.*)
2. How does water break down rock? (*There are several ways that water helps to break down rock. Acidic water can dissolve rock. Water can split rock through freeze-thaw weathering. Water can wash away sand, gravel, and soil.*)
3. How does the wind break down rock? (*Wind can break down rock by pounding it with small particles that chip away at the rock.*)
4. What are several effects of erosion? (*Erosion can cause the formation of valleys, waterfalls, gorges, landslides, sediment deposits, and lakes.*)
5. Explain freeze-thaw weathering. (*Water from rain seeps into a small crack in the rock. The water freezes and expands, causing the crack to widen and allowing more water in the next time. As the temperature rises and falls, the crack continues to grow until part of the rock breaks off.*)

Want More

- **Field Trip** – This would be a good week to visit a local farm and learn about their soil practices. Be sure to have the students ask questions about fertilizing and crop rotation, as well as how the farm prevents soil erosion.
- **Garden** – Plant your own garden in your backyard or in a container. Plan the garden with the students, taking the time to discuss the nutrient needs of the plants you will use and the exposure the garden will have to light and the elements of weather.

Sketch Assignment Week 29

Freeze-thaw Weathering

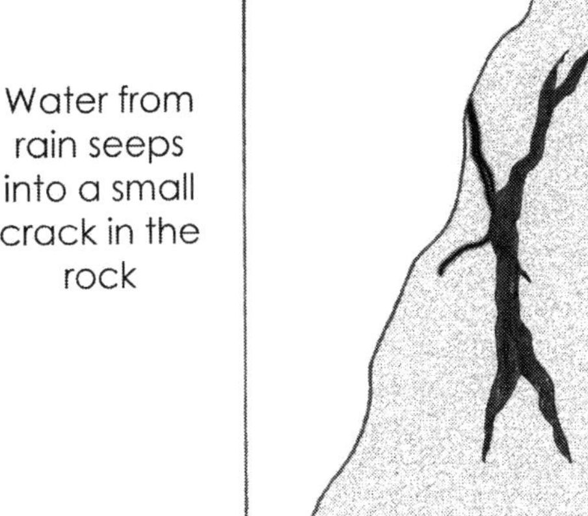

Water from rain seeps into a small crack in the rock

The water freezes and expands, causing the crack to widen and allowing more water in the next time

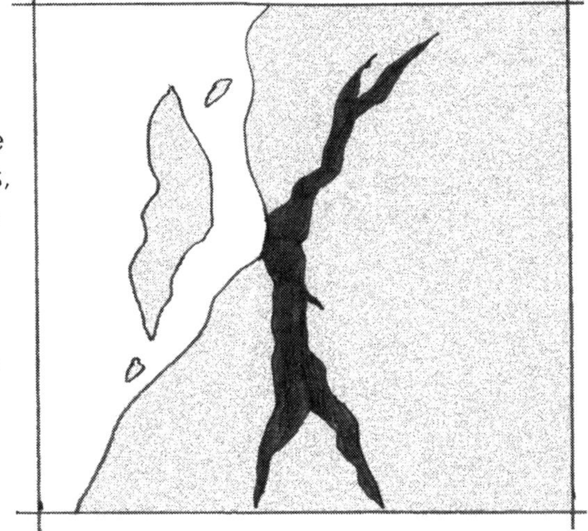

The temperature rises and falls, causing the crack to grow until part of the rock breaks off

Earth Science Unit 5: Geology
Discussion Questions

Week 23

1. What creates the Earth's solid surface?
2. What causes the movement of the tectonic plates of the Earth's crust?
3. What is one difference between oceanic and continental crust?
4. What happens as the tectonic plates stretch? Collide?
5. How can geologists track the movement of the tectonic plates?

Week 24

1. What is a volcano?
2. What does the behavior of a volcano depend on?
3. Name three different types of volcanos and share a characteristic about each.
4. What happens during a volcanic eruption?

Week 25

1. What is an earthquake?
2. Where do earthquakes most commonly occur?
3. What causes the destruction in a earthquake?
4. What are the two scales used to measure earthquakes?
5. Why is it so difficult to create a warning system for earthquakes?
6. What is a seismograph?

Week 26

1. What four factors contribute to the formation and destruction of mountains?
2. What are some of the newer mountain chains around the globe? Older ones?
3. What can the Earth's crust tell us about mountains?
4. Explain how the Himalayan Mountains were formed.

Week 27

Pg. 28 Igneous Rock

1. Describe igneous rock and how it is classified.
2. What are the two ways that igneous rock can form?

Pg. 29 Metamorphic Rock

1. What is metamorphic rock and how does it form?
2. Describe the two types of metamorphic rock.

Pp. 30-31 Sedimentary Rock

1. What is sedimentary rock?
2. What are the three types of sedimentary rock?
3. What are the two main ways of weathering rock (explain both)?

Week 28

1. Describe three ways that mineral deposits can be formed.
2. What is the purpose of smelting?
3. What are types of minerals make up gemstones?

Week 29

1. What cycle drives erosion and weathering?
2. How does water break down rock?
3. How does the wind break down rock?
4. What are several effects of erosion?
5. Explain freeze-thaw weathering.

Earth Science Unit 5: Geology
Unit Test

Vocabulary Matching

1. Continent ____
2. Faults ____
3. Magma ____
4. Lava ____
5. Spreading ridge ____
6. Subduction zone ____
7. Seismic wave ____
8. Richter scale ____
9. Mercalli scale ____
10. Mountain range ____
11. Fossil ____
12. Strata ____
13. Gem ____
14. Ore ____
15. Erosion ____
16. Weathering ____

A. A ridge under the ocean that spreads out sideways as magma wells up along its center.

B. Cracks in the Earth caused by the movement of its plates.

C. An underground shockwave that travels outward from the focus of an earthquake.

D. Any of the seven large landmasses into which the Earth is divided.

E. A scale that rates earthquakes from 1 to 10, based on the power of the vibrations that travel through the ground when the earthquake occurs.

F. Molten rock inside the Earth.

G. The layers of rock found in the Earth's crust.

H. An area where two plates collide and one slips under the other, forming volcanoes & deep trenches.

I. The gradual wearing down of rock by wind or water.

J. A scale that rates earthquakes from I to XII based on the effects of the shaking and the damage caused.

K. A chain, or line, of mountains connected together.

L. The impression or remains of an ancient plant or animal that has been hardened and preserved in a rock.

M. Molten rock at and on the surface of the Earth.

N. A mineral from which we can extract a useful substance, such as a metal.

O. The movement of particles of soil, sand, or rock by wind or water to a new location.

P. A mineral or organic stone that is chosen to be cut, polished, and used, typically in jewelry.

True or False

1. _____________________ The Earth's solid surface is formed by the oceanic and continental crust.

2. _____________________ Geologists cannot track continental drift because it happens so slowly.

3. _____________________ The behavior of a volcano is dependent upon the type of magma that feeds it.

4. _____________________ During a volcanic eruption, the pressure increases.

5. _____________________ Earthquakes usually occur near a plate boundary.

6. _____________________ The hypocenter of an earthquake is the point at which the rock gives way and the earthquake begins.

7. _____________________ The Himalayan mountains and the Alps are two of the oldest mountain chains on the Earth.

8. _____________________ The Earth's crust records the history of the uplift of mountains and the erosional forces that destroy them.

9. _____________________ Intrusive igneous rocks form during volcanic eruptions. Extrusive igneous rocks are pushed up beneath overlying rocks.

10. _____________________ Metamorphic rock is rock that has not been changed.

11. _____________________ Sedimentary rock is made from tiny pieces of rock and dead organic matter that have been compressed into solid layers.

12. _____________________ Smelting is a process used to extract metal from an ore.

13. _____________________ There is nothing that can dissolve rock.

14. _____________________ Wind can break down rock by pounding it with small particles that chip away at the rock.

Short Answer

1. What causes the movement of the tectonic plates of the Earth's crust?

2. Name three different types of volcanos and share a characteristic about each.

3. What is an earthquake?

4. What four factors contribute to the formation and destruction of mountains?

5. What are the two main ways of weathering rock (explain both)?

6. Name the three main types of rock and briefly describe each of them.

7. Explain freeze-thaw weathering.

Earth Science Unit 5: Geology
Unit Test Answers

Vocabulary

1. D
2. B
3. F
4. M
5. A
6. H
7. C
8. E
9. J
10. K
11. L
12. G
13. P
14. N
15. O
16. I

True or False

1. True
2. False (*Geologists can use lasers and satellites to track the subtle continental drift.*)
3. True
4. True
5. True
6. True
7. False (*The Himalayan mountains and the Alps are two of the youngest mountain chains.*)
8. True
9. False (*Extrusive igneous rocks form during volcanic eruptions. Intrusive igneous rocks are pushed up beneath overlying rocks.*)
10. False (*Metamorphic rock is rock that has been changed by heat or pressure.*)
11. True
12. True
13. False (*Acidic water can dissolve rock.*)
14. True

Short Answer

1. The crustal plates float on top of the liquid mantle. Heat from the Earth's core causes the liquid rock in the mantle to move swirl around, which is known as convection. This movement causes the surface plates to slowly move around.
2. The student's answer should include three of the following volcano types—A fissure volcano, which erupts from a narrow slit. A shield volcano, which oozes molten rock over a large area. A dome volcano, which is created by sticky molten rock. A conical volcano, which is formed by volcanic ash. A composite volcano, which can have several side vents. A caldera, which is created by an explosive eruption.
3. An earthquake is a sudden release of energy that makes the ground tremble.
4. The four factors that contribute to the formation and destruction of mountains are volcanoes, earthquakes, continental collisions, and weathering.
5. The two main ways of weathering a rock are chemical weathering and physical weathering. Chemical weathering happens when rocks are changed by water, carbon dioxide, or by organic acids. Physical weathering happens when rocks are fractured or broken apart.
6. Metamorphic – Rock that has been changed by heat or pressure; Sedimentary – Rock made from particles of sand, mud, and other debris that have settled on the seabed and been squashed down to form hardened rock; Igneous – Rock that is formed when magma escapes from inside the Earth, cools, and hardens.
7. Water from rain seeps into a small crack in the rock. The water freezes and expands, causing the crack to widen and allowing more water in the next time. As the temperature rises and

falls, the crack continues to grow until part of the rock breaks off.

Earth Science Unit 6

Weather

Earth Science Unit 6: Weather
Overview of Study

Sequence of Study

Week 30: Atmosphere
Week 31: Climates
Week 32: Weather
Week 33: Clouds
Week 34: Extreme Weather
Week 35: Forecasting

Materials by Week

Week	Materials
30	3 Cups, 2 Colors of food coloring, Hot and cold water
31	3 Foil muffin cups, Soil from outside, Sand, Water , Desk lamp
32	Balloon, Two permanent markers of different colors, A partner
33	2 Liter bottle, Water, Matches
34	Large clear round container, Warm water , Red food coloring, Blue ice cubes
35	Battery powered toothbrush, Sound recording device

Vocabulary for the Unit

1. **Atmosphere** – A blanket of gases that surround the Earth.
2. **Atmospheric pressure** – The force that the air around us exerts.
3. **Currents** – Patterns of circulation of air or water around the Earth that are caused by the Sun's heat.
4. **Climate** – The long-term or typical pattern of weather in a particular area.
5. **Coriolis effect** – The effect of the spinning of the Earth, which forces winds and currents into a spiral.
6. **Weather** – The way the Earth's atmosphere behaves and changes day by day.
7. **Cloud** – A collection of water droplets and dust particles that is caused by a drop in pressure and is visible from Earth.
8. **Precipitation** – Water that falls to the Earth's surface, otherwise known as rain.
9. **Supercell** – A strong, long-lasting, and organized thunderstorm feed by a consistently rotating updraft known as a mesocyclone.
10. **Isobars** – Lines on a weather forecasting map that show atmospheric pressure.
11. **Meteorologist** – A scientist who studies weather and weather forecasting.

Memory Work for the Unit

Layers of the Atmosphere

1. Thermosphere – The outer layer of the atmosphere.
2. Mesosphere – Meteors generally burn up as they reach this layer of the atmosphere.
3. Stratosphere – Planes fly in this layer of the atmosphere.
4. Troposphere – The layer of the atmosphere where weather is created.

Types of Clouds

1. Cirrus
2. Cirrostratus
3. Cirrocumulus
4. Altostratus
5. Altocumulus
6. Stratus
7. Stratocumulus
8. Nimbostratus
9. Cumulus
10. Cumulonimbus

Notes

Student Assignment Sheet Week 30
Atmosphere

Experiment: Does hot water act differently than cold water?

Materials

- ✓ 3 Glasses
- ✓ Red and blue food coloring
- ✓ Hot water (*Do not handle the hot water without the proper protection.*)
- ✓ Ice Cold water

Procedure

1. Read the introduction to this experiment and answer the question.
2. Fill one of the glasses two thirds of the way with cold water and add three drops of blue food coloring. Observe what happens and record the time it takes for the food coloring to completely mix.
3. Next, fill the other glass two thirds of the way with hot water and add two drops of red food coloring. Observe what happens and record the time it takes for the food coloring to completely mix.
4. Then, pour one quarter of the hot red water very slowly into the cold blue water, observe what happens, and record it on your sheet. (***NOTE** – For this part to work, you must pour very slowly down the side of the glass.*)
5. Check the glass after 30 minutes; observe and record what has happened.
6. Draw conclusions and complete your experiment sheet.

Vocabulary & Memory Work

- ☐ Vocabulary: atmosphere, currents, atmospheric pressure
- ☐ Memory Work – Begin to work on memorizing the Layers of the Atmosphere. (*See the sketch labels below for a complete listing.*)

Sketch Assignment: The Atmospheric Structure

- Label the following: Sea Level, Height (be sure to create & label your scale in either km or mi), Thermosphere-outer layer of the atmosphere, Mesosphere-meteors generally burn up as they reach this layer of the atmosphere, Stratosphere-planes fly in this layer of the atmosphere, Troposphere-layer of the atmosphere where weather is created

Writing Assignment

- Reading Assignment: *The Kingfisher Science Encyclopedia* pp. 10-11 Earth's Atmosphere
- Additional Research Readings
  - The Atmosphere: *USE* pp. 134-135
  - Atmosphere: *DKEOS* pp. 248-249

Dates

- 1643 – Evangelista Torricelli invents the barometer, an instrument that measures atmospheric pressure.

Schedules for Week 30

Two Days a Week

Day 1	Day 2
❒ Define atmosphere, currents, atmospheric pressure on SG pg. 202 ❒ Do the "Does hot water act differently than cold water?" experiment, then fill out the experiment sheet on SG pp. 206-207 ❒ Enter the dates onto the date sheets on SG pp. 8-12	❒ Read pp. 10-11 from the *The Kingfisher Science Encyclopedia,* then discuss what was read ❒ Color and label the "The Atmospheric Structure" sketch on SG pg. 205 ❒ Prepare an outline or narrative summary, write it on SG pp. 208-209
Supplies I Need for the Week ✓ 3 glasses ✓ Red & blue food coloring ✓ Hot water ✓ Ice Cold water	
Things I Need to Prepare	

Five Days a Week

Day 1	Day 2	Day 3	Day 4	Day 5
❒ Do the "Does hot water act differently than cold water?" experiment, then fill out the experiment sheet on SG pp. 206-207	❒ Read pp. 10-11 from the *The Kingfisher Science Encyclopedia,* then discuss what was read ❒ Write an outline or list of facts on SG pg. 208	❒ Define atmosphere, currents, atmospheric pressure on SG pg. 202 ❒ Enter the dates onto the date sheets on SG pp. 8-12 ❒ Color and label the "The Atmospheric Structure" sketch on SG pg. 205	❒ Read one or all of the additional reading assignments ❒ Prepare your report, write the report on SG pg. 209	❒ Complete one of the Want More Activities listed **OR** ❒ Study a scientist from the field of Earth Science
Supplies I Need for the Week ✓ 3 glasses ✓ Red & blue food coloring ✓ Hot water ✓ Ice Cold water				
Things I Need to Prepare				

Additional Information Week 30

Experiment Information

- **Introduction** – (*from the Student Guide*) The Sun is responsible for providing light and heat to our Earth. As the Earth heats up, the air and water molecules around the globe also heat up, causing them to rise. As they rise, they cool and fall again. This cycle of rising and falling creates the air and water currents that can be found around the globe. In this experiment, you are going to compare how hot water and cold water molecules behave.
- **Results** – The students should see that it took about 3 times as long for the food coloring to fully mix into the cold water than in the hot water. They should also see that the red water layer (hot) "floats" on top of the blue water layer (cold). After thirty minutes, they should see that the water is now purple because the two layers have mixed.
- **Explanation** – Hot water molecules move faster than cold water molecules, which causes the food coloring in the hot water to mix in much quicker. The hot water molecules are also more spread out, making the same volume of hot water less dense than cold water. This allows the hot water to appear to float on the surface of the cold water. As the hot water cools and the cool water warms up, the two mix, turning the water purple.
- **Troubleshooting** – If the students have difficulty floating the red layer, make sure that:
    - *The cold water is ice cold and the hot water is very warm.*
    - *The water is poured very slowly.*

Discussion Questions

1. What does the atmosphere do? (*The atmosphere contains the air we need to breathe, it affects our weather, and protects us from the extreme temperatures of space.*)
2. Which gas is known as a greenhouse gas and why? (*Carbon dioxide is known as a greenhouse gas because it lets sunlight through to the Earth's surface, but does not let the heat escape.)*
3. What are the layers of the atmosphere from top to bottom? (*The outermost layer of the atmosphere is the thermosphere, then the mesosphere, then the stratosphere, and finally the troposphere.*)
4. What role do animals and plants play in maintaining our atmosphere? (*Animals and plants help to maintain balance in our atmosphere. In the light, plants continually take in carbon dioxide and release oxygen, while animals continually take in oxygen and release carbon dioxide.*)

Want More

- **Create a Poster** – Have the students make a poster explaining the layers of the atmosphere. Be sure they include the earth at the bottom and space at the top. Have them include pictures of what can be found at each layer, as well as a brief explanation of the layer.

Sketch Assignment Week 30

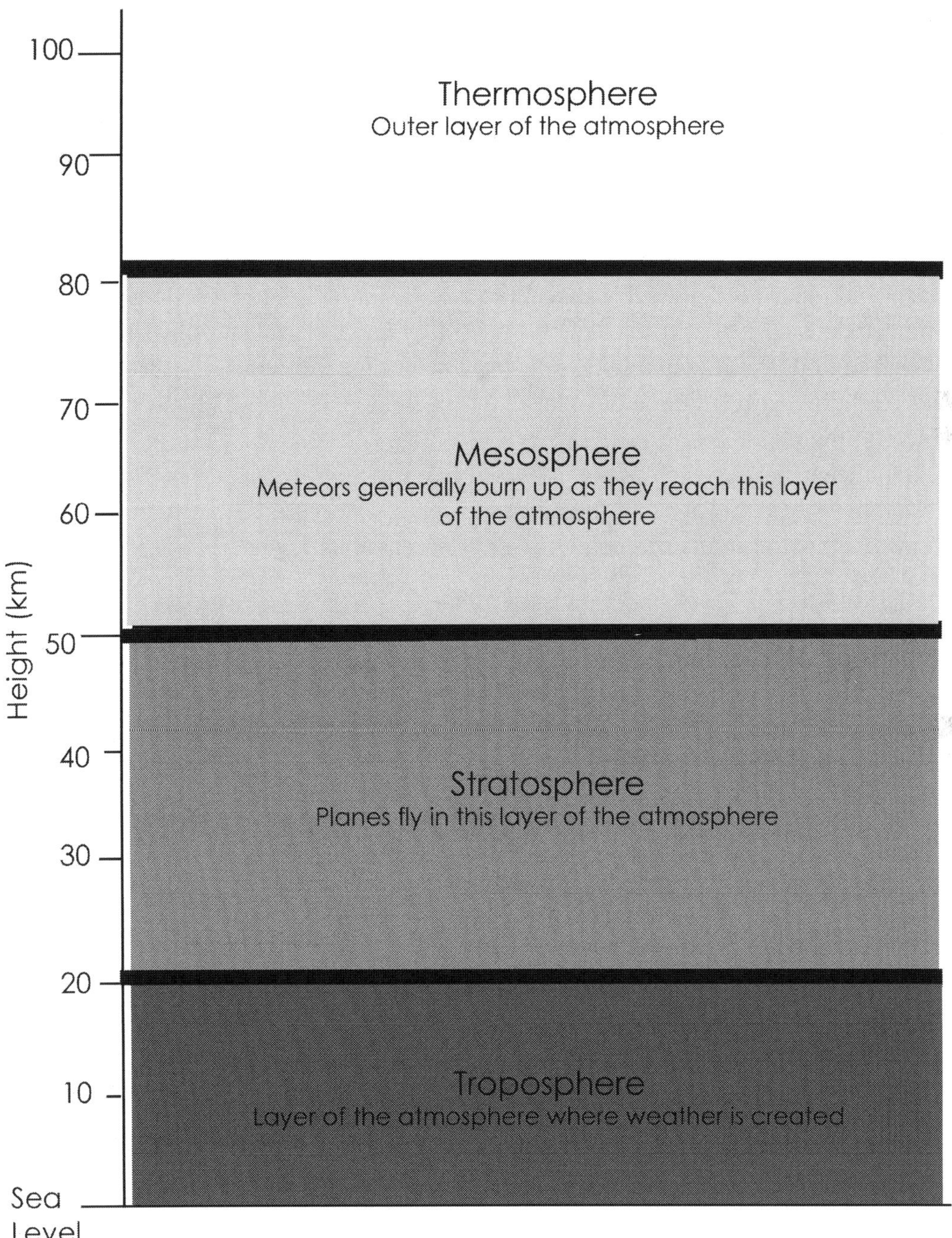

Student Assignment Sheet Week 31
Climates

Experiment: Do different types of surfaces affect the temperature of a region?

Materials

- ✓ 3 Foil muffin cups
- ✓ Darkly colored soil (i.e., potting soil or soil from outside)
- ✓ Sand
- ✓ Water
- ✓ Light source

Procedure

1. Read the introduction to this experiment and answer the question.
2. Fill one muffin cup three quarters of the way with the soil. Repeat with the sand and water and place all three cups on a surface to sit undisturbed for fifteen minutes.
3. Touch the surface of each of the cups and rate the temperature from 1 to 10, with 10 being the hottest and 1 being the coldest. Make observations and record your results.
4. Place all three cups under a desk lamp or out in the sun. Let them sit undisturbed for fifteen minutes.
5. Touch the surface of each of the cups and rate the temperature from 1 to 10, with 10 being the hottest and 1 being the coldest. Make observations and record your results.
6. Draw conclusions and complete your experiment sheet.

Vocabulary & Memory Work

- ☐ Vocabulary: climate
- ☐ Memory Work – Continue to work on memorizing the Layers of the Atmosphere.

Sketch Assignment: The Water Cycle

- Label the following: Clouds become heavy with water and droplets fall as rain, snow, or hail; Water droplets in the air rise and cool, forming clouds; Heat from the sun evaporates water from rivers and seas; Water flows down to the sea in streams and rivers

Writing Assignment

- Reading Assignment: *The Kingfisher Science Encyclopedia* pp. 36-37 Climates
- Additional Research Readings
    - Climate: *USE* pp. 194-195
    - Climates: *DKEOS* pp. 244-245
    - Seasons: *DKEOS* pg. 243

Dates

- c. 5 BC – Strabo, a Greek geographer, proposes the idea of frigid, temperate and tropical climate zones.

Schedules for Week 31

Two Days a Week

Day 1	Day 2
☐ Define climate on SG pg. 202 ☐ Do the "Do different types of surfaces affect the temperature of a region?" experiment, then fill out the experiment sheet on SG pp. 212-213 ☐ Enter the dates onto the date sheets on SG pp. 8-12	☐ Read pp. 36-37 from the *The Kingfisher Science Encyclopedia*, then discuss what was read ☐ Prepare an outline or narrative summary, write it on SG pp. 214-215 ☐ Color and label the "The Water Cycle" sketch on SG pg. 211

Supplies I Need for the Week
- ✓ 3 Foil muffin cups
- ✓ Darkly colored soil (i.e., potting soil or soil from outside)
- ✓ Sand
- ✓ Water
- ✓ Light source

Things I Need to Prepare

Five Days a Week

Day 1	Day 2	Day 3	Day 4	Day 5
☐ Do the "Do different types of surfaces affect the temperature of a region?" experiment, then fill out the experiment sheet on SG pp. 212-213	☐ Read pp. 36-37 from the *The Kingfisher Science Encyclopedia*, then discuss what was read ☐ Write an outline or list of facts on SG pg. 214	☐ Define climate on SG pg. 202 ☐ Enter the dates onto the date sheets on SG pp. 8-12 ☐ Color and label the "The Water Cycle" sketch on SG pg. 211	☐ Read one or all of the additional reading assignments ☐ Prepare your report, write the report on SG pg. 215	☐ Complete one of the Want More Activities listed **OR** ☐ Study a scientist from the field of Earth Science

Supplies I Need for the Week
- ✓ 3 Foil muffin cups
- ✓ Darkly colored soil (i.e., potting soil or soil from outside)
- ✓ Sand, Water & Light source

Things I Need to Prepare

Additional Information Week 31

Notes

- **Additional Memory Work** – If your students have not already memorized the seasons (summer, fall, winter, spring) and their order, you should have them do so this week.

Experiment Information

- **Introduction** – (*from the Student Guide*) A climate is a long-term pattern of weather found in a particular region. Our globe is covered with vastly different climates. These weather patterns determine which types of plants will grow in a region and which type of animals will live in the area. The climate also affects whether people can live in the region. In this experiment, you will be looking at whether a region's surface can help to determine the temperature and climate of the region.
- **Results** – The students should see that the three materials have about the same temperature after 15 minutes of sitting undisturbed. After 15 minutes under the light source, the students should see that the soil got the hottest, followed by the sand, and finally the water. *(**NOTE** – The method of measuring temperature used in this experiment is very subjective. If you would like your measurements to be more precise, you can use a fish tank temperature strip. You will need three strips, one for each cup. Simply place the strip on the surface of the material in the cup while it sit for the 15 minutes and then record the results at the end of the time.)*
- **Explanation** – This experiment was designed to show the students how different land surfaces can affect a region's climate. Different types of land surfaces absorb light rays in different ways. The darker the surface, the more light it will absorb. This means that the darkly colored soil will absorb most of the light rays, while surfaces such as the sand and water reflect a lot of the light rays. Land surface is not the only factor in determining the climate of a region. Proximity to the sun and cloud cover also affect the climate and temperature of a region, which accounts for the variations in regions around the globe that have the same surfaces.

Discussion Questions

1. What two factors influence the Earth's climate? (*The Earth's climate is influenced by energy from the sun and the ability of currents in the oceans and atmosphere to circulate the heat around the globe.*)
2. What is the most important factor in determining an area's climate? Why? (*The most important factor in determining an area's climate is its latitude. This is because the latitude determines how much heat from the Sun the region receives, which affects the plants and animals that can be found there.*)
3. What are some factors that can cause a global climate change? (*Volcanic eruptions, the temperature of the sun, and the amount of oxygen and carbon dioxide in the atmosphere can all affect the global climate.*)
4. What is El Nino? (*El Nino is a reversal in the currents found in the Pacific Ocean. This can cause floods in the Americas and droughts in Southeast Asia.*)

Want More

- **Research Report** – Have the students choose one of the climatic regions to research. (*See the list of major biomes of the Earth that they are memorizing or USE pg. 194-195 for options.*) Have them create a poster or write a report that includes average yearly rainfall, and typical temperatures, as well as the animals and plants found in the region.

Sketch Assignment Week 31

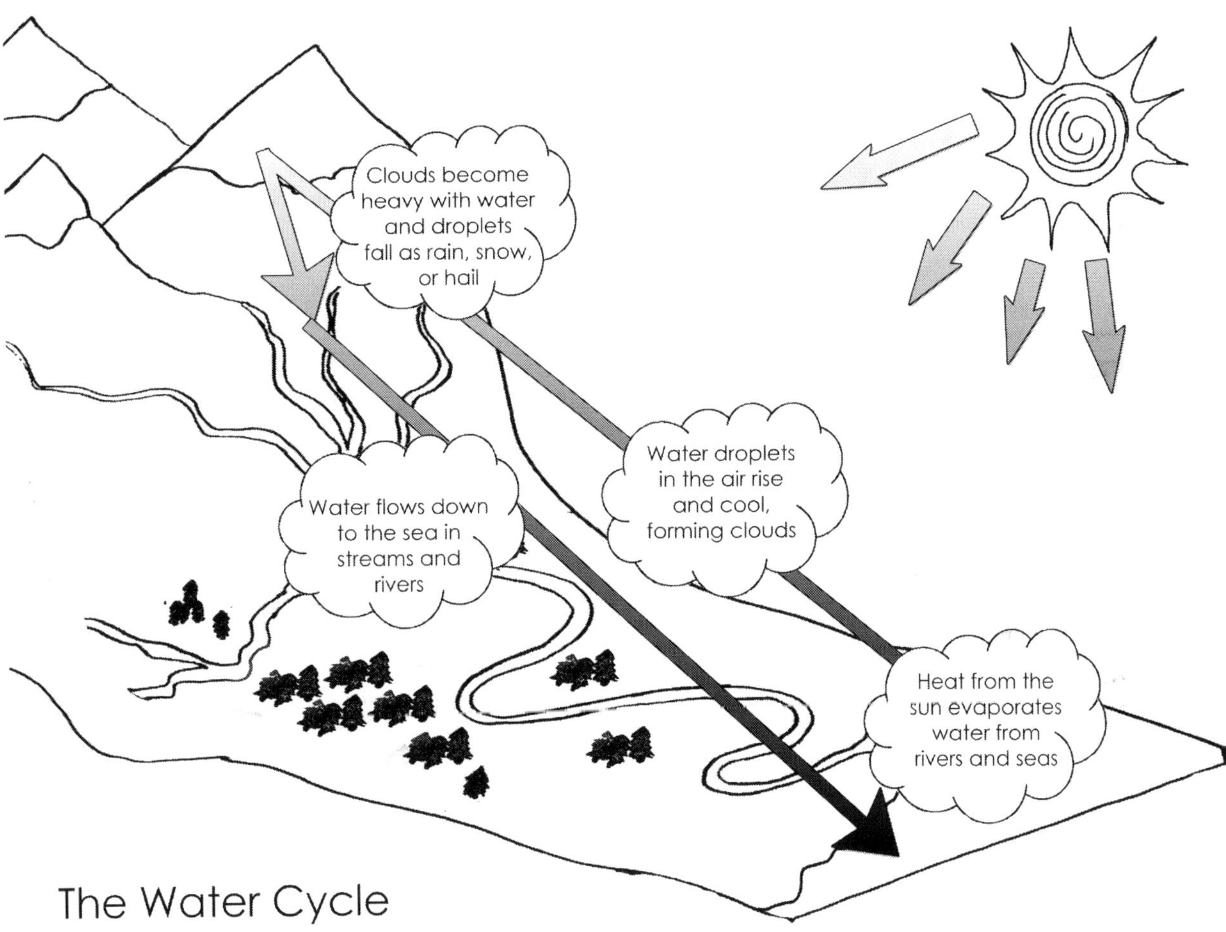

Student Assignment Sheet Week 32
Weather

Experiment: What is the Coriolis effect?

Materials
- ✓ Balloon
- ✓ Two permanent markers of different colors
- ✓ A partner

Procedure
1. Read the introduction to this experiment.
2. Blow up a balloon, draw a straight line around the center for the equator, and hand it to your partner.
3. Have your partner hold the balloon steady as you draw a straight line from the center equator line to the top of the balloon in the same color as you used in step 2. Sketch what the line looked like on the experiment sheet.
4. Now, have your partner spin the balloon in a counter-clockwise direction as you draw a straight line from the center equator line to the top of the balloon in a different color. Sketch what the line looked like on the experiment sheet.
5. Draw conclusions and complete your experiment sheet.

Vocabulary & Memory Work
- ☐ Vocabulary: Coriolis effect, weather
- ☐ Memory Work – Continue to work on memorizing the Layers of Atmosphere.

Sketch Assignment: Seasonal Changes
- Label the following: Sun's rays, March, January, September, June, the sun's rays are concentrated in the center of the globe - warming both hemispheres evenly, the suns rays are concentrated on the northern hemisphere, the sun's rays are concentrated on the southern hemisphere

Writing Assignment
- Reading Assignment: *The Usborne Science Encyclopedia* pp. 192-193 Weather
- Additional Research Readings
  - Rain and Snow: *KSE* pp. 38-39
  - Weather: *DKEOS* pg. 241
  - Seasons: *DKEOS* pg. 243
  - Air Pressure: *DKEOS* pg. 250

Dates
- 1887 – The biggest recorded snowflakes, which were 15 inches across, fall in Montana.

Schedules for Week 32

Two Days a Week

Day 1	Day 2
❐ Define Coriolis effect, weather on SG pg. 202 ❐ Do the "What is the Coriolis effect?" experiment, then fill out the experiment sheet on SG pp. 218-219 ❐ Enter the dates onto the date sheets on SG pp. 8-12	❐ Read pp. 192-193 from *The Usborne Science Encyclopedia,* then discuss what was read ❐ Color and label the "Seasonal changes" sketch on SG pg. 217 ❐ Prepare an outline or narrative summary, write it on SG pp. 220-221
Supplies I Need for the Week ✓ Balloon ✓ Two permanent markers of different colors ✓ A partner	
Things I Need to Prepare	

Five Days a Week

Day 1	Day 2	Day 3	Day 4	Day 5
❐ Do the "What is the Coriolis effect?" experiment, then fill out the experiment sheet on SG pp. 218-219	❐ Read pp. 192-193 from *The Usborne Science Encyclopedia,* then discuss what was read ❐ Write an outline or list of facts on SG pg. 220	❐ Define Coriolis effect, weather on SG pg. 202 ❐ Enter the dates onto the date sheets on SG pp. 8-12 ❐ Color and label the "Seasonal changes" sketch on SG pg. 217	❐ Read one or all of the additional reading assignments ❐ Prepare your report, write the report on SG pg. 221	❐ Complete one of the Want More Activities listed **OR** ❐ Study a scientist from the field of Earth Science
Supplies I Need for the Week ✓ Balloon ✓ Two permanent markers of different colors ✓ A partner				
Things I Need to Prepare				

Additional Information Week 32

Experiment Information

- **Introduction** – (*from the Student Guide*) The Coriolis effect is a principle that was discovered and explained by a French professor as he was trying to understand the various forces that affect machinery. Although he was not interested in earth science, the force he found also affects the movement of wind and water around the globe, which in turn affects our weather. In today's experiment, you are going to examine what the Coriolis effect is.
- **Results** – The students should see that in the first part of the experiment, they were able to draw a straight line from the equator. In the second part, when the balloon was rotating, they should see that the line drawn was a curve.
- **Explanation** – The Coriolis effect is a phenomenon that causes fluids, like water and air, to curve as they travel around the globe. This is caused by the rotation of the Earth. As the Earth spins on its axis, points on the equator spin faster than points on the poles due to the spherical shape of our planet. This phenomenon causes a deflection to the right of the equator in the northern hemisphere and a deflection to the left of the equator in the southern hemisphere.
- **Take it Further** – Watch the following video from PBS on the Coriolis effect:
  - https://www.youtube.com/watch?v=i2mec3vgeaI

Discussion Questions

(**Note** – *The students will be studying clouds next week, so no questions have been included from that section for this week.*)

1. What factors play a part in determining the weather? (*The factors that play a part in determining our weather are temperature of the air, wind speed, air pressure, humidity, the amount of clouds, and the amount of precipitation.*)
2. How does the sun affect the weather? (*The Sun's heat, known as solar radiation, is absorbed by the earth, causing the surface to warm up. This heat rises, causing the air near the surface to warm up. The closer the part of the earth is to the sun, the stronger the effect of the solar radiation.*)
3. How are areas of low pressure created? (*Areas of low pressure are created when warm air expands and rises from the earth's surface.*) High pressure? (*Areas of high pressure are created when cooler air pushes down, forcing the warmer surface air to move.*)
4. What are convection currents? (*Convection currents are formed as warm air rises, cools, and sinks back to earth's surface where it is heated once more.*)
5. Why do we have season on the earth? (*Seasons on the earth are caused by the tilted angle of the globe in relation to the sun.*)

Want More

- **Indoor Rain** – Have the students create a rainstorm in a glass. You will need a clear glass, shaving cream, blue food coloring, and warm water. Fill the glass halfway with warm water and squirt a shaving cream cloud on top of the water. You can pack the shaving cream in a bit before adding an indention in the center so that the food coloring won't run over the "cloud." Now, slowly add 20 to 30 drops of blue food coloring in the center of the shaving cream cloud. Watch and wait for the food coloring "rain" to fall out of the bottom of the shaving cream "cloud."

Sketch Assignment Week 32

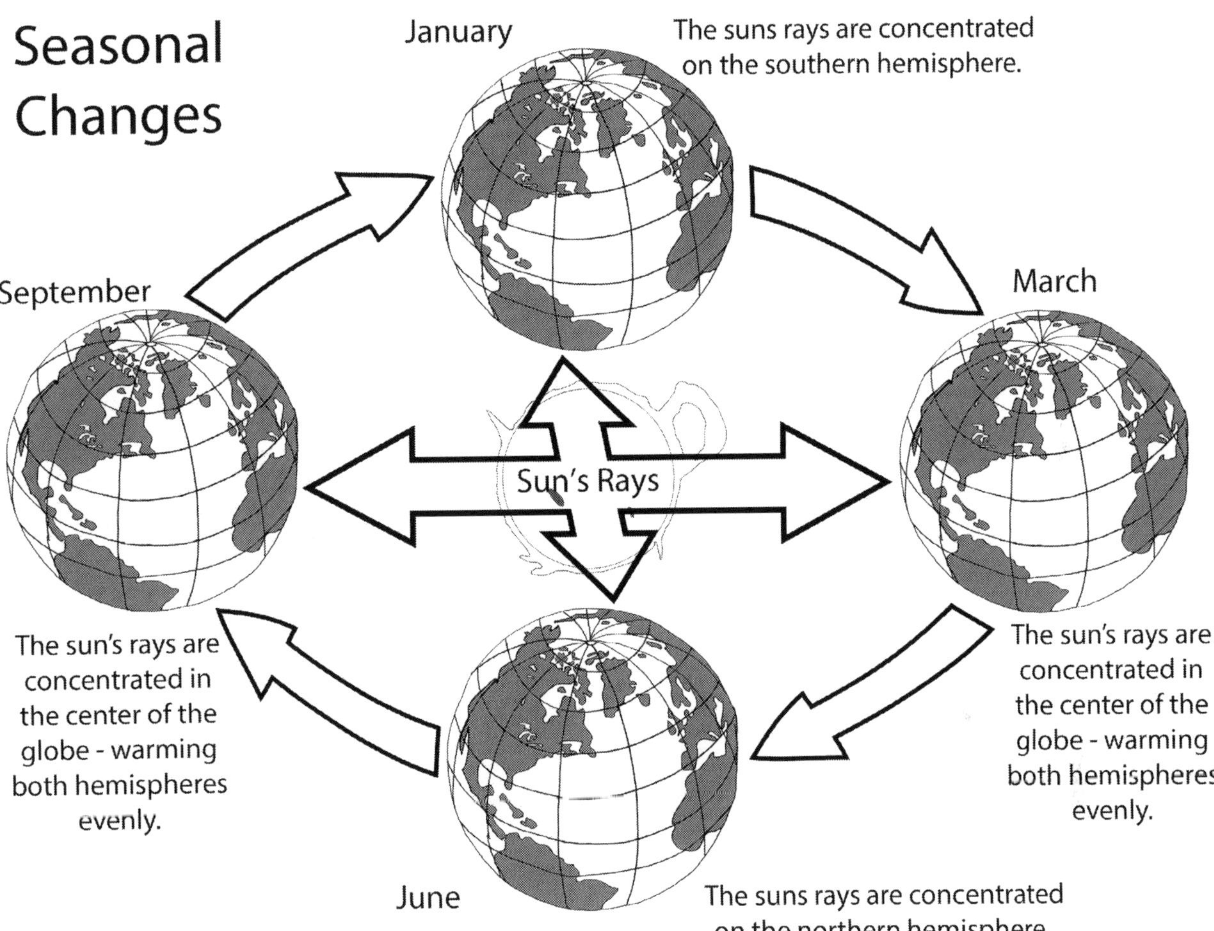

Student Assignment Sheet Week 33
Clouds

Experiment: How do clouds form?

Materials
- ✓ 2 Liter bottle
- ✓ Water
- ✓ Matches

CAUTION
Do not use matches without adult assistance.

Procedure
1. Read the introduction to this experiment and answer the question.
2. Add three cups of warm water to the bottle and cover it with the cap. Wait five minutes and observe what happened.
3. Squeeze your bottle and release, watching carefully to see what happens. Shake down any excess condensation if necessary so that you can see what is happening.
4. Remove the cap from the bottle. Have an adult light a match and drop it into the bottle. Replace the cap quickly so that some of the smoke is trapped. Once again, squeeze your bottle and release, watching carefully to see what happens.
5. Draw conclusions and complete your experiment sheet.

Vocabulary & Memory Work
- ☐ Vocabulary: cloud
- ☐ Memory Work – Begin to work on memorizing the Types of Clouds.
  1. Cirrus
  2. Cirrostratus
  3. Cirrocumulus
  4. Altostratus
  5. Altocumulus
  6. Stratus
  7. Stratocumulus
  8. Nimbostratus
  9. Cumulus
  10. Cumulonimbus

Sketch Assignment: Types of Fog
- Label the following: Advection fog, fog, warm air, cool land; Frontal fog, warm air mass, fog, cold air mass; Upslope fog, fog, moist air; Radiation fog, land loses heat, fog forms

Writing Assignment
- Reading Assignment: The *Kingfisher Science Encyclopedia* pp. 40-41 Clouds and Fog
- Additional Research Readings
  - Clouds: *DKEOS* pp. 260-261
  - Fog, Mist, and Smog: *DKEOS* pg. 263

Dates
- 1803 – Luke Howard, a pharmacist and amateur meteorologist, devises a system to classify the different types of clouds.

Schedules for Week 33

Two Days a Week

Day 1	Day 2
❒ Define cloud on SG pg. 202 ❒ Do the "How do clouds form?" experiment, then fill out the experiment sheet on SG pp. 224-225 ❒ Enter the dates onto the date sheets on SG pp. 8-12	❒ Read pp. 40-41 from the *Kingfisher Science Encyclopedia,* then discuss what was read ❒ Color and label the "Types of Fog" sketch on SG pg. 223 ❒ Prepare an outline or narrative summary, write it on SG pp. 225-226
Supplies I Need for the Week ✓ 2 Liter bottle ✓ Water ✓ Matches	
Things I Need to Prepare	

Five Days a Week

Day 1	Day 2	Day 3	Day 4	Day 5
❒ Do the "How do clouds form?" experiment, then fill out the experiment sheet on SG pp. 224-225	❒ Read pp. 40-41 from the *Kingfisher Science Encyclopedia,* then discuss what was read ❒ Write an outline or list of facts on SG pg. 226	❒ Define cloud on SG pg. 202 ❒ Enter the dates onto the date sheets on SG pp. 8-12 ❒ Color and label the "Types of Fog" sketch on SG pg. 223	❒ Read one or all of the additional reading assignments ❒ Prepare your report, write the report on SG pg. 227	❒ Complete one of the Want More Activities listed **OR** ❒ Study a scientist from the field of Earth Science
Supplies I Need for the Week ✓ 2 Liter bottle ✓ Water ✓ Matches				
Things I Need to Prepare				

Additional Information Week 33

Experiment Information

☞ **Introduction** – (*from the Student Guide*) Clouds are mainly composed of tiny droplets of water or ice. The droplet's weight is so insignificant that they float in the atmosphere. Clouds can appear puffy and large or high and wispy. The way a cloud looks depends on how much water it contains and how fast it was formed. In this experiment, you are going to examine how clouds are formed.

☞ **Results** – The students should see that the warm water caused condensation to form on the inside of the bottle. When they squeezed and released the bottle for the first time, nothing happened. However, when they squeezed and released the bottle after the match was added, they should have seen a cloud form inside the bottle when they released.

☞ **Explanation** – There are three key ingredients for cloud formation. The first ingredient is water vapor, which came from the warm water in this experiment. The second ingredient is a drop in air pressure. When the student squeezed the bottle, this increased the pressure inside the bottle. When the student released the bottle, the pressure inside the bottle dropped. The reason a cloud did not form the first time the student squeezed the bottle is because the third ingredient for cloud formation was missing. The final ingredient is dust, smoke, or other particles in the air, which was provided by the match in this experiment. Water vapor is invisible, so without dust, smoke, or other particles, we could not see the clouds. Every day, invisible water vapor rises into the atmosphere. As it rises, it cools and condenses around dust or other particles found in the atmosphere, forming tiny droplets. When billions of these droplets come together, they become a visible cloud.

Discussion Questions

1. How do clouds form? (*Heat from the sun warms the ground, causing water to evaporate. This water vapor rises and cools, condensing to form clouds or fog.*)
2. What factors affect the type of cloud that forms? (*The factors that affect how a cloud forms include how much and how quickly the warm air cools, whether the warm, moist air meets a mass of cold air, and at what altitude the water vapor condenses.*)
3. How are clouds classified? (*Clouds are classified by their appearance and height.*)
4. Describe the different types of low-level clouds. (*The main types of low-level clouds are stratus clouds, which form unbroken sheets, and cumulus clouds, which form small fluffy balls.*)
5. Describe the different types of mid-level clouds. (*The main types of mid-level clouds are altostratus, which form thin sheets, altocumulus, which are bands of fluffy clouds, and nimbostratus, which are dark and often bring rain or snow.*)
6. What factor is common to all high-level clouds? (*All high-level clouds, or cirrus clouds, are wispy in appearance.*)
7. What is the difference between fog and smog? (*Fog is a cloud that forms at ground level, while smog is the result of air pollution.*)

Want More

- **Make a Poster** – Have the students make a poster that shows and explains the various types of clouds and where they can be found in the atmosphere. Use the picture in *Kingfisher Science Encyclopedia* on pg. 40 to help.

Sketch Assignment Week 33

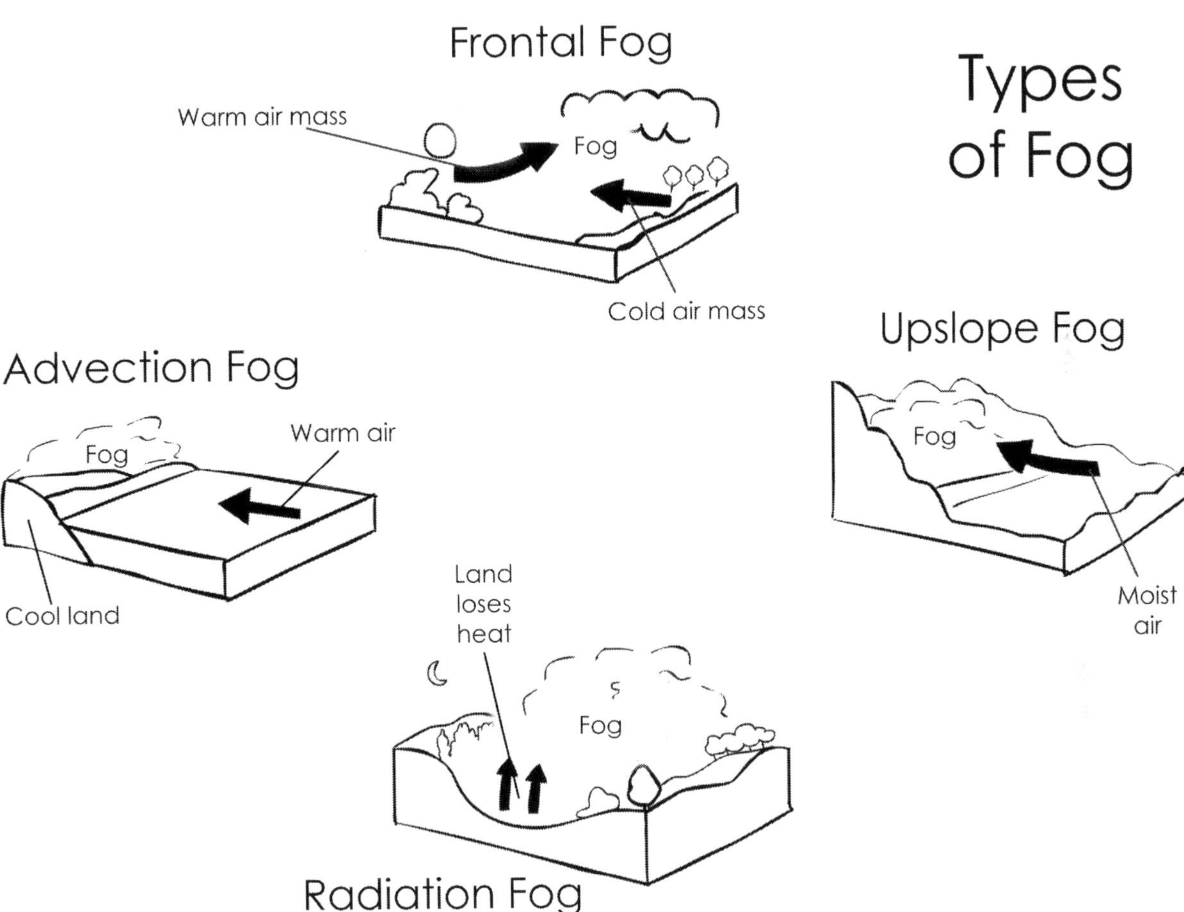

Student Assignment Sheet Week 34
Extreme Weather

Experiment: How does a thunderstorm form?

Materials
- ✓ Large clear round container
- ✓ Warm water
- ✓ Red food coloring
- ✓ Blue ice cubes (*see note below)

Procedure

***NOTE** – You will need to make your blue colored ice cubes the day before. Simply take 1 cup of water, add several drops of blue food coloring, pour into an ice cube tray, and freeze overnight.*

1. Read the introduction to this experiment and answer the question.
2. Fill your container three quarters of the way full with the warm water. Let it set until the water stops moving.
3. Gently add several blue ice cubes to one end of the container and several drops of red food coloring to the other end of the container.
4. Observe what happens and record your results on your experiment sheet.
5. Draw conclusions and complete your experiment sheet.

Vocabulary & Memory Work
- ☐ Vocabulary: precipitation, supercell
- ☐ Memory Work – Continue to work on memorizing the Types of Clouds.

Sketch Assignment: Anatomy of a Hurricane
- Label the following: strong spiral winds, dry air sinks, warm moist air rises, low pressure core

Writing Assignment
- Reading Assignment: *The Kingfisher Science Encyclopedia* pp. 44-45 Wind, Storms, and Floods
- Additional Research Readings
  - Hurricanes: *DKEOS* pg. 258
  - Tornadoes: *DKEOS* pg. 259

Dates
- 1971 – The Fujita scale is introduced by Tetsuya Fujita, a professor at the University of Chicago. The Fujita scale is a way of measuring the strength of a tornado based on the damage they cause, F0 being the weakest and F5 being the strongest.
- December 19, 1898 – President McKinley asks the Weather Bureau, now the National Weather Service, to establish a hurricane warning system.

Schedules for Week 34

Two Days a Week

Day 1	Day 2
☐ Define precipitation, supercell on SG pp. 202-203 ☐ Do the "How does a thunderstorm form?" experiment, then fill out the experiment sheet on SG pp. 230-231 ☐ Enter the dates onto the date sheets on SG pp. 8-12	☐ Read pp. 44-45 from the *The Kingfisher Science Encyclopedia,* then discuss what was read ☐ Prepare an outline or narrative summary, write it on SG pp. 232-233 ☐ Color and label the "Anatomy of a Hurricane" sketch on SG pg. 229

Supplies I Need for the Week

- ✓ Large clear round container
- ✓ Warm water
- ✓ Red food coloring
- ✓ Blue ice cubes

Things I Need to Prepare

Five Days a Week

Day 1	Day 2	Day 3	Day 4	Day 5
☐ Do the "How does a thunderstorm form?" experiment, then fill out the experiment sheet on SG pp. 230-231	☐ Read pp. 44-45 from the *The Kingfisher Science Encyclopedia,* then discuss what was read ☐ Write an outline or list of facts on SG pg. 232	☐ Define precipitation, supercell on SG pp. 202-203 ☐ Enter the dates onto the date sheets on SG pp. 8-12 ☐ Color and label the "Anatomy of a Hurricane" sketch on SG pg. 229	☐ Read one or all of the additional reading assignments ☐ Prepare your report, write the report on SG pg. 233	☐ Complete one of the Want More Activities listed **OR** ☐ Study a scientist from the field of Earth Science

Supplies I Need for the Week

- ✓ Large clear round container
- ✓ Warm water
- ✓ Red food coloring
- ✓ Blue ice cubes

Things I Need to Prepare

Additional Information Week 34

Experiment Information

- **Introduction** – (*from the Student Guide*) A thunderstorm is a storm with thunder and lightning as well as high winds and heavy rain. Thunderstorms are produced from cumulonimbus clouds and they typically occur in the spring and summer during the late afternoon or evening. Three main ingredients are necessary for thunderstorm formation. One is moisture, the second is lift, and the third is warm air. In this experiment, you are going to see how two of those key ingredients work together to help to form a thunderstorm.
- **Results** – The students should see that the colder blue water appears to sit on the bottom of their container. The warmer red water rises to the top of the container and stays there. (**NOTE** – *If you let the container sit for 30 minutes or more, all the water will turn purple because the temperature of the red & blue water have equalized.*)
- **Explanation** – Cool air and warm air both play a part in thunderstorm formation. There must be moisture, lift and unstable air in the atmosphere for a thunderstorm to form. Cool air in the form of a cold front acts as lift, forcing the warmer, unstable air up. Similarly, in the experiment, the colder blue water forced the warmer red water up to the surface. If moisture is present in the atmosphere, a thunderstorm can form.

Discussion Questions

1. How do winds travel around the globe? (*Warm air rises around the equator, causing very little horizontal winds. Around the Tropic of Cancer and the Tropic of Capricorn, there are consistent trade winds. Above these regions, there are strong westerly winds. There are also seasonal winds, like the mistral, sirocco, and harmattan, which change throughout the year.*)
2. How do tornadoes form? (*Tornadoes form when hot, fast, upward-moving air currents meet cold, downward-moving air currents. As the two temperatures of air swirl around each other, they form a suction funnel that reaches the ground.*)
3. What is a tropical cyclone? (*Tropical cyclones are powerful storm systems that can be up to 100 miles wide.*)
4. What is the difference between a tropical cyclone and a hurricane? (*The difference between a tropical cyclone and a hurricane is location. Hurricanes are located in the Gulf of Mexico and the Atlantic.*)
5. What can cause a flood? (*Floods can be caused by storm surges, heavy rains, snow melts, rivers bursting their banks, and high tides.*)

Want More

- **Make your own tornado** – Follow the directions from this website:
  http://personal.monm.edu/BHURCKES/project.htm
- **Storm Safety** – If you live in a tornado or hurricane prone area, this is a good week for you to discuss with the students tornado or hurricane safety. Be sure to discuss what to do if you are caught in the storm, your evacuation plan, and where to meet after the storm if you get separated.

Sketch Assignment Week 34

Anatomy of a Hurricane

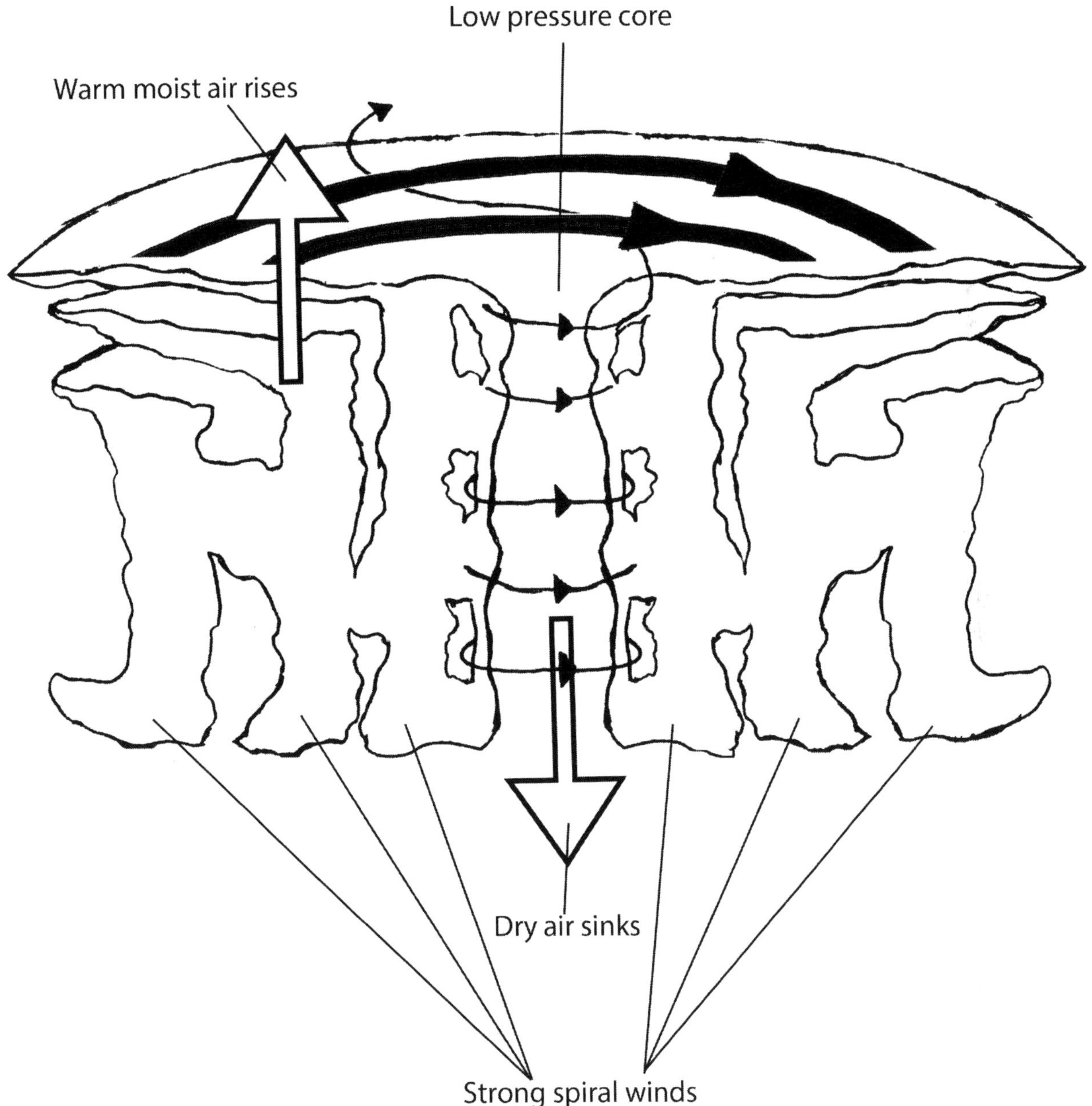

Student Assignment Sheet Week 35
Forecasting

Experiment: What is the Doppler Effect?

Materials
- ✓ Battery powered toothbrush
- ✓ Sound recording device

Procedure
1. Read the introduction to this experiment and answer the question.
2. Place the battery powered toothbrush in front of the microphone of your sound recorder. Turn it on and record the sound for 30 seconds. Then play the recording back and observe how it sounds.
3. Place the battery powered toothbrush in front of the microphone of your sound recorder again and begin recording. This time move the tooth brush back and forth in front of the microphone several times. Also move the toothbrush far away and close to the microphone. Record the sound for 30 seconds as you continue to move the toothbrush. Then play the recording back and observe how it sounds.
4. Draw conclusions and complete your experiment sheet.

Vocabulary & Memory Work
- Vocabulary: isobars, meteorologist
- Memory Work – Continue to work on memorizing the Types of Clouds.

Sketch Assignment: Weather Forecasting Map
- Label the following: Isobars, Cyclone, Isobars close together show a sharp change in pressure, Weather symbols

Writing Assignment
- Reading Assignment: *The Kingfisher Science Encyclopedia* pp. 42-43 Weather Forecasting
- Additional Research Readings
  - Forecasting: *DKEOS* pp. 270-271
  - Fronts: *DKEOS* pg. 253

Dates
- 1842 – Austrian physicist, Christian Doppler, proposes that the frequency of a wave changes for an observer as the source of the wave moves closer to or farther away from the observer. The proposal is later tested and found to be true. It is named the Doppler Effect.

Schedules for Week 35

Two Days a Week

Day 1	Day 2
☐ Define isobars, meteorologists on SG pg. 203 ☐ Do the "What is the Doppler Effect?" experiment, then fill out the experiment sheet on SG pp. 236-237 ☐ Enter the dates onto the date sheets on SG pp. 8-12	☐ Read pp. 42-43 from the *The Kingfisher Science Encyclopedia,* then discuss what was read ☐ Prepare an outline or narrative summary, write it on SG pp. 238-239 ☐ Color and label the "Weather Forecasting Map" sketch on SG pg. 235

Supplies I Need for the Week

- ✓ Battery powered toothbrush
- ✓ Sound recording device

Things I Need to Prepare

Five Days a Week

Day 1	Day 2	Day 3	Day 4	Day 5
☐ Do the "What is the Doppler Effect?" experiment, then fill out the experiment sheet on SG pp. 236-237	☐ Read pp. 42-43 from the *The Kingfisher Science Encyclopedia,* then discuss what was read ☐ Write an outline or list of facts on SG pg. 238	☐ Define isobars, meteorologists on SG pg. 203 ☐ Enter the dates onto the date sheets on SG pp. 8-12 ☐ Color and label the "Weather Forecasting Map" sketch on SG pg. 235	☐ Read one or all of the additional reading assignments ☐ Prepare your report, write the report on SG pg. 239	☐ Complete one of the Want More Activities listed **OR** ☐ Study a scientist from the field of Earth Science ☐ Take the Unit 6 Test

Supplies I Need for the Week

- ✓ Battery powered toothbrush
- ✓ Sound recording device

Things I Need to Prepare

Additional Information Week 35

Experiment Information

- **Introduction** – (*from the Student Guide*) Doppler Radar gives forecasters the information they need to predict the severity of a particular thunderstorm. It measures the wind direction and speed using the Doppler Effect. Doppler Radar can also give estimates on rainfall amounts. Meteorologists use this information, along with information from satellites, to provide early warning for severe thunderstorms and accurate weather forecasts. In this experiment, you are going to see how the Doppler Effect works.
- **Results** – In the first sound recording, the students should have heard that the pitch remained exactly the same for the entire 30 seconds. In the second recording, the students should have heard that the pitch got higher as the toothbrush was closer and lower as it moved farther away.
- **Explanation** – Have you ever noticed that when an ambulance passes you with its sirens on, the pitch changes as it gets closer to you and passes by? This change in pitch or frequency is called the Doppler Effect. Doppler Radar uses the changes in frequency of the signals it receives to determine rate of precipitation, as well as wind speed and direction. It also gives estimates on rainfall amounts and hail size. All this information helps weather forecasters to know how severe a storm will be. This enables them to warn people when necessary.

Discussion Questions

1. What causes weather systems? (*A weather system is caused by sunlight heating up the Earth's atmosphere and surface.*)
2. How can you use natural clues to predict the weather? (*We can use the color of the sunset or sunrise to predict weather. If the sunset is red, it can be a sign of good weather to come. If the sunrise is red, it can be a sign of bad weather to come. We can also watch animal behavior to predict changing weather.*)
3. How do modern weather forecasters predict the weather? (*Modern weather forecasters collect weather data from multiple points and use it to gauge the likely changes in the weather.*)
4. What are some of the tools a meteorologist can use? (*Meteorologists use tools like weather monitoring stations, weather balloons, satellites, and weather-monitory aircraft, along with computer models, to predict the weather.*)
5. What is a weather front? (*A weather front is a region where warm and cold air meet.*)

Want More

- **Weather Station** – Use the following website to make your own weather station, including a rain gauge, wind vane, hygrometer, barometer, and anemometer:
  - http://school.discoveryeducation.com/lessonplans/activities/weatherstation/

Sketch Assignment Week 35

Weather Forecasting Map

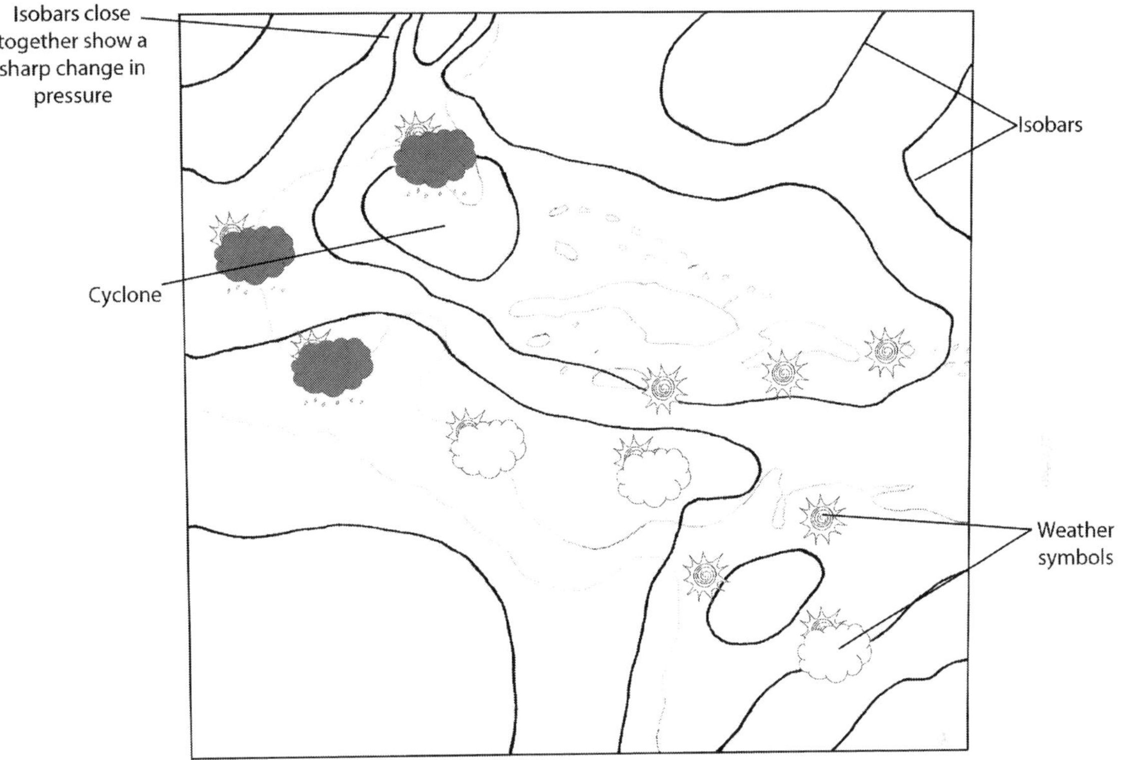

Earth Science Unit 6: Weather
Discussion Questions

Week 30
1. What does the atmosphere do?
2. Which gas is known as a greenhouse gas and why?
3. What are the layers of the atmosphere from top to bottom?
4. What role do animals and plants play in maintaining our atmosphere?

Week 31
1. What two factors influence the Earth's climate?
2. What is the most important factor in determining an area's climate? Why?
3. What are some factors that can cause a global climate change?
4. What is El Nino?

Week 32
1. What factors play a part in determining the weather?
2. How does the sun affect the weather?
3. How are areas of low pressure created? High pressure?
4. What are convection currents?
5. Why do we have season on the earth?

Week 33
1. How do clouds form?
2. What factors affect the type of cloud that forms?
3. How are clouds classified?
4. Describe the different types of low-level clouds.
5. Describe the different types of mid-level clouds.
6. What factor is common to all high-level clouds?
7. What is the difference between fog and smog?

Week 34
1. How do winds travel around the globe?
2. How do tornadoes form?
3. What is a tropical cyclone?
4. What is the difference between a tropical cyclone and a hurricane?
5. What can cause a flood?

Week 35
1. What causes weather systems?
2. How can you use natural clues to predict the weather?
3. How do modern weather forecasters predict the weather?
4. What are some of the tools a meteorologist can use?

5. What is a weather front?

Earth Science Unit 6: Weather
Unit Test

Vocabulary Matching

1. Atmospheric pressure ____
2. Currents ____
3. Climate ____
4. Coriolis effect ____
5. Weather ____
6. Cloud ____
7. Precipitation ____
8. Supercell ____
9. Isobars ____
10. Meteorologist ____

A. The effect of the spinning of the Earth, which forces winds and currents into a spiral.

B. The long-term or typical pattern of weather in a particular area.

C. Lines on a weather forecasting map that show atmospheric pressure.

D. Patterns of circulation of air or water around the Earth that are caused by the Sun's heat.

E. A strong, long-lasting, and organized thunderstorm feed by a consistently rotating updraft known as a mesocyclone.

F. A blanket of gases that surround the Earth.

G. A scientist who studies weather and weather forecasting.

H. Water that falls to the Earth's surface, otherwise known as rain.

I. A collection of water droplets and dust particles that is caused by a drop in pressure and is visible from Earth.

J. The force that the air around us exerts.

K. The way the Earth's atmosphere behaves, changes day by day.

True or False

1. ____________________ The atmosphere contains the air we need to breathe.

2. ____________________ Oxygen is known as a greenhouse gas.

3. ____________________ The most important factor in determining an area's climate is its longitude.

4. ____________________ Volcanic eruptions can cause changes in the globe's climate.

5. ______________________ Temperature, wind speed, air pressure, and humidity all play a role in a region's weather.

6. ______________________ Convection currents are formed as cold air rises, warms up, and sinks back to earth's surface where it is cooled once more.

7. ______________________ Clouds are classified by their appearance and height.

8. ______________________ High-level clouds are all wispy in appearance.

9. ______________________ Tornadoes form when cool, slow, upward-moving air currents meet warm, downward-moving air currents.

10. ______________________ Hurricanes are located in the Pacific Ocean.

11. ______________________ Meteorologists use radars and satellites to help them predict the weather.

12. ______________________ Weather can only be predicted with the use of sophisticated equipment.

Short Answer

1. What are the layers of the atmosphere from top to bottom?

2. What two factors influence the Earth's climate?

3. How does the sun affect the weather?

4. What factors affect the type of cloud that forms?

5. How do winds travel around the globe?

6. How do modern weather forecasters predict the weather?

7. Name five different types of clouds.

Earth Science Unit 6: Weather
Unit Test Answers

Vocabulary

1. J
2. D
3. B
4. A
5. K
6. I
7. H
8. E
9. C
10. G

True or False

1. True
2. False (*Carbon dioxide is known as a greenhouse gas.*)
3. False (*The most important factor in determining an area's climate is its latitude.*)
4. True
5. True
6. False (*Convection currents are formed as warm air rises, cools, and sinks back to earth's surface, where it is heated once more.*)
7. True
8. True
9. False (*Tornadoes form when hot, fast, upward-moving air currents meet cold, downward-moving air currents.*)
10. False (*Hurricanes are located in the Gulf of Mexico and the Atlantic.*)
11. True
12. False (*Weather can be predicted by looking at the clouds or by watching animal behavior.*)

Short Answer

1. The outermost layer of the atmosphere is the thermosphere, then the mesosphere, then the stratosphere, and finally the troposphere.
2. Earth's climate is influenced by energy from the sun and the ability of currents in the oceans and atmosphere to circulate the heat around the globe.
3. The Sun's heat, known as solar radiation, is absorbed by the earth, causing the surface to warm up. This heat rises, causing the air near the surface to warm up. The closer the part of the earth is to the sun, the stronger the effect of the solar radiation.
4. The factors that affect how a cloud forms include how much and how quickly the warm air cools, whether the warm, moist air meets a mass of cold air, and at what altitude the water vapor condenses.
5. Warm air rises around the equator, causing very little horizontal winds. Around the Tropic of Cancer and the Tropic of Capricorn, there are consistent trade winds. Above these regions, there are strong westerly winds. There are also seasonal winds, like the mistral, sirocco, and harmattan, which change throughout the year.
6. Modern weather forecasters collect weather data from multiple points and use it to gauge the likely changes in the weather.
7. Students' answers need to include five of the following – Cirrus, Cirrostratus, Cirrocumulus, Altostratus, Altocumulus, Stratus, Stratocumulus, Nimbostratus, Cumulus, Cumulonimbus

Earth Science & Astronomy: Wrap-up

Year-end Test

Earth Science & Astronomy for the Logic Stage
Year-end Test Information and Answers

Year-end Test Information

The year-end test is on the vocabulary (*Vocabulary Matching section*), short answer questions from the tests (*Multiple Choice section*) and memory work (*Short Answer section*) throughout the year. You can choose to make it open notes or not. The purpose of this test is to help your students gain familiarity with the concept of a final exam, so that it won't be quite so overwhelming when they reach the high school years.

Year-end Test Answers

Vocabulary Matching

1. B
2. M
3. G
4. E
5. A
6. I
7. J
8. L
9. C
10. N
11. P
12. R
13. Q
14. K
15. D
16. H
17. F
18. O
19. W
20. AC
21. V
22. T
23. U
24. AA
25. S
26. AE
27. X
28. AF
29. AG
30. Y
31. AI
32. AH
33. AD
34. AJ
35. AB
36. Z

Multiple Choice

1. B
2. D
3. C
4. A
5. C,A,D,B
6. A
7. E
8. D
9. A
10. B
11. A
12. C
13. B,A,C
14. 3,1,5,2,4
15. D
16. A
17. B
18. D,B,A,E,C
19. D
20. A
21. D
22. B
23. A
24. A,B,C,D

Short Answer

1. Students' answers could include: Blue giant – A hot, large star, Red giant – A large star with a cooler outer layer, Main-sequence star – The typical star, such as the Sun, Red dwarf – A cool, small star, White dwarf – A very cool, small star, Neutron star – The tightly packed remnants of a star, Black hole – A star that has collapsed on itself.
2. Mercury, Venus, Earth, Mars, Jupiter, Saturn, Uranus, Neptune

3. Our galaxy is the Milky Way and it has a spiral shape.
4.

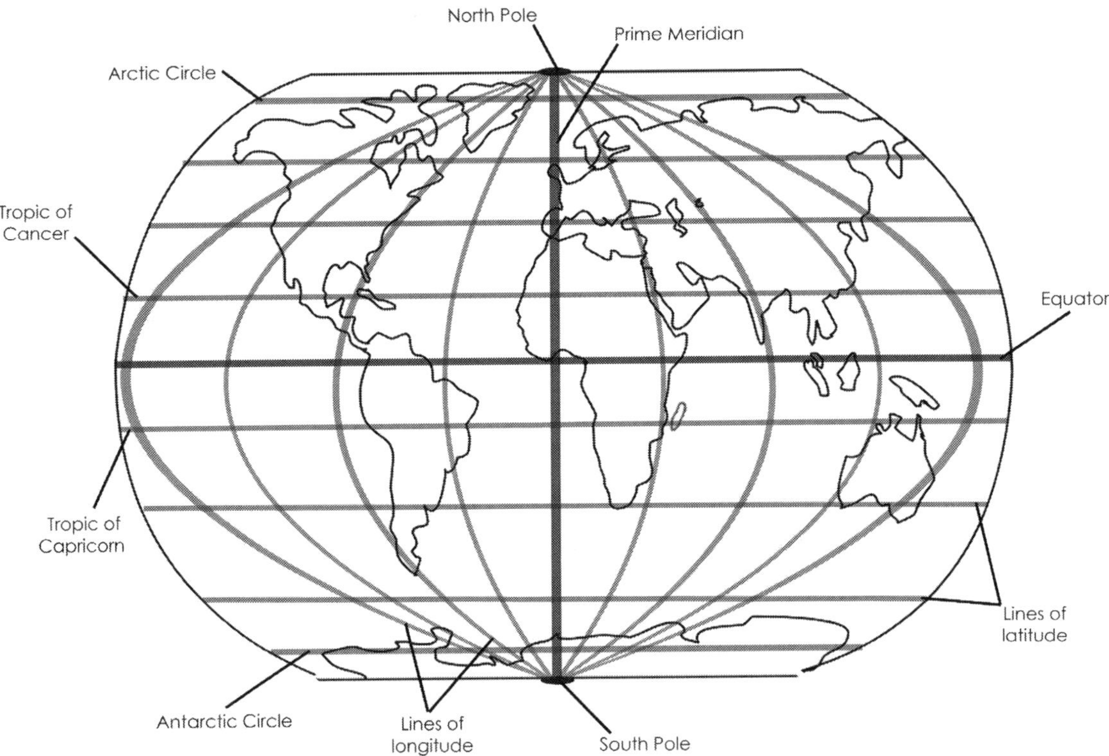

5. Metamorphic – Rock that has been changed by heat or pressure; Sedimentary – Rock made from particles of sand, mud, and other debris that have settled on the seabed and been squashed down to form hardened rock; Igneous – Rock that is formed when magma escapes from inside the Earth, cools, and hardens
6. Thermosphere – The outer layer of the atmosphere; Mesosphere – Meteors generally burn up as they reach this layer of the atmosphere; Stratosphere – Planes fly in this layer of the atmosphere; Troposphere – The layer of the atmosphere where weather is created.

Earth Science & Astronomy for the Logic Stage
Year-end Test

Vocabulary Matching

1. Universe ___
2. Galaxy ___
3. Star ___
4. Nebulae ___
5. Constellation ___
6. Solar wind ___
7. Planet ___
8. Orbit ___
9. Moon ___
10. Eclipse ___
11. Comet ___
12. Meteor ___
13. Astronomer ___
14. Telescope ___
15. Space probe ___
16. Rocket ___
17. Space shuttle ___
18. Artificial satellite ___

A. The pattern that a group of stars seems to make in the sky.

B. The collection of all the matter, space, and energy that exists, also known as the cosmos.

C. A celestial body in orbit around a planet.

D. An unmanned space craft that collects information about objects in space.

E. A cloud of dust and gas found in space.

F. A reusable device capable of delivering objects into space, consists of an orbiter, a fuel tank and two booster rockets.

G. A massive, hot, shining ball of gas.

H. A device capable of delivering objects into space, carries a small amount of cargo and lots of fuel.

I. A constant stream of particles that flow into space from the Sun.

J. A large globe composed of rock, liquid, or gas that revolves around a star.

K. A device used to view objects in space.

L. The path of one celestial body around another.

M. A body held together by gravity that is made of millions of stars, gas, and dust.

N. When one celestial body casts a shadow on another celestial body.

O. A man-made object that orbits a planet and is used to gather or relay information.

P. A chunk of frozen gas and dirt that has an orbit.

Q. A scientist who studies the universe and the objects found in it.

R. A meteoroid that starts to burn as it enters the atmosphere.

19. Lines of Latitude ___

20. Lines of Longitude ___

21. Source ___

22. Tides ___

23. Natural cycle ___

24. Biome ___

25. Continent ___

26. Faults ___

27. Seismic wave ___

28. Mountain range ___

29. Fossil ___

30. Erosion ___

31. Atmosphere ___

32. Currents ___

33. Climate ___

34. Coriolis effect ___

35. Weather ___

36. Supercell ___

S. Any of the seven large landmasses into which the Earth is divided.

T. The daily movement of the sea up and down the shore, they are caused by the gravitational pull of the moon.

U. The exchanging of essential elements, such as nitrogen, carbon, and oxygen.

V. The beginning of a river.

W. Lines that run parallel around the globe, dividing the globe into flat slices; the lines never meet.

X. An underground shockwave that travels outward from the focus of an earthquake.

Y. The movement of particles of soil, sand, or rock by wind or water to a new location.

Z. A strong, long-lasting, and organized thunderstorm feed by a consistently rotating updraft known as a mesocyclone.

AA. A region of Earth that contains unique plants and animals and is characterized by a distinct climate.

AB. The way the Earth's atmosphere behaves and changes day by day.

AC. Lines that run from the North to the South pole, dividing the globe into segments, they all meet at the poles.

AD. The long-term or typical pattern of weather in a particular area.

AE. Cracks in the Earth caused by the movement of its plates.

AF. A chain, or line, of mountains connected together.

AG. The impression or remains of an ancient plant or animal that has been hardened and preserved in a rock.

AH. Patterns of circulation of air or water around the Earth that are caused by the Sun's heat.

AI. A blanket of gases that surround the Earth.

AJ. The effect of the spinning of the Earth, which forces winds and currents into a spiral.

Multiple Choice

1. Within our solar system astronomers use ________ to measure distance.

   A. Meters

   B. Astronomical Units

   C. Light Years

2. What factor(s) do astronomers believe helps to shape a galaxy?

   A. The amount of material

   B. The speed of spin

   C. The rate at which the stars form

   D. All of the above

3. All stars start with a core made from ____________.

   A. Oxygen

   B. Nitrogen

   C. Hydrogen

   D. Iron

4. How are galaxies classified?

   A. According to their shape

   B. According to their size

5. Match the minor member of our solar system to its description.

____	Asteroid Belt	A. A group of asteroids found after Neptune.
____	Kuipter Belt	B. A round object of rock, ice, or gas not large enough to be considered a planet.
____	Comets	C. A group of asteroids between Mars and Jupiter.
____	Dwarf Planets	D. A chunk of ice and dirt that orbits in the Ort Cloud.

6. A comet's tail forms as it gets ___________ the sun.

   A. Closer to

   B. Farther from

7. Which of the following planets are gas giants?

   A. Jupiter

   B. Saturn

   C. Uranus

   D. Neptune

   E. All of the above

8. Which planet has a red, rocky surface?

   A. Mercury

   B. Venus

   C. Earth

   D. Mars

9. What did Copernicus believe that changed astronomy forever?

   A. He believed that the earth revolved around the sun.

   B. He believed that the sun revolved around the earth.

10. What is escape velocity?

   A. 2 miles per second

   B. 7 miles per second

   C. 15 miles per second

   D. 100 miles per second

11. How do telescopes work?

A. Telescopes use one lens to collect and focus light and another lens to magnify the object.

B. Telescopes use one lens to collect light and magnify the object.

C. None of the above.

12. Where to artificial satellites get their power?

A. Earth

B. Internal combustion

C. Solar panels

D. All of the above

13. Match the layer of the earth with its description.

_____ Crust	A. The extremely hot layer that consists of molten rock made from iron and nickel.
_____ Mantle	B. A solid upper layer, which consists mostly of dense silicate rock.
_____ Core	C. The thinnest layer, which floats over the layers below.

14. Place the stages of a river in order beginning with the source.

_____ Water meanders through the landscape forming big loops.

_____ Water flows from a spring or from a point high up in the mountains.

_____ Water reaches the sea.

_____ Water moves quickly downhill and smaller streams join in.

_____ Water spreads out forming an estuary or delta.

15. Which process(es) are important to the water cycle?

A. Evaporation

B. Condensation

C. Precipitation

D. All of the above

16. Glaciers are _____________.

A. Rivers of moving ice

B. Stationary slabs of ice

C. Only found in the tropics

17. What is an earthquake?

A. A moment of fear on the earth

B. A sudden release of energy underground

C. None of the above

18. Match the volcano type with its description.

____ Fissure volcano	A. Created by sticky molten rock
____ Shield volcano	B. Oozes molten rock over a large area
____ Dome volcano	C. Composed of several side vents
____ Conical volcano	D. Erupts from a narrow slit
____ Composite volcano	E. Formed from volcanic ash

19. Which of the following factor(s) contribute to the formation of mountains?

    A. Volcanoes

    B. Earthquakes

    C. Continental collisions

    D. All of the above

20. Which statement correctly describes the two main types of weathering?

    A. Chemical weathering happens when rocks are changed by water, carbon dioxide, or by organic acids, while physical weathering happens when rocks are fractured or broken apart.

    B. Physical weathering happens when rocks are changed by water, carbon dioxide, or by organic acids, while chemical weathering happens when rocks are fractured or broken apart.

21. What factor(s) influence the Earth's climate?

    A. Heat from the sun

    B. Currents in the atmosphere

    C. Currents in the ocean

    D. All of the above

22. Clouds are formed from _______________.

    A. White cotton balls

    B. Condensed water vapor

    C. Liquid Nitrogen

    D. None of the above

23. Which statement is correct about the formation of tornadoes?

    A. Tornadoes form when hot, fast, upward-moving air currents meet cold, downward-moving air currents.

    B. Tornadoes form when cool, slow upward-moving air currents meet warm, downward-moving air currents.

24. Meteorologists can use the following tool(s) to predict the weather. (Circle all that apply.)

A. Types of clouds

B. Radars

C. Computer models

D. Animal behavior

Short Answer

1. Name and describe three types of stars.

2. What are the names of the planets in our solar system in order from the sun?

3. What is the name of our galaxy and what shape is it?

4. Label the globe below with the Arctic Circle, Prime Meridian, Equator, Tropic of Cancer & Tropic of Capricorn, North & South Pole.

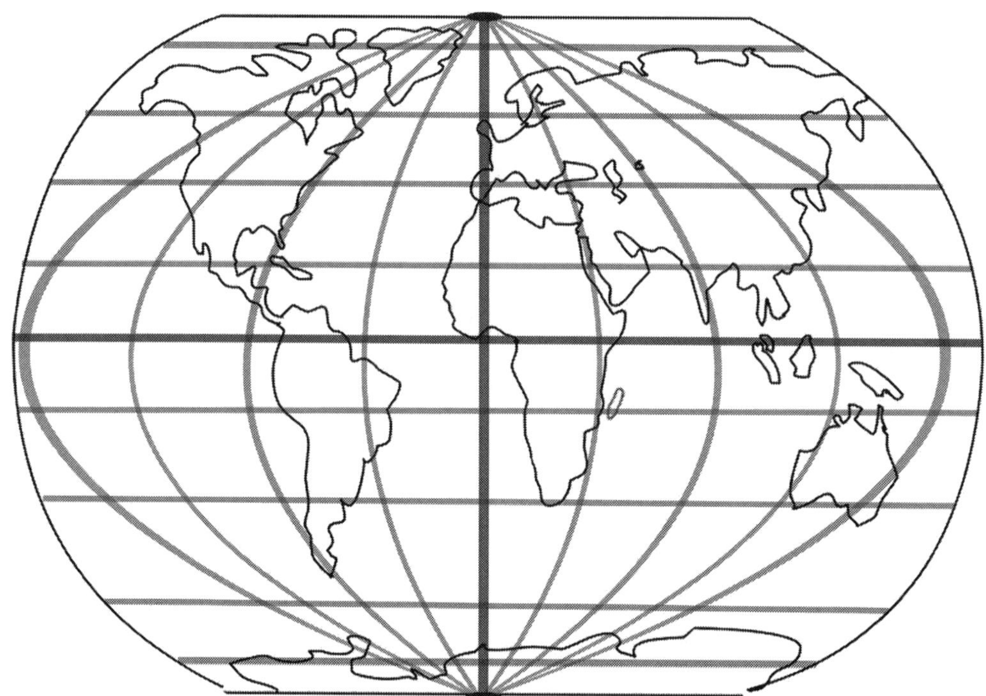

5. Name and describe the three main types of rock.

6. What are the four main layers of our atmosphere? (Be sure to include brief description of each.)

Appendix

Ancients 5000 BC–400 AD

- 3300 BC – The Indus Valley Civilization uses rivers for navigation.
- 7th century BC – Babylonian astronomers use a coordinate system resembling the Zodiac.
- ca. 50 BC – A relief called the Dendera zodiac is the first known depiction of the classical zodiac of twelve signs.
- c. 5 BC – Strabo, a Greek geographer, proposes the idea of frigid, temperate and tropical climate zones.
- 79 AD – Mount Vesuvius, in Italy, erupts and destroys Pompeii.
- c. 30 AD – Prominent geographer, Strabo, suggests that there might be continents that are not yet known to the Greeks.
- 2nd century – Ptolemy names forty-eight different constellations in his book *Almagest.*
- 132 – The Chinese invent the first seismograph, in which precisely balanced metal balls fall if the ground shakes.

Medieval-Early Renaissance 400AD-1600AD

- 1538 – Gerhard Mercator, a Flemish cartographer, devises a fairly accurate way to represent the Earth's surface on a map.
- 1546 – Georgius Agricola, a German metallurgist, first uses the term "fossil" when referring to the rock-like remains of animals and plants.

Late Renaissance-Early Modern 1600 AD-1850 AD

- 1609 – Galileo invents the first telescope.
- 1610 – Galileo makes the first systematic study of Jupiter's 4 largest moons.
- 1620 – Dutch physician, Cornelis Drebbel, builds the world's first submarine and makes several trips in the River Thames near London at a depth of about 12 or 15 feet.
- 1643 – Evangelista Torricelli invents the barometer, an instrument that measures atmospheric pressure.
- 1647 – Johannes Hevelius publishes the first lunar atlas.
- 1655 – Dutch scientist, Christiaan Huygens, correctly identifies Saturn's rings.
- 1656-1742 – English astronomer, Edmond Halley lives. He correctly predicts that a comet will return to Earth's night sky in 1758, 1835, and 1910.
- 1660 – Robert Hooke reports a giant spot on Jupiter's surface.
- March 13, 1781 – William Herschel discovers Uranus using a homemade telescope.
- 1784 – Charles Messier finds several blurry objects that he records as nebulae. These are later discovered to be galaxies.
- 1785 – James Hutton, a Scottish geologist, says that moutains are formed by hot rock erupted from volcanoes.
- 17th-18th centuries – Forty more constellations are named, for a total of eighty-eight named constellations.
- 1800 BC – Egyptians begin using very simple techniques to measure water depths.
- 1803 – Luke Howard, a pharmacist and amateur meteorologist, devises a system to classify the different types of clouds.
- 1822 – Friedrich Mohs, a German mineralogist, creates the first hardness scale based on 10 common minerals to use as a reference.
- 1824-1910 – British astronomer William Huggins lives. He is the first to use spectroscopy in astronomy.
- 1842 – Austrian physicist, Christian Doppler, proposes that the frequency of a wave changes for an observer as the source of the wave moves closer to or farther away from the observer. The proposal is later tested and found to be true. It is named the Doppler Effect.
- 1845 – Lord Rosse draws the galaxy M51, without knowing what it is.
- 1846 – Johann Galle finds the planet Neptune.

Modern 1850 AD-Present

- 1868-1938 – George Hale lives. He is an American astronomer who studied sunspots and discovered the magnetic fields within them.
- 1887 – The biggest recorded snowflakes, which were 15 inches across, fall in Montana.
- 1896 – Svante Arrhenius, a Swedish chemist, shows that CO_2 helps to trap heat in the atmosphere.
- December 19, 1898 – President McKinley asks the Weather Bureau, now the National Weather Service, to establish a hurricane warning system.
- 20th century – Tropical and temperate rainforests experience heavy logging, which leads to a reduction of the forests' sizes.
- 1906 – Ejnar Hertzsprung, a Danish astronomer, discovers that a star's temperature and luminosity are linked. He then arranges them into families, from hot and bright to cool and dim.
- 1924 – Edwin Hubble presents the first evidence of other galaxies.
- 1926 – Robert Goddard launches the first liquid fuel rocket.
- 1929 – Edwin Hubble proves that the universe is expanding.
- 1930 – Clyde Tombaugh, a US astronomer, discovers Pluto.
- 1930 – French astronomer, Bernard Lyot, invents the coronagraph, allowing scientists to view the Sun without waiting for a total solar eclipse.
- 1931 – American astronomer, Karl Janley, collects the first evidence of radio radiation coming from space.
- 1935 – Charles Richter, a US seismologist, develops a scale for reporting the strength of earthquakes.
- 1942 – The first rocket, launched by Germany, reaches space.
- 1957 – A rocket delivers the first Russian satellite, *Sputnik*, into space.
- October 1959 – Russian spacecraft *Luna 3* transmits the first images of the far side of the moon back to the Earth.
- 1960 – A two-manned submarine, named *Trieste*, dives to what was believed to be the deepest point in the Mariana Trench, which was 10,915 meters.
- 1965 – Scientists find heat waves in the universe that they believe are leftover from a vast explosion.
- 1965 – Tuzo Wilson, a Canadian geophysicist, explains how the plates on the ocean floor move.
- July 20, 1969 – US astronauts Neil Armstrong and Edwin Aldrin became the first humans to walk on the moon.
- 1971 – The Fujita scale is introduced by Tetsuya Fujita, a professor at the University of Chicago. The Fujita scale is a way of measuring the strength of a tornado based on the damage they cause, F0 being the weakest and F5 being the strongest.
- 1974-1975 – *Mariner 10* flies past Mercury three times to take overlapping photos of the surface of the planet.

Modern 1850 AD-Present

- 1976 – The second largest iron and nickel meteorite in the United States is found.
- 1976 – Two American space probes land on Mars to test for signs of life, but find none.
- 1979 – *Pioneer II* explores Saturn's rings.
- May 18, 1980 – Mount St. Helens, in Washington, erupts.
- 1981 – NASA launches the first reusable space shuttle.
- 1986 – The space probe *Giotto*, is sent inside Halley's comet, giving people the first look at a comet's nucleus.
- 1989 – The satellite *Hipparcos* is launched. Its job is to map the night sky.
- 1990-1994 – *Magellan* maps 98% of the surface of Venus.
- 1992 – *Keck I*, the first telescope to use a segmented mirror, is completed.
- 1992 – The satellite *Cosmic Background Explorer* traces background radiation and ripples in the universe that are thought to be leftover from the Big Bang.
- 1995 – The *Galileo* probe reaches Jupiter. It studies Jupiter's atmosphere and its moons.
- 1997 – *Pathfinder* lands on Mars and delivers the robotic rover *Sojourner* to explore the surface of Mars.
- 1997 – The comet *Hale-Bopp* is in the Earth's night sky. It won't return for another 2,400 years.
- 2004 – *Cassini* arrives at Saturn to study the planet's moons and rings.
- 2004 – Mobile robots, called *Spirit* and *Opportunity,* explore the surface of Mars.
- 2006 – Pluto is reclassified as a dwarf planet.
- 2011 – NASA's four reusable space shuttles are retired.

The Science Fair Project Presentation Board

The science fair project board is the visual representation of the students' hard work. Below is a list of the information that needs to be included, along with where it is typically found on the project board. The students can certainly mix things up a bit, but be sure to remind them that their information needs to be placed in such a way that it is easy for someone else to follow.

The left section of the board typically has:

- ✓ Introduction
- ✓ Hypothesis
- ✓ Research

The center section of the board typically has:

- ✓ Materials
- ✓ Procedure
- ✓ Pictures, Graphs and Charts from the Experiment (Note — *The students can also display a portion of their projects or a photo album with pictures from their experiments on the tables in front of their boards.*)

The right section of the board typically has:

- ✓ Results
- ✓ Conclusions

When purchasing a presentation board, you are looking for a tri-fold board that is at least 36" high and 48" wide, with the two side sections folding into the center section. If you search the internet for science fair project boards, you will find plenty of options, some with header boards, some without. You can usually purchase a project board at most local WalMart, Target, or Michael's stores.

Here is a description of what the students need to prepare for their presentation boards.

- **The Introduction** — *Have the students turn their questions from step one into a statement. Then, they should write two to three more sentences explaining why they chose their specific topics. The students should end their introductory paragraphs by sharing the questions that they were trying to answer with their projects.*
- **The Hypothesis** — *Have the students type up and prepare their hypotheses from step three for their project boards.*
- **The Research** — *Have the students type up and prepare their research reports from step two for their project boards.*
- **The Materials** — *Have the students type up a list of the materials they used for their projects.*
- **The Procedure** — *Have the students revise the experiment design they wrote in step four so that it is written in the past tense.*
- **The Results** — *Have the students turn the trends in the observations they noted and the results they interpreted in step six into a paragraph.*
- **The Conclusion** — *Have the students type up and prepare their concluding paragraphs from step six for their project boards.*

The Scientific Method Explained

The scientific method is a method for asking and answering scientific questions. This is done through observation and experimentation.

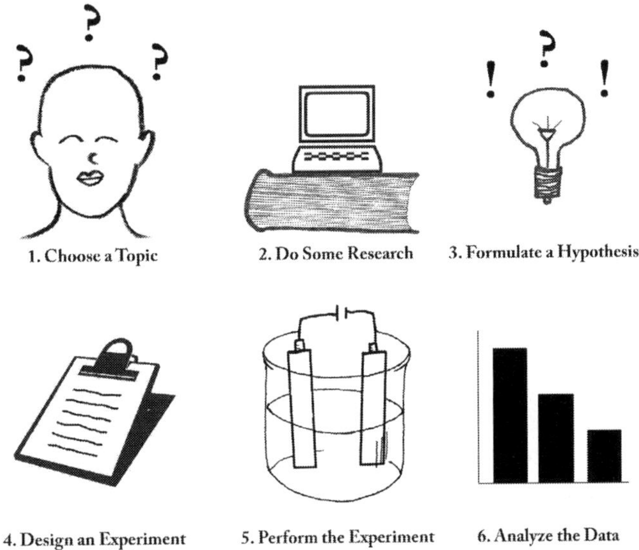

The following steps are key to the scientific method:

1. **Ask A Question** — The scientific method begins with asking a question about something you observe. Your questions must be about something you can measure. Good questions begin with how, what, when, who, which, why or where.

2. **Do Some Research** — You need to read about the topic from your question so that you can have background knowledge of the topic. This will keep you from repeating mistakes made in the past.

3. **Formulate a Hypothesis** — A hypothesis is an educated guess about the answer to your question. Your hypothesis must be easy to measure and answer the original question you asked.

4. **Test with Experimentation** — Your experiment tests whether your hypothesis is true or false. It is important for your test to be fair. This means that you may need to run multiple tests. If you do, be sure to only change one factor at a time so that you can determine which factor is causing the difference.

5. **Record and Analyze Observations or Results** — Once your experiment is complete, you will collect and measure all your data to see if your hypothesis is true or false. Scientists often find that their hypothesis was false. If this is the case, they will formulate a new hypothesis and begin the process again until they are able to answer their question.

6. **Draw a Conclusion** — Once you have analyzed your results, you can make a statement about them. This statement communicates your results to others.

Reading Assignments for Younger Students

Astronomy Unit 1: Space

Week	Topic Studied	Resource & Pages Assigned
Week 1	Universe	*DK First Space Encyclopedia* pp. 22-23
Week 2	Galaxies	*DK First Space Encyclopedia* pp. 16-17, 18-19
Week 3	Stars	*DK First Space Encyclopedia* pp. 102-103, 104-105
Week 4	Constellations	Read *The Stars & Thier Stories* along with your older student
Week 5	Zodiac	Skip the constellations research project and just read *DK First Space Encyclopedia* pp. 112-113

Astronomy Unit 2: Our Solar System

Week	Topic Studied	Resource & Pages Assigned
Week 6	Sun	*DK First Space Encyclopedia* pp. 52-53, 54-55
Week 7	Mercury, Venus, Mars	*DK First Space Encyclopedia* pp. 56-57, 58-59, 64-65
Week 8	Earth/Moon	*DK First Space Encyclopedia* pp. 60-61, 62-63
Week 9	Jupiter & Saturn	*DK First Space Encyclopedia* pp. 68-69, 70-71
Week 10	Uranus, Neptune & Minor Members	*DK First Space Encyclopedia* pp. 72-73, 74-75
Week 11	Comets & Meteorites	*DK First Space Encyclopedia* pp. 76-77, 82-83

Astronomy Unit 3: Astronomers & Thier Tools

Week	Topic Studied	Resource & Pages Assigned
Week 12	Astronomers	Get a library book on an astronomer for this week.
Week 13	Looking Into Space	*DK First Space Encyclopedia* pp. 10-11, 12-13
Week 14	Exploring Space	*DK First Space Encyclopedia* pp. 24-25, 36-37, 38-39
Week 15	Satellites	*DK First Space Encyclopedia* pp. 44-45

Reading Assignments for Younger Students

Earth Science Unit 4: Our Planet

Week	Topic Studied	Resource & Pages Assigned
Week 16	Inside the Earth	*DK First Earth Encyclopedia* pp. 6-7, 8-9
Week 17	Maps and Mapping	*DK First Earth Encyclopedia* pp. 102-103, 104-105
Week 18	Rivers	*DK First Earth Encyclopedia* pp. 30-31
Week 19	Oceans	*DK First Earth Encyclopedia* pp. 64-65
Week 20	Glaciers	Have the students read about the arctic on *DK First Earth Encyclopedia* pp. 50-51
Week 21	Natural Cycles	*DK First Earth Encyclopedia* pp. 28-29
Week 22	Biomes and Habitats	*DK First Earth Encyclopedia* pp. 46-47, 48-49

Earth Science Unit 5: Geology

Week	Topic Studied	Resource & Pages Assigned
Week 23	Continents	*DK First Earth Encyclopedia* pp. 10-11
Week 24	Volcanoes	*DK First Earth Encyclopedia* pp. 16-17
Week 25	Earthquakes	*DK First Earth Encyclopedia* pp. 18-19
Week 26	Mountains	*DK First Earth Encyclopedia* pp. 20-21
Week 27	Rocks	*DK First Earth Encyclopedia* pp. 14-15
Week 28	Ores and Gems	Have the students read about the earth's resources on *DK First Earth Encyclopedia* pp. 88-89
Week 29	Erosion and Weathering	*DK First Earth Encyclopedia* pp. 26-27

Earth Science Unit 6: Weather

Week	Topic Studied	Resource & Pages Assigned
Week 30	Atmosphere	*DK First Earth Encyclopedia* pp. 12-13
Week 31	Climate	*DK First Earth Encyclopedia* pp. 38-39
Week 32	Weather	*DK First Earth Encyclopedia* pp. 36-37
Week 34	Clouds	Check out a book from the library for this week about clouds.
Week 35	Extreme Weather	*DK First Earth Encyclopedia* pp. 38-39
Week 36	Forecasting	Check out a book from the library for this week about weather forecasting

Templates

Two Days a Week Schedule Template

Week: ____________________ Topic: ______________________

Day 1	Day 2
Supplies I Need for the Week	
Things I Need to Prepare	

Week: ____________________ Topic: ______________________

Day 1	Day 2
Supplies I Need for the Week	
Things I Need to Prepare	

Five Days a Week Schedule Template

Week: ____________________ Topic: ____________________

Day 1	Day 2	Day 3	Day 4	Day 5
Supplies I Need for the Week				
Things I Need to Prepare				

Week: ____________________ Topic: ____________________

Day 1	Day 2	Day 3	Day 4	Day 5
Supplies I Need for the Week				
Things I Need to Prepare				

Galaxy Cards

NGC 7217 	• Found in the Pegasus constellation • Pinwheel shaped • Contains mostly new stars • Has a large bulge with tightly wrapped arms

Messier 100 	• Found in the Virgo cluster in the Northern Hemisphere • Pinwheel shaped with a small central bulge • Contains mostly young stars, as well as large amounts of gas and dust • Has loose, lumpy spiral arms

NGC 4156 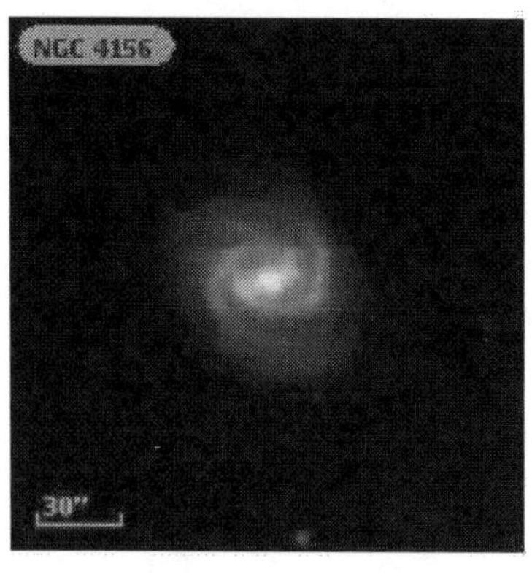	• Found in the Canes Venatici constellation • Contains many new stars with large amounts of gas • There is a "bar" of stars, dust and gas running across the center of this galaxy • Pinwheel shaped

NGC 4881 	• Ball-shaped galaxy • Contains mostly older stars and a small amount of gas • Found in the Canes Venatici constellation • 352 million light years away from Earth

NGC 3377 	• Part of a dozen galaxies that cluster together in the constellation Leo • Contains mostly older stars and a small amount of gas • Has a well-defined oval shape • Contains a black hole at the center
NGC 5253  Big Stellar Clusters in the Blue Dwarf Galaxy NGC 5253	• Found in the constellation Centarus • Contains both young and old stars • Has no definite structure • Contains large amounts of gas and dust • Dwarf galaxy

Andromeda	
	• Found in the Andromeda constellation • Contains young and old stars • Pinwheel shape • Contains close to one trillion stars • Approximately 2.5 million light years from Earth

Milky Way	
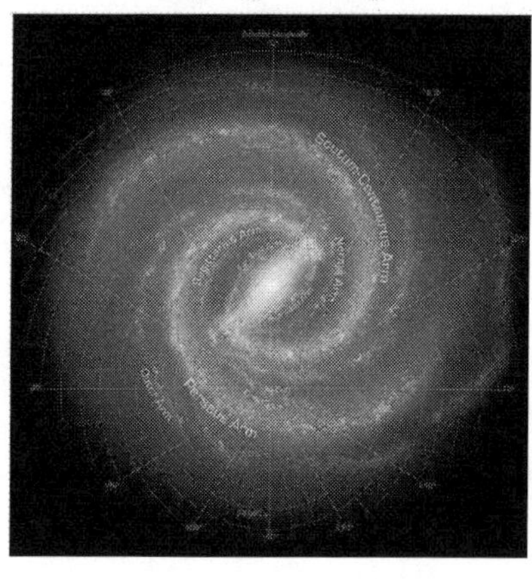	• Our solar system is located on the Orion Spur of this galaxy • Contains young and old stars • There is a "bar" of stars, dust and gas running across the center of this galaxy • Contains close to 200 billion stars

Solar System Fact Book Templates

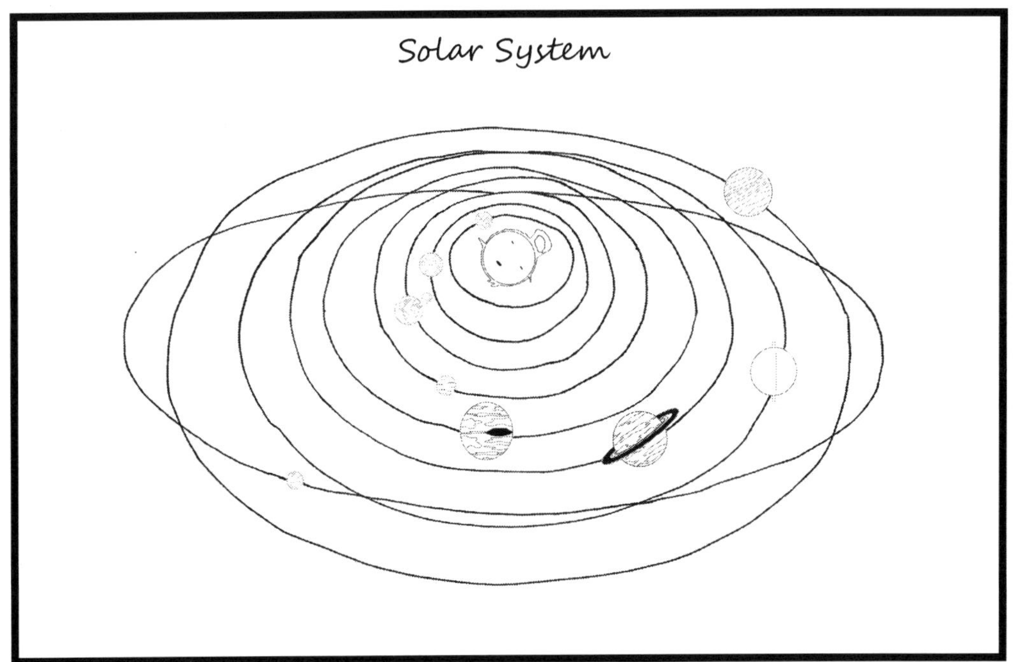

Solar System Fact Book Templates

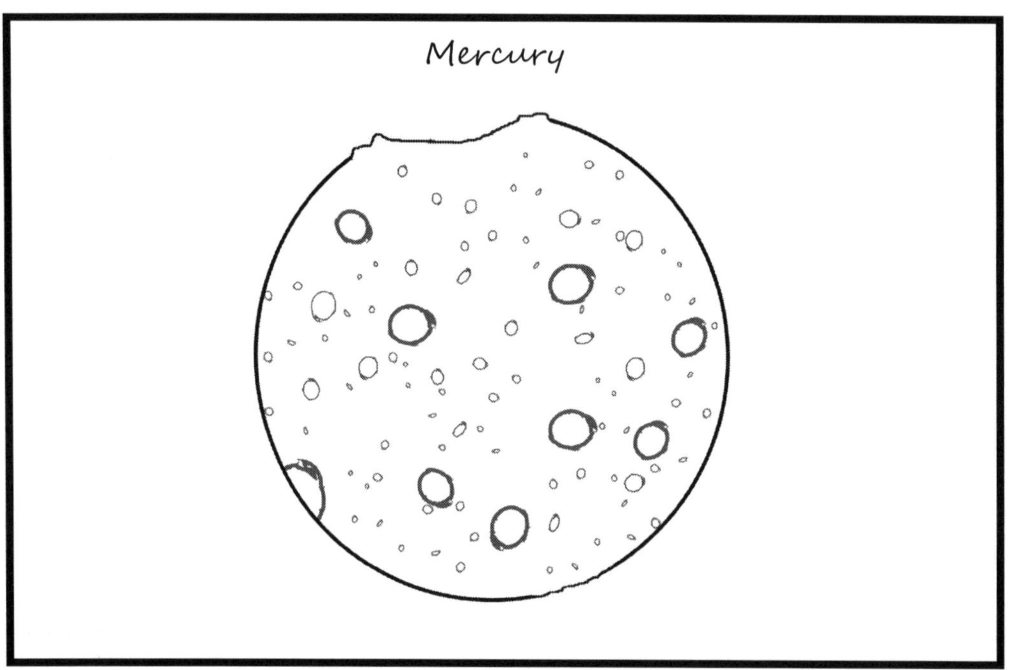

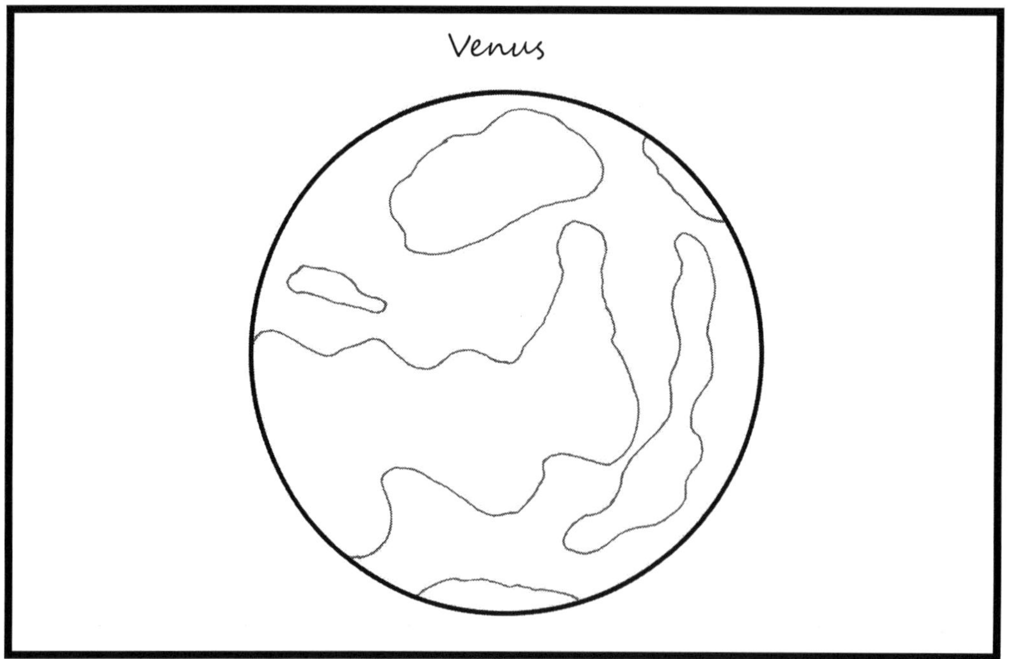

Solar System Fact Book Templates

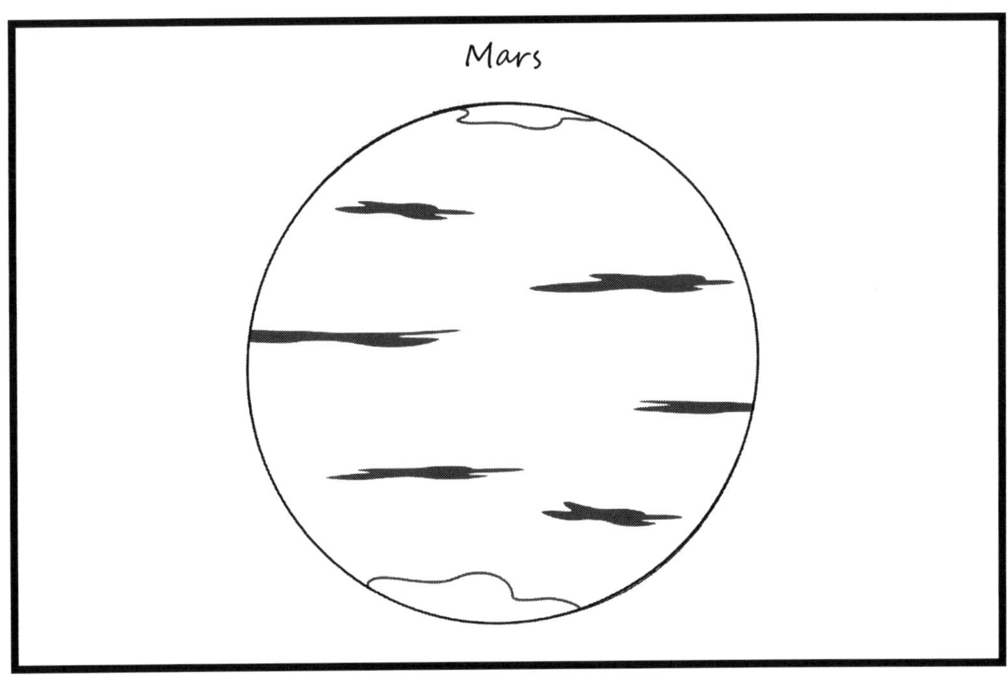

Solar System Fact Book Templates

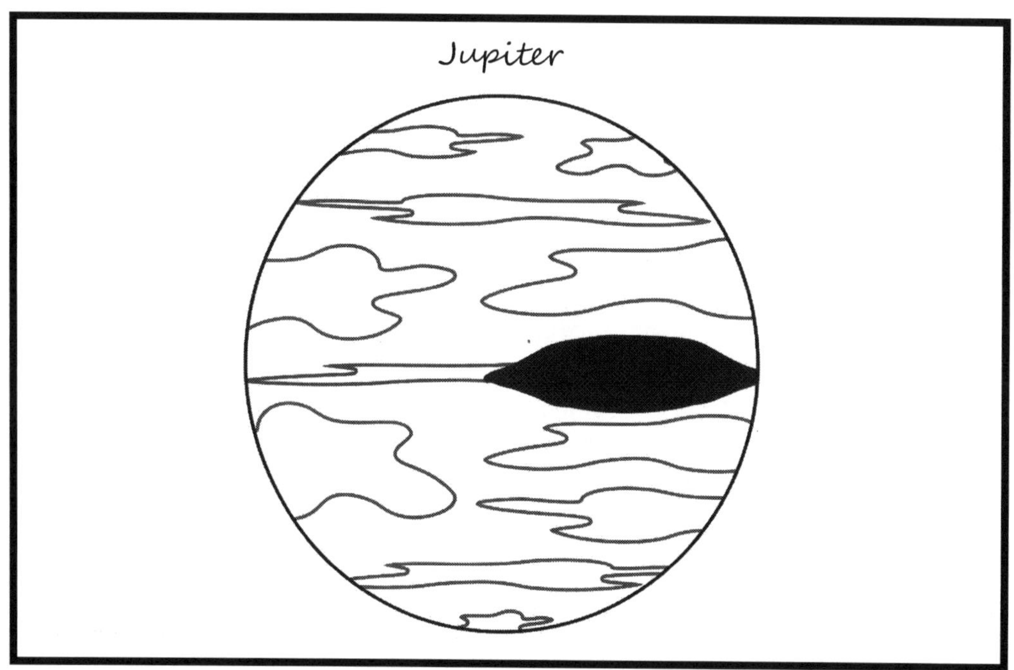

Solar System Fact Book Templates

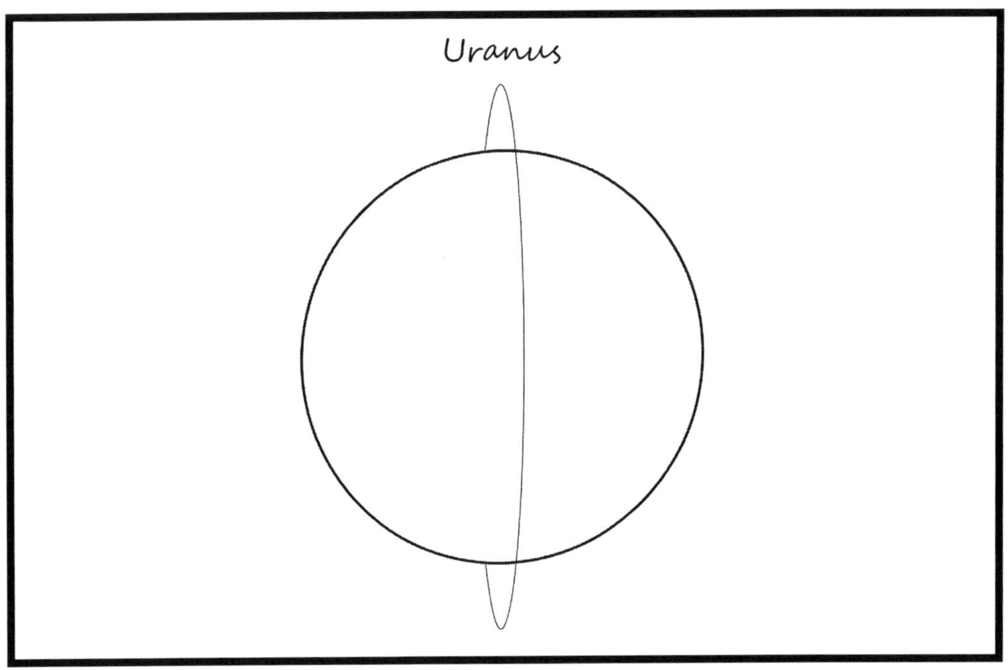

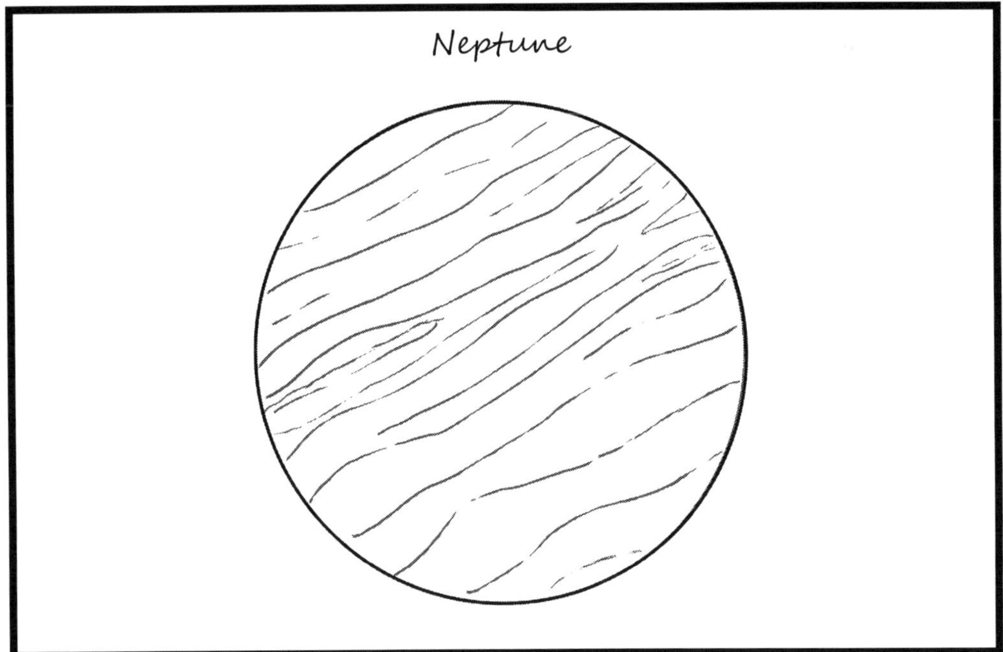

Solar System Fact Book Templates

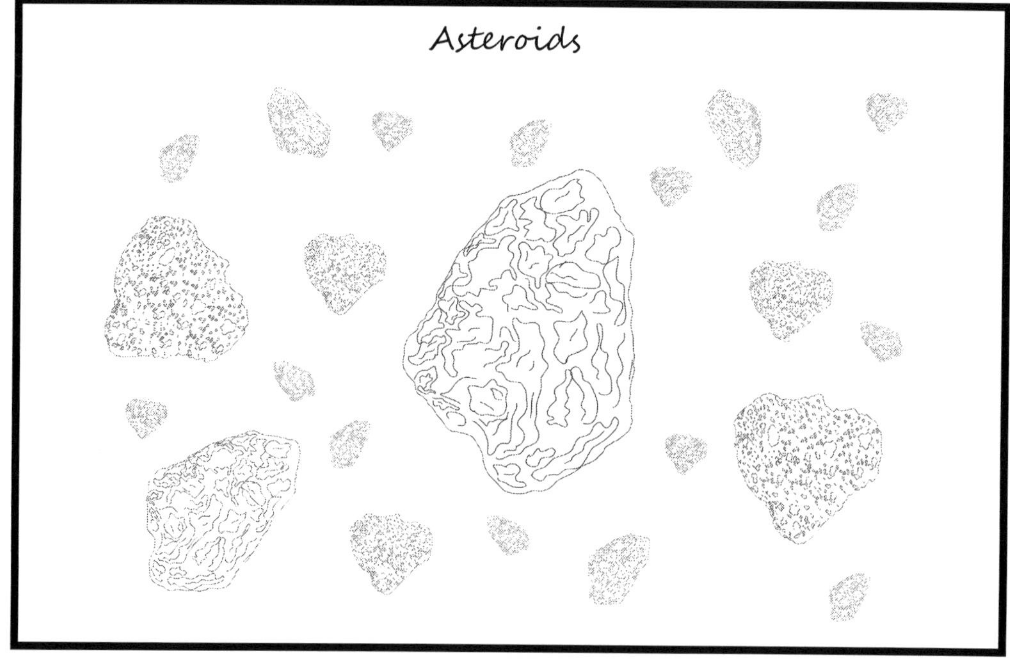

Solar System Fact Book Templates

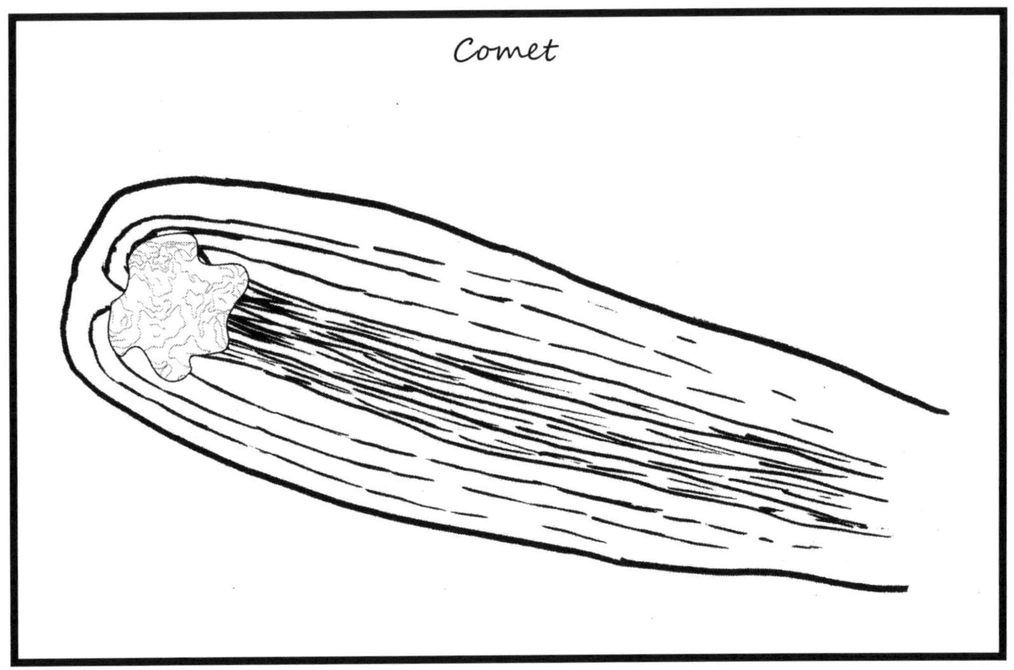

Made in the USA
Columbia, SC
14 January 2024